First published in Ireland 2020 by
Artisan House Ltd., Letterfrack,
Connemara, Co. Galway, Ireland.

www.artisanhouse.ie

Editorial Director	**Mary Ruddy**
Creative Director	**Vincent Murphy**
Author	**Peter Vine** *peter@petervine.com*
Copy-editors	**Stan Carey** and **Siobhán Mannion**
Proofreading	**Kate Murphy**
Typesetting	**Dominic Carroll** Ardfield, Co Cork.
Printing	**KPS**
Photographs	**© Peter Vine** unless otherwise credited.
Copyright	**© Peter Vine** 2020

Set in Adobe Caslon Pro and Frutiger.

A CIP catalogue record of this book is available from the British Library.

ISBN **978-1-912465-08-8**

Artisan House Publishing is committed to using papers sourced from sustainable forests
to ensure a better future for planet Earth. *Spirorbis* is printed on paper certified by the
Forest Stewardship Council (FSC) so you, our reader, can be assured of our commitment.

SPIRORBIS

To Sarah with best wishes

Peter Vine

Stories from my Life

PETER VINE

Foreword by Doug Allan

The hills of Connemara.   © Paula Vine

Contents

Foreword   Doug Allan

Autobiographies are difficult to write, and sometimes even harder to read. But Pete Vine's decision to tell stories from his life rather than the story of his life makes *Spirorbis* engaging, intriguing, honest, and uplifting.

Pete in person is all those and more, but when I was asked once to pick a single word to describe him, I chose *generous*. I saw that quality very soon after meeting him and Paula for the first time in 1974 in the Red Sea. I'll always be grateful for their Bacon Sarnie Sudanese Sunday Breakfasts.

There are many loveable and endearing sides to Pete's character. He's self-effacingly modest about his achievements while simultaneously making sure in the gentlest sense that you hear all about them. Insights abound from the first page.

In birth as in life, he was special. As he points out in the preface, his *en caul* birth was a 1 in 80,000 event and meant fate favoured him with special protections. Good grief, we think, the man is a rarity from the word go. Pete never did venture near a battlefield, but he certainly took his chances underwater with me in the Red Sea. Or was it me taking my chances with him?

I smiled to myself at how he describes Paula's presence at the lectures he gave at Galway University: 'She recounts that, deeply tanned, with long hair and a well-formed physique, I had caught her eye as she sat, well positioned, in the front row.' Not the slightest trace of poetic licence there, I'm sure.

As I read *Spirorbis*, I sensed one recurrent theme. Pete recognises that as he has moved through his life, he is the sum of all his experiences; he's never afraid to reinvent himself. At one point he confesses to having a life plan, but he also acknowledges he's been nudged by chance. You might be tempted while reading his book to think he's been more serendipitous than simply lucky. You're right, up to a point, but behind his wry sense of values he also lives by the old adage, 'The harder I work, the luckier I get.'

Though Pete and I have slipped in and out of each other's lives for over forty-five years, there's one omission in the book. I was with him in the Red Sea in January 1976 when a telegram arrived for me. Six months earlier I'd been turned down for the research diver's post with the British Antarctic Survey. Now I read: 'Unexpected vacancy for diver Antarctic Base H. Please reply soonest.' When I showed it to Pete, he was typically decisive: 'You must grab this chance, you lucky man. It'll be fantastic.' So I did, and my life was changed forever. Thanks, Pete – you certainly knew serendipity when it came calling for me.

A word on the biological naming of living creatures. We're all familiar with *Homo sapiens* or a reference to a *Boa constrictor*. While commonly used, these pairs of words are actually the final levels in the classification system used throughout biology. *Homo* is the genus, the group of humans that contains the unique species *sapiens*. The genus *Boa* includes many kinds of snakes, but only one of them is the species *constrictor*.

Most explorers and scientists would be flattered to have a single species named after them, but Pete has gone much further. In *Vinearia* he has his own entire spirorbid *genus*. That's a word only one letter short of *genius*: surely a reminder, if we needed one, of the man himself.

Doug Allan with a colony of emperor penguins in the Antarctic. © Doug Allan

Let me die a youngman's death.

Let me die a youngman's death
not a clean and in-between-
the-sheets, holy-water death,
not a famous-last-words,
peaceful, out-of-breath death.

When I'm 73
and in constant good tumour
may I be mown down at dawn
by a bright red sports car
on my way home
from an all-night-party

or when I'm 9I
with silver hair
and sitting in a barber's chair
may rival gangsters
with ham-fisted tommyguns burst in
and give me a short back and insides

or when I'm IO4
and banned from The Cavern
may my mistress
catching me in bed with her daughter
and fearing her son
cut me into little pieces
and throw away every piece but one

Let me die a youngman's death
not a free-from-sin, tiptoe-in
candle-wax-and-waning death
not a curtains-drawn, by-angels-borne,
'what a nice way to go' death.

Good man, Roger. My thoughts entirely.

'Let me die a youngman's death' by Roger McGough (© Roger McGough, 1967)
is printed by permission of United Agents (www.unitedagents.co.uk) on behalf of
Roger McGough.

Preface

My mother used to claim, hopefully in jest, that I was 'the misfortune of a warm night', whilst my Arabian friend Kasim suggested that she actually meant 'the good fortune of a cool night'. Either way, the implication is that I was an unplanned addition to the global population, which on my birthday in October 1945 had just passed two billion. Hot or cold, there was no debate about the fact that I emerged encased in a caul, which is widely regarded as an omen of good luck and occurs in less than 1 in 80,000 births. My mother promptly gave the caul to a hospital nurse whose fiancé worked in the merchant navy. I am glad to say that good fortune has lasted throughout my life, but less pleased to note that an inexorable expansion of our numbers indicates that approximately six billion more babies have already followed me onto our planet, almost quadrupling the global population in the past seventy-five years to just under eight billion in 2020 – and it doesn't stop there. By the end of this century, the global population could almost double, to 15.6 billion.

Back in 1945 the world was a very different place. Part of the post-WWII 'bulge', I entered the swinging sixties at the age of fifteen, probably one of most formative years of my life. Disregarding the advice of a garda I once met on the streets of Dublin – 'I wouldn't have started from here, if I was you' – and following some brief introductory notes, I have chosen to begin this memoir with stories from the early 1960s. Fortunately, as my stories relate, and unlike the stereotypical image of that decade, I *do* remember living through it, or at least some of it. Not only did I soak up these years, but I did so for a while within the sounds of Liverpool's musical drumbeat. The Beatles, Gerry and the Pacemakers, and the Spinners were part of a dynamic culture embracing original visual and aural arts, including a group of local poets led by Adrian Henry and Roger McGough. When I first read Roger's poem 'Let Me Die a Youngman's Death', I realised it was an allegorical plea to live life to the full, not to dramatise or romanticise death. While searching through old documents, I discovered a copy of this poem that I had typed out in red ink on my old Remington typewriter, in order to send to my parents. The words speak for themselves.

Peter, in 1948, at the age of about two-and-a-half years, displaying an
early sense of adventure and a love of the sea.

1   Why *Spirorbis*?

I am on first-name terms with *Spirorbis*, having a whole genus (*Vinearia*) named after me and having published descriptions of several new species belonging to the spirorbid dynasty. Each time I came across a previously undescribed species, I had the privilege to name it after one of my colleagues or connected entities.

Spirorbids are tiny tube worms that live on rocks, shells, weeds, boat hulls, marine structures, and other drifting objects. Viewed under the microscope, each has its own unique structure and physiology, displaying features that establish its identity within a genus or species. Once a type is recognised as different from its cousins, representatives (i.e. 'type specimens') are preserved in small glass tubes, methodically catalogued and stored at qualified museums, such as the British Museum of Natural History, and labelled with a scientific Latin or pseudo-Latin name. Subject to peer review and acceptance by qualified curators, they thus enter the official biological record with details of their anatomy, ecology, type locality, distribution, and other details recorded in published scientific literature such as the *Zoological Journal of the Linnean Society*.

I was introduced to these diminutive worms in the 1960s by my academic mentor, Professor Wyn Knight-Jones, who unfailingly encouraged me in my travel and diving adventures. 'Bring back a few spirorbids, old boy?' would be enough to turn my adventures into expeditions and, more than likely, these exploits into scientific publications. His guidance led me to submit a Ph.D. thesis describing spirorbids in New Zealand, Hawaii, and the Red Sea. So, thanks to *Spirorbis*, I became Dr Vine, a title that tickled me to the core. I owe the sub-family a debt of gratitude and perhaps a word of apology for throwing the cat among the pigeons with my discovery of *Anomalorbis*: a new species and genus that breaks some of the previously established taxonomic rules separating Serpulidae and Spirorbidae.

As I have made my way through life, I have often paused to wonder at the infinite spiral form. Starting with a dot – as we all do – it gradually wraps around itself, growing in size and connections – as we all do. I leave you to extend these philosophical ramblings, and I promise you will hear no more of them from me. I hope you enjoy this collection of stories from my life and will come to appreciate how a lowly tube worm could play such a starring role.

2   Albums and Shoeboxes

Much of this book owes its existence to the thoughtful actions of a local friend and building contractor, the late Peter Guy. Tired of sorting through old suitcases and piles of papers, magazines, clothes, souvenirs, and kids' toys – all of which cluttered our attic – I asked Peter to dump everything into the skip that he had placed on our driveway. Dutifully following my instructions, the clearout moved ahead at a great pace until something caught Peter's eye. It was a shoebox full of letters from the Gilbert and Ellice Islands, written in 1964 and 1965. Peter stopped work and started reading. About half an hour later, he descended from the attic, carefully clutching the shoebox. 'Are you really sure that you want me to chuck these out, Pete?' he asked me. Paula and I had recently rescued, also thanks to Peter, our old photo albums and figured we had preserved the most valuable memorabilia, so I was reluctant to abandon our strict decluttering drive. I delved into the box: 'Dear Loving Teacher,' one letter began, whilst another detailed how I killed an octopus with my teeth. A third aerogramme was devoted to describing my voyage from Fiji to Tarawa and my shock at discovering the remnants of one of the most lethal WWII battles that took place in the Pacific.

Then Peter brought me a larger box containing records from my schooldays. Among the unsorted documents was a mixed collection of photographs, letters, postcards, and the odd newspaper cutting that brought back memories from my youth. Climbing into the skip, I began rescuing the forgotten treasure chest of items that set me on a journey through time. Without Peter's timely action, I doubt that this voyage of personal discovery would ever have begun, let alone turn into a book.

Where to begin? Various documents recorded my birth in Swansea in 1945 and the short period we spent in Cardiff before the family – Dad, Mum, sister Sue, and brother Andy – moved north to be near Dad's civil service work in Liverpool. We settled first in Wallasey, and then, in 1950, in Hoylake, famous for its hosting of the British Open golf championships, birdwatching in the Dee Estuary, Hilbre Island, and its location on the Wirral Peninsula that served, during Cromwell's time, as a landing point for troops from Ireland.

I frequently flick though these records, many of which are now stored on my computer, dragging memories from the past into active parts of my brain. Early images speak of a happy child with relatively few worries, unless you count my vivid, frightening nightmares: fear of being bullied if I failed my eleven-plus exam and finished up at the secondary modern school rather than the grammar school; and a sharp reaction to the threat of a mysterious initiation ceremony into the Boy Scouts known as 'marmalading', which I eventually escaped by hiding out in the hills. I should not forget to mention an overbearing embarrassment towards my body shape and an inability to sing, dance, or display any other social skills that would have a chance, at least, of attracting members of the opposite sex. I was no good at football or any other organised sports, especially those that involved training after school. My ambition was to become Elvis Presley, or, in my more developed phase, Jacques Cousteau, or Hans Hass – especially if his beautiful wife, Lotte, came as part of the deal. My main memory from these teenage years is that I was excited by life and ready for action.

3   Boats and Boating

A big breakthrough came on my eighth birthday, when I demonstrated an ability to swim by jumping off the top diving board in Hoylake Baths wearing flippers. This intrepid and daring feat became the trigger for our father to make good on an oft-repeated promise to provide us with a sailing dinghy once all three of us children could swim. He took over half his bedroom to build our first boat, a 2.3-metre-long Gremlin sailing dinghy. My dream of sailing the seven seas was thus set in motion as we manually towed the tiny *Mischief* down to the shore or along Meols Drive to West Kirby and its Marine Lake. Once Andy and I could sail the Gremlin, Dad bought a Heron sailing dinghy – a 3.4-metre gaff-rigged dinghy and a welcome step up from our diminutive *Mischief*. We honed our skills in the Heron and slowly graduated through various friends' boats, racing in Cadets, GPs, Fireflies, Enterprises, Operas, and Falcons, not forgetting our small bilge-keel Silhouette cabin cruiser.

Our adult yachting saga has involved various larger yachts, crewed, borrowed, or bought, including *Silver Dipper* (Sadler 32), *Harmony* (Najad 36), *Suaimhneas* (Malo 45), and our present boat, *Saoirse* (an 8-metre Cornish Crabber). Sailing, and the sea, thus became one of the guiding influences and loves of my life. I am eternally grateful that my wife, Paula, has shared my passion for messing about in boats. Thanks to Dad (and Mum, who hated boats) for helping Andy and me to take the first meaningful steps towards not just a rewarding hobby but a whole career that has wrapped itself around our planet's amazing marine world.

By the time I was eleven, sitting the eleven-plus and thankfully starting my grammar school education, I was an accomplished sailor who regularly sailed for the school team and was familiar with the sand banks and channels that criss-crossed the shores of the Dee Estuary. Andy, being eighteen months older, tended to take the lead in our increasingly adventurous cruising and overnighting at Hilbre Island and the coast of north Wales.

While sorting through my papers from this time, I came across a hard-backed notebook titled '1962 Log Book' that describes some sailing in the latter years of my Calday Grange Grammar School days, when I was seventeen years old. Our summer cruise had been on *Spindrift*, Colin Evans's homebuilt Caprice sailing boat, which was one step up from

Ljubljana, the Silhouette. My notes of the time make regular reference to notoriously unreliable weather forecasts. In hindsight, we had some fairly close shaves, and this was fifteen years before the infamous 1979 Fastnet Race disaster that really drew attention to how hit-and-miss weather planning was at that time.

1962 Summer Cruise

Our 1962 fortnight summer cruise around Anglesey was due to begin on Friday 3 August, on the midnight tide. Unfortunately a depression centred over Scotland was creating strong north-westerly winds that delayed our departure. On Saturday, winds were still strong, but SW force 4–5 was forecast for that night, so we made new preparations to leave on the Sunday midnight tide. Saturday afternoon brought heavy rain. The crew, Colin Evans, my brother Andy, and I decided to visit the cinema in Birkenhead to see *The Four Horsemen of the Apocalypse*, which I later learned received such bad reviews that it threatened the survival of MGM.

After watching the movie, we drove to Sandhey Slipway in Meols, to assess the weather. We also telephoned the Garston Meteorological Office, which forecast slightly improved weather, persuading us to finally leave. Having slipped our mooring at 01:00 hours on Sunday morning, we headed off on a dead beat. I took the first sleep down below while Colin and Andy sailed the boat. They soon needed to reef the sails, with the wind blowing force 5 from the Great Orme making it impossible to lay a course directly for the headland. We headed off on port tack until we reckoned we would be able to clear the Point of Air on starboard tack. The wind continued to freshen, throwing up steep seas, and we fitted the storm jib.

It soon became obvious that the forecast team at Garston had underestimated wind strengths and that we were in for a strong blow. We put about and headed for the sheltered waters off Hilbre Island. A strong tide set us towards Liverpool, and we were surprised to pass near HE3 and HE6, the spit buoys. We altered course and headed for the flashing red light on Hilbre Island, reaching this relatively safe haven at 03:45 and anchoring in the channel before everyone fell into their bunks in the warmth of the cabin.

Waking late on Sunday morning, we enjoyed a hot breakfast, tidied the cabin after the rough night, and prepared to sail to Mostyn on the coast of north Wales. We left Hilbre at 11:00 and set our course for Mostyn harbour in a strong but gradually diminishing wind. We lay there, tethered to the deep harbour wall as the tide receded, revealing a quagmire of mud. At 01:00 that night we were woken by a fellow sailing club member, Rex Taylor, who had sailed into Mostyn on the previous high tide. He asked if we were planning to stay in this muddy place until next high tide, or leaving on this one in the middle of the night. Energised by his enthusiasm to keep going, we quickly slipped our lines, hoisted sails, and were on our way again.

A close reach with full sail took us along the Welsh coast towards the Point of Air that marks the entrance to the River Dee Estuary. Once around the Point, we pulled our sails hard in and commenced a beat towards the seaside holiday town of Rhyl that we had reconnoitred by road earlier in the day. At 03:30 an entry was made in the log commenting that a dawn glow was already lighting the night sky. Rhyl appeared in the distance as a row of golden lights, probably from the casino, helping us considerably. A mackerel sky with mare's tails patterned the early-morning horizon, presaging a strong NW wind, but our wind had swung to the SW and was blowing a more comfortable 3–4. With sails pulled hard in, we were just managing to lay a route parallel to the coast.

Reaching Rhyl at 05:45 on Monday morning, we held a cockpit conference. Rather than stop in Rhyl, we decided to carry on for Great Orme's Head, a key landmark en route to the Menai Straits. We had tide with us, carrying the ebb all the way along the coast as far as Llandudno, when we met a strong counter-current, the start of a flooding tide that threatened to bring us to a halt. With only a light wind to fight the flow, we swallowed our pride, attached an outboard engine to the stern, and headed for the Orme before the current became too much for our diminutive vessel and underpowered outboard.

At 09:00 we finally struggled around the Orme and set a course for Puffin Island. An uncooked breakfast renewed our energies, and we let the engine carry us to the island since wind had now dropped to force 1. We reached Puffin at 11:30 and went ashore in the hope of catching some rabbits for lunch. Unfortunately, myxomatosis had reached the island a few months before us, and the terrain was overgrown due to the removal of herbivores.

So there were no wild rabbits for lunch, and all the island's paths had been hidden by uncontrolled vegetation. Even the remains of the monastery were unrecognisable. But the surrounding waters were unaffected, and we enjoyed a swim before heading back to the boat. Up anchor, up sail, and we were on our way again towards the Menai Straits town of Beaumaris – the perfect place to shop for supplies and to enjoy local facilities, from cinemas to pubs. It had been agreed that Colin and Andy would pick me off the pier at 23:30, after the cinema, but they remained fast asleep. I 'borrowed' a local punt and rowed out to the Caprice. Once woken, the crew quickly returned the stolen boat to its mooring, and we all slept with clear consciences.

Next morning, after a late start, we headed out to meet the 'Swellies', one of the world's most notorious stretches of whirlpools. There is only one safe way to pass through this treacherous body of water, and that is at slack low or high water. Although only half a mile long, they present scores of eddies, whirlpools, overfalls, and fast-flowing currents together with dangerous rocks and shallow waters. Thanks to a late wake-up call, we were at the 'gate' half an hour after low water and foolishly decided to give it a try.

Despite some 10-knot currents, we succeeded in motoring halfway through the Swellies and started to congratulate each other. However, a lapse in concentration was all that was needed to turn success into imminent failure. Not heeding instructions in the *Anglesey & North Wales Coastal Pilot* (the local navigational instructions), we almost ran aground. Fighting to regain control of the boat, we swung its bows back towards the entrance and rode the current back to the Menai Bridge, which marked the start of the Swellies. Once back in calm waters, we dropped anchor to wait for the next slack water. Meanwhile the Mostyn Arms provided a comfortable and welcoming haven.

We spent six hours watching boats taking part in one of the Straits regattas, and at 15:00, shortly before high tide, we went through the Swellies, riding a current that took us along at 9 knots. We arrived at the beautiful town of Caernarvon at 16:10 and entered the harbour to replenish our water supply and obtain a weather report from Valley Airport: light NW winds increasing to moderate and possibly reaching force 5 in the night. With plenty of daylight left, we set sail for Rhoscolyn on the south-west coast of Anglesey, a few kilometres south of Holyhead. By 17:35 we were at the entrance of the channel over Caernarvon Bar, and fifty minutes later we were off Llandwyn Island – an average speed of 5¼ knots, under just motor. At this point of our passage we laid bets among us on when we would reach Rhoscolyn. Colin and Andy bet on 20:15, whilst I predicted that we would not drop anchor before 21:00. With the challenge in mind, we sailed along the beautiful Anglesey coast on a summer's evening with light NW winds and scattered clouds occasionally covering the sun.

The weather was so good that we hung all our wet clothes out to dry and hoped that nobody on shore would mistake them for distress signals. At 50 seconds to nine o'clock, we dropped anchor in Rhoscolyn Bay, in the lee of Ynys Traws. The bay is encumbered with many rocks, and it is dangerous to take a yacht any further in than the lifeboat slip. Our first acquaintances were the owner of a motor launch and his family, who had friends in Hoylake Sailing Club. Much impressed by our efforts, he told us that it had taken him a week to take his boat 5 kilometres along the coast, from Treaddur Bay. He kindly gave us petrol and told us all about Rhoscolyn.

That evening we decided to stretch our legs by taking a cross-country run in search of friends reported to be camping nearby: Wendy Hartley and Jane Elliot. If you count leaping over 5-metre drainage channels and running through knee-deep bog, the mission was partially accomplished, but as for achieving the real goal, it was a dismal failure. We returned to the boat exhausted and in need of 24 hours' sleep. Next morning, after 12 hours' sleep, we went ashore to the post office housed in the front room of a small house in the village. Phone calls were made and postcards sent, and we learnt of other Hoylake residents who had decamped for their summer holidays in Anglesey. It felt quite like home, and we happily accepted various forms of hospitality.

Weather forecasts were against us heading back to open water any time soon. Thursday brought more gales, and after moving our anchorage closer to the shelter afforded by Ynys Traws, we resigned ourselves to another day at Rhoscolyn. Friday was slightly better. We visited the White Eagle to drown our sorrows and telephoned Valley for a weather forecast, which they gave as force 6 SW moderating and going around to the NW – something we thought we could handle. Andy rowed ashore and was told by the coastguard that it would be too rough outside the bay – we should make for Malltraeth, just north of Llandwyn Island.

At 13:45 we prepared *Spindrift* for a fast sail back towards the sheltered waters of Menai Straits. We set sail with a small jib and four rolls in the mainsail. It was a close reach along the coast, and navigation was a simple process of counting the headlands as we passed by, making good speed to our destination. The wind began to strengthen rather than weaken, and we decided that the infamous Caernarvon Bar would be out of the question. Instead, we heeded the coastguard's advice and in preparation for entering Malltraeth we studied the *Anglesey & North Wales Coastal Pilot* and were met with the following text: 'Caution. If a heavy groundswell is running in the bay the passage into the River Cefni should not be attempted.' This came as a surprise, since there was indeed a heavy groundswell, and we expected another dangerous, Caernarvon Bar type of rollercoaster entry. Our guardian angels kicked in, however, and with little wind in our sails we shot across the bar in record time, soon wallowing in sheltered waters and heading for Malltraeth Boat Yard. Apart from running aground for a while, the final stage was uneventful. We anchored in the channel about three cables southwest of the bridge.

We tidied up and went ashore to buy stores. The locals were extremely helpful, and we returned to the boat in rising spirits, only to be met by strengthening winds and a gale that was approaching force 10. Battening down securely, we chocked ourselves into our bunks and tried to settle down to sleep. The cabin was waterproof, but when we woke in the middle of the night our sleeping bags were soaking wet and drips were coming from the coach roof. Condensation. There was no way to avoid it, since it was impossible to arrange suitable ventilation.

We rolled over and listened to the gale howling outside. Through the portholes you could just make out the disturbed surface of the sea as a mass of white foam and spray. The waves were short and steep during the flood, but when the wind went against the tide the sea became very confused. The light which eventually replaced darkness on Saturday morning was simply an apology for a miserable dawn. We stayed in our bunks as long as possible, and when we did eventually poke our heads out of the hatch, we were greeted by a scene of utter confusion. The tide had been driven an extra 50 metres up the beach, and a yellow boat had capsized at its mooring. More gales and heavy rain were forecast.

It was time to consider our options. The idea of parents to the rescue, with trailer and tow bar and a local tractor to get us over the mud, was hard to resist. At 09:30 on Sunday morning, the rescue brigade arrived, followed – right on cue, at 10:30 – by a local tractor that rescued the rescue vehicles, heaving us all onto firm ground. It was a beautiful sunny morning, and it seemed sad to be back on the road, all the way back to Hoylake. But *Spindrift* did not have a dry bottom for long. At 19:30 that evening, we returned her to the mooring that we had left seven days before. And that was the end of our 1962 summer cruise.

Emerald Cruise

The logbook also records part of a delivery sail that I did that same year on board *Emerald*, from the Isle of Man to Rock Ferry on the River Mersey, through the night, setting off at 18:40 with Peter Bailey, Glynne Attersall, and Brian McAlister. The old traditional vessel sailed beautifully with the helm lashed and the mizzen sail allowed to flap a bit. She rarely went more than 5 degrees off course and steered herself better than any of us could have done. I was on the midnight to 2 a.m. dog watch, keeping an eye out for shipping and trying to interpret various lights. Reciting 'Green to green and red to red; perfect safety go ahead' or 'If to starboard red appear, 'tis your duty to keep clear' was all well and good, but what was I to do with the ship coming up right behind me?

When I guessed the approaching vessel was about half a mile away, I showed it my torch light, which might have been fine if the torch was working correctly. Unfortunately, faulty connections made it flash, and the ship's signals officer must have thought I was signalling in Morse code.

The next thing I knew, the ship was signalling to me with an Aldis light. Our efforts to respond in Morse failed due to a faulty Aldis, and the ship approached within 75 metres so it could take a closer look at this mysterious sailing craft. They steered around us, overtaking in the dark, and eventually my watch came to an end with Glynne taking over the helm.

I recently chased down the history of this beautiful old boat, designed by Albert Strange and owned at the time of our sail by a Mr John C. Richardson of Liverpool. Peter Bailey was a friend of the Richardson family, and hence probably the commission to deliver her back to her home port at that time. She is still going strong, owned at present by Richard Wynne of Woodbridge, Suffolk.

My Fair Lady and Hurricane Faith

On 9 September 1966, ninety-eight passengers and forty-six crew were on board the *MF Skagerak* ferry which was returning to Denmark from Norway across Skagerrak Strait. In good conditions the one-year-old ferry could make the crossing in about five hours. Shortly before dawn on the same day, three other crew members and I set off from the Danish port of Grenaa in the 12-metre yacht *My Fair Lady*, owned and skippered by Hems Kalis (a friend of Peter Bailey), to deliver the yacht back to her home port of Southampton. Like ourselves, the train ferry's captain had waited for an easing of the winds of the tropical storm Faith, born weeks before in the South Atlantic, before setting sail. And, like the ferry captain, we were impatient to make the passage. We had been held up in Grenaa by engine problems and a storm that was more typical of warm Atlantic waters than these cold northern seas.

We also shared a blissful ignorance of the tremendous wind forces that were still wrapped up in the ominously named weather system. The ferry was 60 kilometres into her voyage when weather conditions deteriorated dramatically – high-speed wind accompanied by torrential rain. Our own yacht experienced similar conditions, and we were battening down the hatches at roughly the same time that the vehicle deck hatches on *MF Skagerak* broke and tons of water poured into the lower regions of the ship.

For our part, we hove to about 15 kilometres away from where the ferry drama was unfolding and took to our bunks, leaving one person at the wheel. We had arrived in the mother of all storms and were prepared for the worst after hearing an ominous Mayday call broadcast over the crackling airwaves. *That could soon be us*, we reflected, listening to roaring waves and bracing ourselves as each one threatened to capsize us. We were glad to hear that the Royal Danish Airforce was out in strength to rescue the ferry's passengers and crew, and there was nothing we could do to help in that operation except to focus on our own survival and not call on their valuable resources to rescue us.

We remained drifting and hove to for the next four and a half days, by which time we had been flung across the Dogger Bank and felt the full force of Hurricane Faith – a storm that meteorologists had expected to have blown itself out by the time it reached so far north. Over this frightening period I was violently seasick and managed to eat only a packet of Maryland cookies and an orange. I struggled up to the cockpit to take my turn at the wheel, increasingly weakened by lack of food, water, and sleep. I was even beginning to hallucinate – not the best of safety-first drills.

We only learnt the full details of Faith's story after we escaped its vicious clutches. They do say hindsight is a wonderful thing, and had we known then what we know now, we would never have left Grenaa until the storm had completely disappeared from the weather map. By the time I consumed the orange, having lost track of our dead-reckoning navigation, we thought that we were drifting off Edinburgh and would seek shelter there. When we did take sight of Britain's east coast we were close to Hull, a straight-line distance of about 300 kilometres from Edinburgh. No wonder I failed my GCE Navigation certificate.

A rescue operation was launched by the Royal Danish Sea Air Rescue Squadron 722 to assist the passengers and crew of *Skagerak*. In a later report they revealed that the operation lasted over eight hours as they faced 50-knot winds and 40-foot waves. The ferry sank in 75–80 feet of water about 6 miles from the coast after drifting 17 miles. Miraculously, all passengers and crew were rescued, although one person later died from injuries. Three other people lost their lives in two separate incidents.

Once on dry land, we were all exhausted and weakened by the physical abuse that we had been subjected to by the storm. Little was said between us, but we were all glad to be alive and grateful for our skipper's cool head and experienced guidance through the worst weather any of us had ever seen, or were likely to see. I caught a train and bus back home to Hoylake and enjoyed a few days' recuperation. Not keen to return to *My Fair Lady*, nor even sure that Hems would want me back aboard, I was moved by the call he had with my father, urging me to complete the trip. I took the train back to Hull, boarded the gallant yacht, and we all sailed in perfect autumn sunshine all the way to Southampton.

Lough Ness Monster

My early love of sailing was an introduction to an ever-expanding world of adventure, starting with a birdwatching holiday with my fifth-form classmate John Harriman on Bardsey Island and quickly followed, in the summer of 1962, by the Observer Lough Ness Monster Expedition, on which I was the youngest member. Led by WWII hero and single-handed Atlantic sailor Herbert 'Blondie' Hasler, the expedition was run like a military operation. I was fascinated by the whole process, including sailing the famous junk-rigged yacht *Jester*, in which our leader, in 1960, had challenged Sir Francis Chichester to a single-handed transatlantic race. I treasure the letter that Blondie instructed his assistant, and soon-to-be wife, to write to me on 14 April 1962. It confirmed that I should plan on joining the expedition from 21 to 31 July, and that if our Silhouette was available we could bring it to join in the search. We did not take up the offer of using *Ljubljana*, but I did arrive on the prescribed date, after months of anticipation.

The expedition that I joined had already been working for six weeks, and I was to be present for the final fortnight. On my first day I was met by Colonel Hasler, who explained that the project was aimed at investigating the biology of the lough, with particular reference to the likelihood or otherwise of a surviving enigmatic creature, commonly known as 'the monster'. Before our attempt at scientific recording of the monster, recent sightings had been reported by multiple observers: two fishermen, one policeman, one water bailiff, and twenty guests at the Clansman Hotel. I was to integrate into the research programme, which comprised a twenty-four-hour watch of the lough being maintained for ten weeks, without a break. The watchkeeper had two powerful pairs of binoculars, a telescope, a cine camera, and two still cameras, all of which were kept adjusted for prevailing conditions. This shore-based surveillance was supported by a twenty-four-hour patrol onboard *Jester*, whose crew was also equipped with two pairs of binoculars, two still cameras, one flash, one cine camera, and a 'feeling pole', together with hydrophone gear and a Morse-code-ready Aldis lamp. In addition, we operated hydrophone gear from a dinghy, together with eel-fishing gear. The hydrophone survey was deemed to be important, since it was based on the assumption that any creature of the size imagined would be likely to emit detectable echolocation sounds, like those of a dolphin.

On 29 June, researchers Marc Barton and Dave Dunn were sailing approximately 270 metres off the south shore, opposite Urquhart Bay. They had deployed their high-frequency (HF) microphone listening device at 25 metres and noticed ripples about 18 metres astern. Gybing the boat around to investigate, they described the ripples as a small disturbance in the water, moving slowly away from the shore:

> As we approached . . . I saw what I took to be the back fin of a fish at the head of the ripple. At about 15 yards I saw there were two separate disturbances and that they persisted. I took a few photos but the light was bad . . . the disturbances remained separated at a constant distance apart which I estimated at eight to ten feet and each disturbance was rotating. These little whirlpools seemed to rotate in different directions. There were no bubbles . . . all the water appeared quite dark except when it reflected the sky and I could see nothing below the surface.

There was more to come. The disturbances lasted for about five minutes, and after they subsided there were clicks recorded on the HF recording equipment. These were totally different in nature to anything that the team had heard before. Unlike the constant hum of atmospheric crackle, these sounds lasted for ten minutes or so and then disappeared. Ten minutes later they were back, once again gradually diminishing before disappearing. Three hours later and about a mile away, whilst becalmed off Urquhart Bay, Barton and Dunn again saw two counter-rotating eddies, about 3 metres apart at a range of approximately 15 metres. These were followed a short time later by a third eddy forming a triangle with the other two. A small dark hump then replaced each eddy: 'dark brown or black with smooth shiny skin. These were in view for five minutes and then disappeared. *Jester* could not move closer because she was becalmed.'

The pattern was repeated an hour later, about 6 metres away, and again an hour later when four humps appeared. These recordings were the closest we got to proving the existence of the monster, but we soon learned the error of our ways. After sending the recordings for specialised analysis in Scandinavia, we received the qualified statement that the 'sonar clicks' emanated either from one large marine creature or from a small group of them. But by that stage we had realised that the mysterious clicks were due to the underwater microphone knocking against the protective cage that surrounded it. Much to everyone's disappointment, this potentially exciting discovery was just one more false alarm in the long-running saga of the Lough Ness monster. To its believers, eddies, probably caused by rising salmon, were readily claimed as 'suspicious sightings', whilst out-of-focus blobs on pictures were still being presented as proof of the monster's existence.

At the behest of Colonel Hasler, I had suspended my disbelief, but I had been sceptical from the beginning to the end of the expedition. I did not think it provided any evidence for the existence of the monster, but I had been sworn to secrecy and was not permitted to share my views until his report was published in the newspaper later that year.

Plesiosaurs or no plesiosaurs, the lough delivered a fantastic experience and one that opened doors to even more adventures in the years that followed. I will always be grateful to Blondie Hasler for the opportunity to participate in such a fun expedition.

Clifden Boat Club: Finding and Founding
Once Paula and I had built our house on the shores of Clifden Bay, I was keen to sail its waters. In 1975 we brought over from England a GP14 wooden-hull dinghy, and I got back into the habit of yelling at my crew

to 'get your arse out'. We were generally the only leisure boat on the sea, with the exception of Adrian O'Connell, who sailed a traditional *gleoiteog*. One sunny day in midsummer, we met on the bay.

'I can't understand why more people don't do this,' I said.

'They have a different attitude here to what you're used to in the UK. Boats are for fishing and transportation, but even those traditional boats are almost extinct,' he replied.

'What we need is a sailing club where the young people can learn to sail.'

'We could buy some Mirror dinghy kits. You raise the money and I'll build them.'

And so it began.

I soon learnt that there were plenty of keen supporters living in the region, and at our first meeting to gather support for such a club, we were presented with a surprise. We were asked why we were starting a sailing club when the Clifden Boat and Sea Angling Club already existed. This long-forgotten entity had a single surviving member, Tom Connolly, however, it owned a large building on Clifden Quay. With a little help from its friends, Clifden Boat and Sea Angling Club was resurrected and its property taken in hand to raise finance for a clubhouse. The existing building was acquired by the local fish farm and as an initial base for the RNLI, while Clifden's revived boat club built its new clubhouse. This went from strength to strength and is now a firm fixture of Clifden's maritime activities, having been instrumental in teaching hundreds of people to sail. How things have changed!

Gerry's Ordeal and Rescue

Another chance encounter with Adrian O'Connell led indirectly to the establishment of an RNLI station in Clifden. It was in the early days of our fish farming in Ardbear Bay. I had switched to writing for a living, which I did in our old garage, looking out over the garden and sea. Meanwhile, my brother-in-law Eugene and his friend Gerry were running the salmon farm. Suddenly the garage doors burst open and a very anxious-looking Eugene urged me to come and help him. The two of us rushed down to the slipway at the bottom of our road. Only minutes earlier you could hardly have imagined a more tranquil scene – no wind and a flat calm sea. Eugene explained to me that he had come ashore from the cages to fetch a spanner, since they were doing some maintenance work. He had picked up the spanner and was about to push off in our small wooden curragh when a blast of wind nearly knocked him off his feet. It seemed to have come from nowhere, and we found it impossible to get the curragh back into a depth where we could use the outboard. On top of a raging gale, it was January and freezing cold.

'Gerry is still on the raft,' Eugene shouted across the storm, checking that I could hear him. There was no need for further explanation. We had to get him ashore before he died of hypothermia. He was not wearing heavy-weather gear and, despite his rugby toughness, he could only survive for an hour or so in these conditions. We rang the helicopter rescue service in Shannon, but they told us it was too rough to fly. 'You're on your own, I'm afraid. Can't you get a local boat to assist?' Eugene and I knew there were no boats accessible in the bay, with one possible exception. Adrian O'Connell was running a small boat-building and marine maintenance business, and I knew he would do his best. We spoke on the phone. 'You'll have to come over this side,' he told me.

I quickly put on my diving wetsuit and drove through hail and vicious gusts, 5 or 6 kilometres around the head of the bay and along Errislannan peninsula, to meet up with him. When I reached his boatyard he was struggling to launch an inflatable dinghy whilst a huge door was being blown off its hinges. 'Jump in,' he ordered, and we were off. 'The throttle cable is not connected to the engine,' he shouted. 'You do the throttle, and I'll steer.'

Once outside the shelter of his little harbour, we were faced by huge waves that threatened to overturn the dinghy. Peering ahead, I could just make out the raft, where Gerry was standing bold upright like a stone statue. As we approached, I slowed the engine and Adrian brought us alongside. I signalled Gerry to get in, but he was already immobilised by the cold. Jumping onto the fish cage walkway, I grabbed him and pushed him, quite roughly, to the dinghy. Immediately we were all aboard, Adrian steered away from the bucking raft, and I grabbed the engine throttle to make sure we kept clear. For a moment, Adrian headed us into the waves, but it was apparent that all we could do was to surf the wave train up the bay, as far as the Salt Lake road bridge, where we ended up and were taken in by French sailor Luc Hellaire. Gerry eventually warmed up, and we all breathed big sighs of relief.

Years after this incident, a planning officer from the RNLI visited Clifden at the behest of Adrian and a few other local mariners. 'We need evidence that there is a need that the RNLI can meet,' the official told the meeting. Adrian prepared a report, explaining how an inflatable boat had saved Gerry's life. 'The RNLI would be well placed to save more lives from a base in Clifden,' he told the lifeboat team. That marked the beginning of a long and highly successful lifeboat service that continues to thrive, run by a valiant volunteer crew.

That Sinking Feeling

Once we moved into yacht ownership, our sailing waters extended from Achill Island to the north of our home on the west coast of Ireland to the south coast of England, on the River Hamble. The latter was the home of the largest yacht marina in the UK, and it tended to be where we went to buy or sell our yachts. The delivery voyages were often the highlight of our sailing season, full of excitement at owning a new and increasingly complex sailing boat. For most of these voyages we were blessed by Breton skipper Hervé Le Guen, who knew more about sailing and navigation than the rest of us put together. John Ruddy and Padraic de Bhaldraithe were regular and reliable crew members, and Damian Ward also made some deliveries for us, ensuring the boat was always well cared for. On a few voyages between the south coast of Ireland and Clifden, it was just Paula and me on our 10-metre Sadler, *Silver Dipper*, 11-metre Najad, *Harmony*, or 14-metre Malo, *Suaimhneas*. It was on the last of these boats that one of our scariest episodes occurred.

Hervé, Paula, John Ruddy, and I were sailing *Suaimhneas* along the south coast of England and had picked up a mooring buoy in Fowey harbour so we could go ashore for dinner. Well fed and generously watered, we came back on board at around 10 p.m., ready to hit our bunks. Just as John put his head on the pillow, he heard a trickling sound and decided to investigate. Opening the engine hatch, he peered inside to discover that seawater was lapping around the engine, and the bilges were about to overflow onto the floorboards. We were slowly sinking.

Not sure about the source of our leak, John raced for the electric bilge pumps, which failed to operate. No matter – we would use the high-volume hand bilge pump in the cockpit. We pumped away, but nothing happened. It was blocked. John dived back into the engine compartment and found that the offending pipe was part of our desalination freshwater system. I had been fiddling with it earlier in the day, and it had started to siphon water into the hull rather than act as an overflow pipe. He switched off the pipe, and we began to wonder how to drain the bilges. John confirmed that the engine would start, and then he removed the seawater intake pipe from the closed-off through-hull valve, dropping the pipe that normally sucked in cooling water from outside, to suck water from the bilges once the engine was restarted. Half an hour later, the bilges were dry and we switched back the pipe to perform its usual function. John had saved the day, and we completed our passage to Ireland without further incident.

Cruising in Connemara and Joyce's Passage

While Gerry's rescue happened in horrendous weather conditions, it is remarkable how many rescues happen on perfectly calm sunny days. So it was with one of our much-loved sails along the west coast of Ireland, when I decided to take a famous shortcut, sneaking inside Slyne Head. Known as Joyce's Passage, it is a short, narrow gap between two small islands. I had seen yachts sail through at full speed and was convinced that my duplicate GPS chart plotters were all I needed to navigate a safe passage. Motoring between the jumble of rocks at 8 knots, I swung our bows into the gap. 'Are you sure this is safe?' Paula asked. 'No problem. I can see it on the—' My sentence was cut short by a violent crash into solid rock at lower keel level, beneath the yacht. Paula was thrown forward into the cockpit canopy – dazed and bloodied. A knife that had been sitting on the sink slab took off like a flying dagger, lodging itself firmly in a varnished teak panel. When I entered the cabin to check if we had holed the hull, the knife was still quivering.

Hovering about 3 metres above the mast top, there just happened to be a rescue helicopter. A quick scan of the horizon confirmed that the two of us – 14-metre yacht and hovering copter – were the only human activity in sight. The eye in the sky was on a mission to locate the bodies of two people who had drowned a few days earlier. When the pilot saw me charge into the narrowest navigable passage in these waters, he decided to hang along for the ride. Our sudden stop probably came as no surprise. I had only been vaguely aware of the helicopter before the keel banged into the seabed, but now it formed part of my rescue plan.

'Rescue helicopter, rescue helicopter, rescue helicopter. This is yacht *Suaimhneas* in Joyce's Passage off Slyne Head. Over.'

'Yacht *Suaimhneas*, this is Rescue Helicopter 115. Over.'

'Rescue Helicopter 115, please stand by while I check our vessel for leaks after hitting a rock in the channel. Over.'

'Yacht *Suaimhneas*, this is Rescue Helicopter 115. Standing by. Over.'

I felt the reassurance of a professional at the other end of my radio and pulled up the floorboards to peer into the deep, narrow bilges. My fear and remorse were overbearing. What had I done to our beautiful yacht, and why hadn't I heeded Paula's cautionary comments? Her face was covered in blood – what had I done to her? I shone a torch into the darkest recesses of the hull. No sound nor sight of water. Miraculously, the boat had survived the violent impact, and just I was about to report all OK, the coastguard in Dublin came on line.

'Yacht *Suaimhneas*, Yacht *Suaimhneas*, Yacht *Suaimhneas*, this is the coastguard. We have launched the lifeboat from Clifden. They will be with you in twenty minutes. Please describe your vessel and how many people are on board.' I had not given any thought to the fact that my call to the helicopter, which was within 10 metres of our boat, would be monitored with equal clarity by the country's rescue service, listening on Channel 16, 200 or so kilometres away. I backed *Suaimhneas* out of the passage and headed around Slyne Head. The lifeboat seemed to arrive in minutes. How do they manage such rapid responses? Although we were not imperilled, it was good to see the crew escort us back to Clifden. Several days later the marine surveyor came to Kilrush, where we had taken the yacht to check on her. 'A GPS-assisted grounding' was how it was reported.

OceansWatch

On our visit to New Zealand in 2006 we chartered a skippered yacht to sail through the Bay of Islands for a few days. Our skipper, Chris Bone, and his partner, Julia Alabaster, were full of ideas about how to harness the facilities and interests of the international yachting community to support social, environmental, and economic development among remote island communities in the Pacific. I tuned in to his progressive thinking, and in 2007, between us, we established a new charity: OceansWatch (OW) (www.oceanswatch.org). Over the years, the charity has had some notable successes and a few frustrating disappointments. Under Chris's leadership, OW gained a reputation for professionally managed development programmes in island communities, providing environmental surveys, conservation training, education, infrastructure, and healthcare in areas that were in need of help. By listening to these traditional island communities, and working in partnership with them to address their needs, OW gained the support of key organisations, from village councils to international development bodies. On the website, Chris writes: 'We respond to the requests of communities that are struggling with declining marine or terrestrial resources and help them through resourcing, empowering and facilitating processes to implement locally managed protected areas to protect their biodiversity.'

As a co-founder of OW, a member of its board of directors, and one of its patrons, I took a close interest in its various projects, particularly in the Eastern Solomon Islands, where Chris focused much of his efforts. Over the years, one issue occupied more and more of the organisation's time and efforts: deforestation of sustainable woodlands to make way for commercial mining. It proved to be an exhausting and sometimes dangerous mission that was reported to be heavily influenced by misinformation, bribery, and corruption, splitting communities and leaving devastation in its wake. As OW's website emphasises, forests are an important habitat for several reasons. In OW's project areas, they are home to critically endangered species such as the Temotu ground dove. They provide a suite of ecosystem services such as providing clean water, reducing landslides and erosion, regulating local weather patterns, and serving as a vital source of food and construction materials.

ABOVE & OPPOSITE
John Harriman, my birdwatching buddy in fifth class at Calday Grange Grammar School, handed me these sketches, torn from the pages of an exercise book, after returning from an Easter holiday together on Bardsey Island. I failed in my efforts to trace John, who is clearly a talented artist.   © John Harriman

TOP   Our first boat, a Gremlin dinghy, on West Kirby Marine Lake. My father built this tiny boat on his bedroom floor at Sandtoft Hotel.

ABOVE   Andy and I competed to make and race a raft on West Kirby Marine Lake.

TOP Fireflies racing on West Kirby Marine Lake. Teams came from all over the UK to compete for the Wilson Trophy for team racing.

ABOVE My father fitted a 1.5 h.p. Stuart Turner marine engine to our much-loved Silhouette cruising boat, *Ljubliana*, in which we explored North Wales and the Dee Estuary. She did all of 3 to 4 knots at full revs. Andy was also a practical guy who helped with such jobs.

Hilbre Island is at the mouth of the Dee Estuary, between the Wirral Peninsula and the hills of North Wales. It was the starting point for many of our adventures.
© Alamy

ABOVE The Swellies in the Menai Straits are challenging, but we made it through by timing our passage to low tide. © Glyn Davies

OPPOSITE TOP Peter Bailey was my physics teacher at school and my mentor in all things marine.

OPPOSITE The gaff-rigged yawl *Emerald* mostly steered herself on our delivery passage from the Isle of Man to Southampton. She was built in 1938 at Deganwy, North Wales, by Williams & Parkinson. © Richard Wynne

Jester was the Chinese junk-rigged folkboat in which Lieutenant Colonel 'Blondie' Hasler had raced Francis Chichester across the Atlantic in the first Observer Singlehanded Transatlantic Race in 1960. We sailed the famous yacht all over Lough Ness in search of the elusive monster. The long pole we carried on *Jester* was an attempt to get a skin imprint on a lump of plasticine at the end of the probe. The long box at the stern was used for looking underwater from deck level.

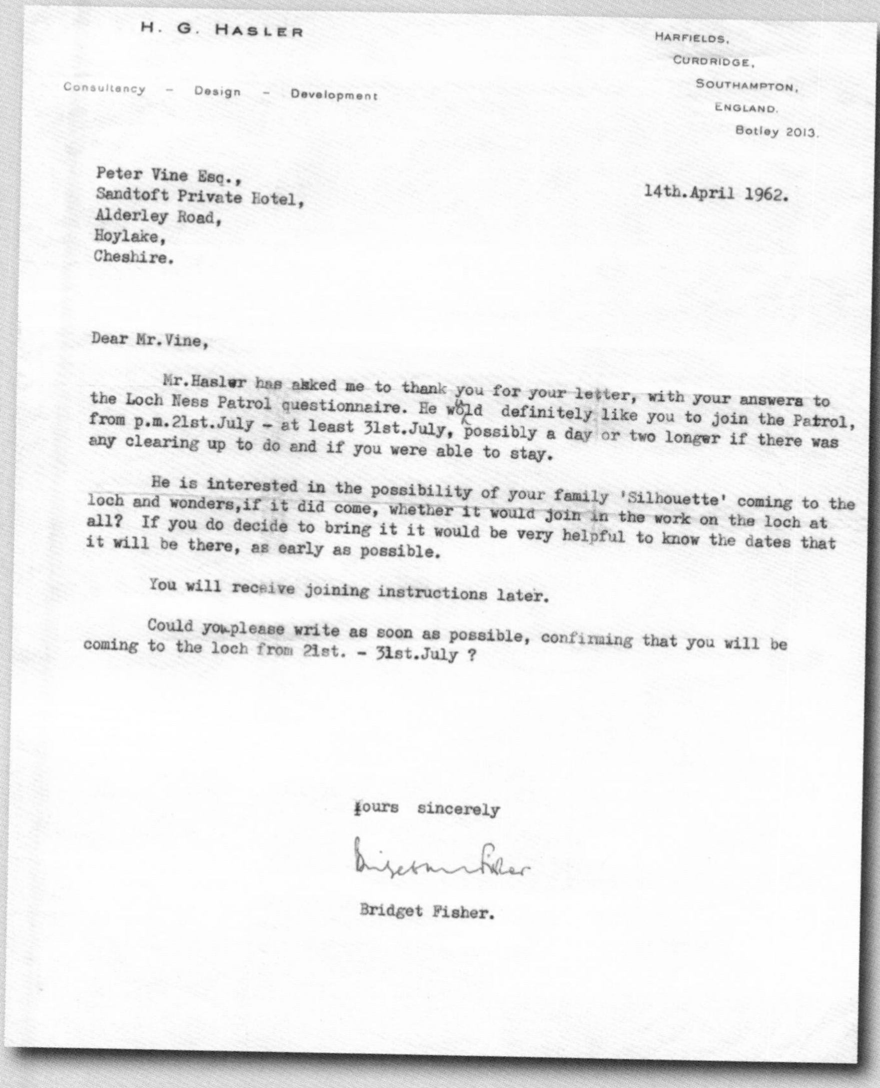

H. G. HASLER

Consultancy — Design — Development

HARFIELDS,
CURDRIDGE,
SOUTHAMPTON,
ENGLAND.
Botley 2013.

Peter Vine Esq.,
Sandtoft Private Hotel,
Alderley Road,
Hoylake,
Cheshire.

14th. April 1962.

Dear Mr. Vine,

Mr. Hasler has asked me to thank you for your letter, with your answers to the Loch Ness Patrol questionnaire. He would definitely like you to join the Patrol, from p.m. 21st. July - at least 31st. July, possibly a day or two longer if there was any clearing up to do and if you were able to stay.

He is interested in the possibility of your family 'Silhouette' coming to the loch and wonders, if it did come, whether it would join in the work on the loch at all? If you do decide to bring it it would be very helpful to know the dates that it will be there, as early as possible.

You will receive joining instructions later.

Could you please write as soon as possible, confirming that you will be coming to the loch from 21st. - 31st. July ?

Yours sincerely

Bridget Fisher.

I became the youngest member of the Observer/'Blondie' Hasler
1962 Lough Ness Expedition.

TOP   Hurricane Faith, which almost sank us in the North Sea in September 1966, had the longest track of any recorded hurricane up to that time.
© The Weather Channel

ABOVE   *My Fair Lady* carried us safely through the five-day voyage from the Baltic to Hull, placing us over a hundred miles off course thanks to Hurricane Faith.
© Hems Kalis

TOP *Leenane Head* was an Isle of Man 'nobby' that was expertly sailed between Cleggan and Inishbofin by Paddy O'Halloran. For many years this was the main way to get out to the island.

ABOVE Paula and myself, sailing *Harmony* in Clifden Bay. *Harmony* was an 11-metre-long Najad yacht, built in Sweden. She was a near-perfect boat for exploring Irish waters: very strong and very seaworthy.

ABOVE Opening day of the new clubhouse at Clifden Boat Club, 3rd June 1990.
© Barry McInerney

Back Row
Saul Joyce, Catriona Vine, Pete Vine, John Stanley, Paddy McDonagh,
Julia Awcock, Liam Clarke.

Middle Row
Susie Ward, Emer Joyce, Doris Lindemann, Jean LeDorvan, Barry Ward.

Front Row
Francie Mannion, Donal O'Scanaill, Padraig McCormack, Talbot O'Farrell,
Jackie Ward, Adrian O'Connell. Damian Ward (inset).

OPPOSITE Our Malo 45, *Suaimhneas*, was a joy to sail but over-equipped in almost
every way. Nevertheless, Paula and I were happy to sail her without additional crew.
My own propensity for seasickness prevented the longer voyages that she was built
to undertake. © Olivier Bauduin

This fine working boat, a Red Sea sambuk, sailed past us in Sudanese waters.
She was crewed by Yemeni sailors who dived for fish and shellfish and probably
conducted a bit of low-key smuggling.

TOP The UAE brought two racing dhows to Galway to mark the famous Volvo Ocean Race. They were supposed to race against a local púcán but, once rigged, the first dhow sailed off so fast that she quickly disappeared from sight. A cold, wet crew, plus semi-waterlogged dhow, were eventually rescued by a friendly Galway RNLI lifeboat.   © Boyd Challenger

ABOVE The *Nora Bheag* played host to Emirati sailors when they visited Galway. © Boyd Challenger

The hooker *American Mór* sailing at Cashel Regatta in 2005.

The days of sail in Arabia were drawing to a close in the 1960s, but they will not be forgotten. I was often struck by the classic sails of both dhows and hookers – efficient, challenging, and above all, graceful.   © Ronald Codrai

Fungie, the Dingle dolphin, used to greet us when we sailed our Mirror sailing dinghy in the entrance to Dingle harbour. Here he is again, doing an impressive 'spy hop'.

For our first underwater encounter with Fungie, three of us shared one set of snorkelling gear: one mask, leaving two of us to open our eyes underwater; two flippers, leaving one without any, and a single snorkel that was not much use to any of us. Paula took the picture of my encounter without a mask. Meanwhile, Triona vividly recalls her meeting, without a wetsuit and only able to flip with one leg. Fungie took it all in his stride and made lots of eye contact. I will never forget his playfulness in these magical meetings.

4 Folk Music and the Clubs

Winter of 1963 saw the establishment of what was to become one of Cheshire's most popular folk clubs. The *Liverpool Daily Post* recorded the event as follows:

> . . . at the West Kirby inn, next Saturday sees the start of a folk song club formed by Andrew Vine, the nineteen year old son of the proprietor of another local hotel. A specialist in sea shanties, he has recruited a new folk song group the Leesiders comprising a girl from West Kirby and two young men from Liverpool. 'We intend to give guests the chance to stand up and sing before an audience,' he told me.

The news was repeated in more detail in the Friday 31 January 1964 edition of *Hoylake News and Advertiser*, and so Dee Folk Club was born.

Whilst we were experiencing a strong revival of folk music, the big story was the rock music pioneered by Bill Haley and Elvis Presley in the States, and by our own homegrown lads from Liverpool and Birmingham. We felt part of the Beatles' surge in popularity and were proud of our local bands. I skipped school to attend a lunchtime concert at the Cavern, and was at the Empire Theatre concert where the Beatles were supposed to be supporting, but completely outshone, a confused Little Richard. 1963 and 1964 were years to remember, but there was a lot to take in. Buzzing with music, both folk and rock, fashion became another important part of the scene, with the miniskirt – thanks to Mary Quant and her Bazaar – raising testosterone levels off the dial. Part of the War Bulge generation, we were ready to take over the world if the world didn't get us first.

I followed these events with a deep sense of belonging. The Beatles were our own lads. They had played at our local YMCA, and John Lennon's wife, Cynthia, lived on our road in Hoylake. 'Love Me Do' was followed in February by their first number one single, 'Please Please Me', which became the title track of their first album, released in March. Meanwhile the Rolling Stones had their first hit single with 'Come On' released in the UK. And in August, much to our chagrin, the Beatles gave their final performance at the Cavern Club. On 15 October, the

Daily Mirror used the term 'Beatlemania' in a story about the group's concert the previous day in Cheltenham. The rest is history.

Despite the overwhelming success of the rock and roll movement, folk music remained popular, and our Friday nights would be spent at the Spinners club in Liverpool. Over that summer of '63, Andy and I mixed sailing with music – often returning to Hoylake by train from Liverpool after the pubs closed, and heading off from our mooring in Meols soon after midnight at the start of a weekend cruise that might take us north of the Mersey or westwards, towards Hilbre and the beckoning coast of Wales.

Though we had an extremely positive start to the folk club at the Dee Hotel in West Kirby, turning away over fifty people on the first two nights, the new management of the rather stuffy hotel did not like what they were seeing: young people enjoying themselves. We were told to find alternative accommodation, and so began a search for a more suitable venue. It wasn't until October that we reopened with the Fo'castle Club at Black Horse Hotel. The management there was extremely grateful for the vibrant trade that we attracted every Tuesday night, and the future again looked bright. Just as this whole scene was heating up, I left it all behind to spend a year in what was, for me at least, paradise.

5 Voluntary Service Overseas – a Year in Paradise

'. . . have recommended you for service with V.S.O.,' stated the letter dated 7 November 1963. It was signed by E.R. Chadwick, assistant director of Voluntary Service Overseas (VSO) and my new 'best friend'. Despite the burst of adrenaline the letter generated, there were a few bridges to cross before I would land in paradise – not least the small matter of my A levels and the acquisition of a university place. I managed the former (A levels in physics, chemistry, biology, and general studies), much to the surprise of my teachers at Calday Grange Grammar School. Actually the real shock had come two years earlier, in June 1962, with my eight O levels, one of which was in Seamanship, Signals, and Rules of the Road. Having been assigned into the least academic stream for five years, thanks to a perception among staff that I was a renegade, I had been expected to pass one or two O levels; sixth form had never been considered.

There were a few people who recognised a slow burner when they saw one. Peter Bailey, my physics teacher, sailing companion, and mentor, was a source of inspiration during my latter years at Calday, not just because he treated me as an adult and believed in me, but also for his guidance in my career choice as a marine biologist. Without Peter Bailey I don't think I would ever have reached university. The next major influence was the Professor of Zoology at Swansea University, Wyn Knight-Jones, who said, 'Jolly good, old boy' more times than I care to recall. My final report from grammar school was issued by the headmaster, Eric Hawkins, when I was eighteen years and eight months, just before sitting my A levels in July 1964. At that stage I was vice-captain of the school and ready to take on the world. In the few months between leaving school and departing for VSO I enjoyed a mixture of travel and temporary employment.

VSO did not give its volunteers a choice in where they would be stationed. The movement, which still operates today, had been established by Alec Dickson six years earlier. Dickson saw that the post-war ending of National Service created an opening for a voluntary youth service that would work to the advantage of both young volunteers and the people they could help. There was already a nascent organisation called Year-In-Between, founded by the Bishop of Portsmouth, Launcelot Fleming.

What Fleming had started in 1958 with eighteen graduates in various countries had been rebranded and expanded. By 1964 there were five hundred volunteers in fifty-six countries. Three hundred of these were school leavers, like me, who were expected to pass on skills and know-ledge gained through our modern education system, in both practical and academic fields. A letter dated 25 June 1964 revealed the final details of my year away: 'I am glad to inform you that your services have been accepted in the Gilbert and Ellice Islands where you will be assisting with welfare work and general administration duties under the District Commissioner, mostly in urban communities.'

Journey to the Sun

By sheer serendipity, I had been posted to the one country I was des-perate to visit, then known as the British Colony of Gilbert and Ellice Islands, later to become Kiribati and Tuvalu. These are both independent island nations forming part of the great chain of undersea mountains that crops up between Hawaii in the north and New Zealand in the south. They are also two of the countries most threatened by sea-level rise caused by global warming. The predicted response to further rise in sea level is emigration, but this option is not readily available to islanders who have limited skills and generally lack financial resources to settle and work overseas.

My own experiences of life in these most attractive islands belong to a different era, when the population was more manageable and tra-ditional livelihoods were still possible. Arthur Grimble's book *A Pattern of Islands* had painted for me a vivid image of far-flung coral atolls with strong cultural links to the sea, navigation, and marine life. But first I had to get there. I found myself at London Airport on a cold, wet, and foggy 5 October 1964 – an eighteen-year-old kid, going on nineteen – about to fly for the first time in his life. A letter written at the start of my journey captures my mounting frustration with the experience:

> You just won't believe this but it is now 3 p.m. and I have been here since 9 a.m. It is a hole. During the last six hours I have lost count of the number of re-routings we have been

through. We have retrieved our baggage from the bowels of planes twice. Now, wait for it, we are going to Australia. God knows why.

A word of explanation regarding my confusion is required. Flights had been carefully researched and booked by Hickie Borman Grant and Co., commencing with the one that we had been trying to board all day, from London to Honolulu, touching down in New York and San Francisco before arriving at Honolulu Airport. From there we were scheduled to take a connecting flight to Nandi in Fiji. After that we would fly across Fiji to Suva and board the colony's ship, the *Moana Raoi* (*Queen of the Seas*), to steam north through the islands of Fiji, the Ellice islands, and eventually Tarawa, the capital of the Gilbert and Ellice Islands. It was a hugely exciting travel plan full of firsts for me. At home I read and reread the route on numerous occasions before the designated rendezvous when I met up with two fellow volunteers, Gary Gross and Ben White, at what is now Heathrow Airport.

On arrival at check-in, we presented our treasured, heavily thumbed tickets and were immediately warned of problems. Fog and the imminent arrival of the Queen's flight had created a series of knock-on delays that left us sitting on our cases for hour after hour. All of a sudden, it seemed we were going nowhere. For the nth time I returned to the check-in attendant for news. 'We've rerouted you on the Kangaroo Route, since you were going to miss the boat,' she said, somewhat reassuringly. We gathered at the desk and stared in eager anticipation as new blocks of tickets were pinned to our cancelled ones. The route was unfamiliar and confusing. Instead of flying to America, we would go via India, the opposite way around the world. Beirut, Cairo, Karachi, Calcutta, Singapore, Darwin, Sydney was our new route for a plane that would take us all the way to Australia before switching to Fiji Airways' flights to Nandi and Suva. All my reading about the Hawaiian islands was redundant – where exactly were Beirut, Cairo, Karachi, Calcutta, Singapore? Geography was not my best subject.

Our British Overseas Airways Corporation (now British Airways) plane required regular refuelling, and at each stopover we were released from the stuffy aircraft cabin to stretch our legs on the tarmac. Remarkably, our replacement plane to Sydney was only five minutes late on its schedule but hopelessly late on ours. We eventually landed in Nandi, Fiji, almost two days later than originally planned. Nandi Airport, set among the palm trees of Viti Levu, is an international airport used as a refuelling stopover for planes crossing the Pacific from Australia to Honolulu. Unfortunately we saw very little of it, since we arrived at midnight and left at 5.30 a.m. We were put up at the Mocambu Hotel, which had, according to the hotel's literature, the ultimate luxury of 'a shower and bathroom in each bedroom'.

I wrote to my parents 'Man, that shower is a necessity – I had three showers in the night. The climate is hot – eighty to ninety degrees Fahrenheit – and also quite humid.' The morning taxi drive back to the airport took us along a wonderful country road with shades of England in familiar traffic signs. As the airport came into view, we caught sight of teeming, brightly coloured birds alongside Indian staff in white shorts and equally brightly patterned shirts. The journey was not all idyllic, however. We saw poverty and squalor that would make the slums of Liverpool look like five-star hotels. A piece of corrugated iron leaning against a palm tree was the home of about a dozen people, their toilet the surrounding ground. Water for drinking and washing was a stagnant pool.

We flew from Nandi to Suva in a twenty-seater four-engine Heron aircraft with unpressurised cabin. The terrain was rugged, luscious, and dramatic, with steep-sided needle peaks shrouded in clouds and fertile valleys that would draw the envy of farmers throughout the world. Our plane climbed almost vertically above the green and brown landscape of Fiji's Viti Levu. My dream of Pacific paradise was just hours away. I was just out of school and on my way to the adventure of a lifetime. Pangs of homesickness fought with the excitement that gripped my whole being.

A sharp pinnacle peak of an extinct volcano veered into view ahead, and the pilot banked towards it, levelling off to let it pass beneath us. We soon banked again and flew between two peaks, the tallest of which was shrouded in cloud. Looking down, I could see a thickly forested landscape penetrated by a few ravines that carried gushing water. Near one of these was a small village set in a clearing, its thatched huts visible as brown specks. Suddenly the pilot executed a sharp turn and pointed our nose towards the ground, and the sharply contrasting terrain of the other, drier side of the mountains was revealed. Beyond the fertile land and muddy rivers lay the dazzling blue of the Pacific, and somewhere along this coastline was Suva, the capital, where *Moana Raoi* was hopefully still awaiting our arrival.

The drive from airport to harbour was fascinating and memorable, taking us through the centre of the city, a mixture of primitive and modern buildings whose highlights included a large fruit and vegetable market alongside a bustling fish market. It enabled an all too brief encounter with Fijian society – just long enough for me to meet and engage with a young Indian Fijian student who was lobbying for help to reach the UK to complete his education. Deo Dutt impressed me strongly. Here I was, enjoying many privileges, and here was Deo, who had probably studied twice as hard, achieved every certificate available to him, and yet remained severely disadvantaged in terms of opportunities. At the root of this situation was something that still acts as a cancer in our so-called civilisation: prejudice based on skin colour. How could I help? Writing to my family to support Deo, I nevertheless felt obliged to explain this fine young man's colour:

> If you or anyone else can find someone willing to employ
> him in a job that would give him time for part-time study, I
> and he would most appreciate it. He can produce references
> and certificates. I should, I suppose, mention that he is a
> Fijian with fairly dark skin . . .

What possible relevance did this have, or should it have had, for Deo's prospects? And yet there it was. My parents, like many of their generation, simply could not rid themselves of what was described as colour prejudice, although they would have regarded themselves as liberal and open-minded.

Eyes not seeing, ears not listening, hearts not feeling, so many of us subconsciously chose to ignore the issue. Meanwhile, amid mounting frustration and anger, protests against the basic injustices and humiliation that racial prejudice engenders were gaining momentum, leading to abolition of apartheid and the emergence of spontaneous responses such as the Black Lives Matter movement. In today's turbulent world, I find hope in the responses of people from all nationalities and ethnic backgrounds who are, increasingly, joining efforts to cure the racial pandemic that threatens some people just as much as Covid-19.

Before reaching the harbour, we rushed around Suva town, where I picked up a pair of flip-flops and a hat – essential items for equatorial life. We met briefly with the British Council representative, Mr Halstead, and his wife, and they presented us with a large water melon and a bunch of bananas for the voyage. Finally, our Land Rover taxi entered between the massive port gates and sped along the wharf, giving us no opportunity to quiz the driver about where exactly he was taking us. He hurled his dilapidated vehicle between cranes, dockside sheds, and rows of oil drums, laughing loudly as he exchanged waves with the groups of Fijians who lined the quays, and then came to an abrupt stop alongside a smartly white-painted ship about 30 metres in length. My luggage was thrown on the ground and I struggled to stop it toppling into the water while I searched for the taxi fare. As soon as he saw the money in my hand, he grabbed at it without mentioning a price, hopped back into his vehicle, and was away again, tooting his horn at Indian labourers playing cards in the ship's shade.

A very English voice bellowed down at us from the bridge. 'Do you realise we could be halfway to Funafuti by now? Where the hell have you been? We've been waiting for three days.'

Not having heard of Funafuti and feeling at peace with the world, I shouted up: 'Good day.'

'Of course it's a good day. It's been a good day since last Friday, but we've been sitting in dock waiting for you. We're leaving in five minutes, and let's hope it remains a good day.'

'I'd like to speak to Captain Ward,' I told my unfriendly accuser.

'Who the hell do you think I am?' came the reply, and, in mild shock, I reappraised this brawny, tanned man in oil-stained shorts. This was *the* Captain Vic Ward, legend of seafaring among the islands of the South Pacific. I recalled the British civil servant in London who had told me with a wry grin that the Pacific was like heaven and Captain Ward like a sea-god. Timidly I carried my cases up the gangplank and was pleased to find a helpful crewman. The real adventure was about to begin.

On Board *Queen of the Seas – Moana Raoi*

Suva's quay was packed with islanders. Some were there as passengers carrying their rolled-up mats containing all their worldly possessions, and many were friends and relatives come to say their goodbyes. Unbeknown to us, our delay had potentially huge consequences for scores of people, many of whom were camped out on the quay alongside the ship's gangway. As we climbed on board, a whole mass of restless islanders jumped to their feet and started to sing their farewells to the passengers that crammed along the ship's rail. The captain cast another stern gaze in our direction, ordered the plank to be raised, warps to be released and the wheel turned to edge our way out to deeper water and the open ocean. With only one or two trips to the island each year, this colony supply vessel was our only option to reach Tarawa. There was no suitable airport there at that stage – that was to become VSO volunteers Gary and Ben's project – and there was a danger of having to cancel our entire mission if we had literally missed the boat.

As the ship drew away from the quay, both the farewell party and the passengers continued their exquisitely harmonious song. We passed out through the lagoon into the open sea, and everyone on board lent a hand in erecting awnings over the decks. They would live, sleep, and eat under the shade of this canvas for the next 2,000 or so kilometres.

That evening my first impressions of a rather gruff skipper were quickly revised, as a charming, hospitable captain invited us to join him for dinner and apologised for his outburst of a few hours earlier. Then, with a glint in his eye, he asked what faith I had come to preach to the tolerant islanders. He was renowned for pulling the legs of innocent missionaries that regularly came this way, and I quickly disabused him of any presumption that I must be planning to convert more islanders to the Bahai or Christian religions.

On our first morning out of Suva, we sailed close to some Fijian islands, low sand cays fringed by coconut palms. Two small boats seemed to be waiting for us about a mile offshore. The main engine was stopped in order to liaise with the islanders' boat, and I was struck by the natural grace of the ballet being performed before us. Two boat crews sprang into action. They were soon joined by about a dozen outrigger canoes that appeared, as if by magic, from several directions, all making a beeline for our exotic, garlanded *Queen of the Seas*, the *Moana Raoi*. An elderly man in a dugout canoe was having no difficulty keeping pace with his younger colleagues, propelling his tiny vessel with a sculling motion from one side of the stern. We were boarded by these scantily clad islanders swarming up ropes and along planks in what resembled a multipronged assault by friendly pirates. But there was no cause for alarm: the only treasures they came to capture were the hugs, kisses, and smiles of friends and relatives – some of whom were disembarking and some joining us.

After about half an hour, the skipper sounded the fog horn and they returned to their boats as quickly as they had arrived. Bursting into song, they waved at us until we sank beneath their horizon. We could hear their music above the sound of our engine for at least a hundred metres. It was the last island we would call at before arriving, four days later, off the Ellice Island of Funafuti, known today as Tuvalu.

I sank into the tropical ship's soporific routine: up at 5 a.m. when it was still cool, consume a few bananas off the massive stalk hanging over the afterdeck, breakfast and afterwards some ropework to quell boredom. At least once a day there would be a surge of excitement, be it a waterspout or an big tunny on the fishing line. Flying fish were plentiful, and many landed on deck where they were gathered up by our passengers. It all seemed so far away from the sweaty chaos and confusion we had experienced at our journey's beginning in London.

In the days that followed, the true character of Captain Ward, his crewmen, and his passengers revealed itself. My first friend was James, a Solomon Islander whose brand of pidgin English was a source of amusement to everyone on board, including himself. He was about seventy to seventy-five years old and told us that he had been a slave in his youth. Jumping around like a young child, he re-enacted the scene where white traders had captured him and his family by offering them a lift to another island. His family were not the only ones to be tricked by this deception, thrown into the ship's dark cargo holds with masses of their fellows, many of them too weak to crawl away from their own excrement. James was considered some of the most valuable cargo, since young boys (he was probably about ten years old at this point) could fetch a good price if they arrived at the slave centre in good health. For this reason he was taken to the open deck after a few days and set to ship-cleaning tasks in more healthy conditions, along with some of his colleagues.

'Long-time voyage much like ship roly-poly. No see family, Maybe they big much money people in them States,' he told me. Nobody told him that his parents had probably not even survived the sea voyage, and as for making a success of life in the States, the chances would have been slim, to say the least. James himself got lucky, in relative terms, since the skipper of the ship decided he could use him as a young seaman and signed him on as an unpaid crew member. The end of slavery simply meant that he could get drunk more often and have enough cash to buy his own girl in Fiji. Now he worshipped Captain Ward and was really only happy when he was at sea.

Blackbirding in the South Pacific

I recently turned to available documents from the late nineteenth century to see if James's story tallied with known incidents of slavery in the Solomons and other areas of Melanesia. The first shipment of human cargo to Moreton Bay was on board the *Don Juan* in 1863 – thirty years after the UK passed the Slavery Abolition Act, abolishing slavery in most parts of the British Empire. *Don Juan* was owned by British mariner and blackbirder Robert Towns, after whom Townsville takes its name; a statue of Towns in the centre of the city is a matter of controversy today in the current debate ignited by the Black Lives Matter movement.

Over 60,000 Pacific islanders were lured or kidnapped onto boats and transported to Australia between 1863 and 1904. The practice was known as 'blackbirding'. It was a quasi-legal exercise, as the islanders unwittingly 'signed' contracts with their employers, primarily sugar cane and cotton plantation owners. Most of the indentured labourers were from Vanuatu, previously New Caledonia, and the Solomon Islands, but also from Tuvalu (Ellice Islands), Kiribati (Gilbert Islands), and Fiji.

Kidnapped islanders, known as *Kanakas* (now considered an offens-ive term), played a key role in Australia's development, particularly in the cotton and sugar industries, in the second half of the nineteenth century. Their contribution remains largely unacknowledged, and they derived little benefit from subsequent government intervention. In 1868, a first attempt was made by the Queensland government to regulate the labour market. The Polynesian Labourers Act provided for some limited protec-tion of labourers, but it did not outlaw blackbirding; instead it established a licensing system for 'recruiters'.

It was toothless legislation, and some of the most notorious and brutal blackbirders retained their licences. British government acts, such as the 1872 Pacific Islanders Protection Act, introduced measures that reduced the incidence of blackbirding by British subjects, but the ongoing demand for labour in Queensland meant the practice continued to flourish to the end of the century. Blackbirding was finally brought to a close in 1904, but its end was as ignominious as its beginning. In 1901, the Commonwealth government ordered the deportation of the entire Islander community. This was only one element of a wider policy aimed at limiting the size of the non-European-origin population in Australia. This so-called White Australia policy resulted in islanders being deported en masse to communities that were no longer known to them. It was a travesty, and there is a growing call for acknowledgement of this part of Australian history.

Visit to Idyllic Funafuti

Soon after 5 p.m., as the *Moana Raoi* entered the perfectly shaped atoll, I had my first close view of a real desert island. A Bahai missionary, Vitoli, took us ashore and we were met by the entire village of about three hundred people. It was a happy event for the islanders, most of whom were smiling and joining in with the singing of traditional welcome songs. We were guided towards the missionary's house, and as we filed along the carefully tended coral road, the tropic sun was setting beneath the horizon, providing an intensely hued romantic backdrop of slanting palms that hugged the shoreline. It was an evocative, serene experience, and I drank in the sheer beauty that surrounded us: azure shallow waters, dazzling white coral sand, lush green palms, and pandanus trees – too much for my very basic Bantam camera and Kodak film to capture in its entirety.

Darkness was fast approaching, and at Vitoli's palm-thatched house we all sat on mats around a hurricane lamp. Out of the crowd of children who had been following us, several entered the room, all entirely naked. These were all members of Vitoli's family, and together with great-grandparents, grandparents, Vitoli's wife, and all the young adults, teenagers, children, and infants, we counted at least twenty-five people. The youngest was an eight-month-old baby in arms. It was not only the size of the family that impressed us but the fact that they all slept under the same roof. Boys, we learnt, married at sixteen, whilst girls could do so as young as thirteen. Protection of virginity until marriage was a key tenet of their moral law, underpinning the custom for girls to marry at such a young age. Coconuts were split open and handed around with an invitation to drink their juice. 'It is the nearest thing to nectar that I have ever tasted,' I enthused.

Next day we were shown into a meteorological station run by one of Funafuti's few white men, a Mr Dunbar. I told him that it felt like paradise, and he shared a knowing smile but said little to confirm or deny his state of rapture. After the weather station visit, Vitoli took us for a swim in the crystal-clear waters of the lagoon. It was a first and highly impressionable experience for me. I could hardly believe the vast array of fish in all shapes, colours, and sizes, swimming in and out of intricate coral formations. After half an hour lazing in this enchanting world, we emerged onto the shore, where we were presented with more refreshing coconut water. Finally, before our return to the ship, Dunbar entertained us in his air-conditioned house, serving fresh bread, ice cream, and chocolate. I felt as if I was being propelled directly up to heaven.

Funafuti to Tarawa

Continuing on my voyage from Fiji to Tarawa, the final leg – Funafuti to Tarawa – passed by in a continuation of the hot and steamy first half of the trip. We lived for four days from one meal to the next. When not eating, it was a clear case of 'laze now, do later'. The midday sun was unbearably hot, and no one ventured out under its penetrating rays. Waterspouts were common in this area of the Pacific. Watching columns of dark water slowly rise up to join with twisting clouds that sank to meet them, forming mini-tornadoes, was quite mesmerising, if not a little frightening. I could not help imagining the plight of one of the local canoes caught up in such destructive phenomena. When the water column and cloud column were joined, the whole spout would move around in what appeared to be a large arc. Fortunately, none approached us too closely.

The throb of our ship's engines was like the *thump-thump* of an excited heart, and as we steamed north we all felt mounting excitement. Our *Queen of the Seas* steadily chewed up the sea miles, and the crosses that marked our midday positions on the wheelhouse chart drew closer and closer to Tarawa. In the evenings, after a conversational joust at the captain's table, I would stroll to the poop deck at the stern of the vessel, a natural gathering place for passengers and crew. Cool evening breezes gave respite from the day's heat. I helped to pull in fishing lines and struck up a lively banter with my fellow passengers.

Sitting along the gunwale of the small workboat, which was lashed down on the hatch covers, a group of young men sang soothing Pacific music to the accompaniment of one or two guitars. Around the outside of this group, and interspersed with the occasional parent, were a dozen or more girls sitting on their palm-woven fans. Evading the gaze of young handsome men singing of young love and feminine beauty, every now and then eyes locked and a discreet wink would provide a signal to surreptitiously creep back into the shadows. By dawn, acquaintances had evolved. A little later in the evening, a tall slim girl, with long black hair flowing over a yellow dress, crept quietly up the ladder to the captain's cabin. Everyone knew this story. A giggle floated down on the night air, and lights were dimmed. No longer the brash, rude, tough king of local legend, the captain transformed into a gentle, passionate, seagoing lover who brought his sweetheart along for the ride.

Dusk – dawn – dusk – dawn: the heartbeat never faltered, and the spirit of carnival only intensified. A waterspout to the west, a school of whales ahead, a frigate bird, a new tuna on the line: every experience was a new one, but the greatest of all was the experience of building friendship with the ship and its people – especially between sea-king and sea-queen, as I had come to think of Captain Ward and *Moana Raoi*.

Following the Money – the Colonial Way

The British colonies were on their way out when I arrived on Tarawa in October 1964. They had served the UK well during their existence, providing a rich and varied supply of raw materials for the manufacturing hubs of Great Britain. In the case of the Gilbert and Ellice Islands, and the Central and Southern Line Islands, these valuable assets comprised copra (dried coconut husks) and bird droppings or guano, which was high-grade phosphate used in vast quantities in soil fertilisers.

Banaba Island, also known as Ocean Island, was the Gilbert and Ellice Islands' cash cow. Mining of phosphate had turned it into a derelict, virtually uninhabitable wasteland. It was visibly shrinking and had produced more than 335,000 tons of phosphate in 1960 alone. The British Phosphate Company had earned a reputation for poor industrial relations, with two major strikes by its workers in 1961. It had no long-term plan other than grabbing as much phosphate as it could before the country became independent and its activities would be placed under closer scrutiny.

Soon after I began teaching at King George V (KGV) School for Boys, on the last day of term, 4 December 1964, a Speech Day was held at which the resident commissioner delivered a keynote address. It was textbook colonialism, reminding the indigenous people that they owed a huge debt of gratitude to Great Britain and that the current situation was becoming more and more precarious as a result of the rapidly depleting reserves of guano on Ocean Island. It did not seem to be acknowledged that this depletion of valuable resources was being carried out at huge profit to the British Phosphate Company and its shareholders. The resident commissioner told the boys that on leaving school they 'owed the colony' a living rather than the colony owing them one. 'It will be impossible to maintain the same standard of living when Ocean Island's phosphate deposits are worked out in a few years' time,' he told them.

Tarawa

Tarawa lies close to where the equator and International Date Line transect, in the west-central Pacific, 4,500 kilometres north-east of Australia. Other low-lying islands of the group include Makin, Butaritari, Marakei, Abaiang, Maiana, Abemama, Kuria, Aranuka, Nonouti, Tabiteuea, Beru, Nikunau, Onotoa, Tamana, and Arorae. Covered with coconut palms and pandanus trees, their inhabitants, the i-Kiribati, are Micronesians as opposed to Melanesians or Polynesians. The islands derive their English name from Capt. Thomas Gilbert, who sighted Tarawa in 1788 and whose name was officially given to the islands in the 1820s. In 1892, Capt. E. H. M. Davis proclaimed the Gilberts a British protectorate, and in 1916 the group became part of the Gilbert and Ellice Islands Colony.

A brief word on names and their pronunciation is required, since it is still a source of some confusion. The name *Kiribati* is based on the local spelling of Gilbert. There is no 'g' in their language, so the hard 'g' sound is written with a 'k', There is also no 's', so this is written with 'ti'. Thus Kiribati is pronounced 'Giribass'. Meanwhile, the Ellice islands, with their main island of Funafuti, were named after Edward Ellice, a British politician and merchant, who sighted the islands in 1819. The two island groups were administered as the Gilbert and Ellice Islands Protectorate, and then Colony, from 1892 to 1976, when they each became independent: Kiribati and Tuvalu.

Sir Arthur Grimble's personal account of living on Tarawa, the best-selling book *A Pattern of Islands*, was first published in 1952 and covered the author's assignment there from 1913 to 1919. As with my own stories of a year in 'paradise', also written decades after the experience, *A Pattern of Islands* was written with the help of diaries, letters, and reports that were compiled in real time, describing events as they happened. As I thumb through my own fifty-year-old letters and notebooks, it is as if I can feel that tropical sun on my back, smell the frangipani and hibiscus flowers that were woven into necklaces worn as signs of affection, and hear the ocean's swell rolling across the reef top. It was a life-changing experience that taught me far more than I was able to impart to my pupils, but I am acutely aware that Tarawa (Kiribati) and Funafuti (Tuvalu) are no longer the paradise that I once knew and loved.

Some claim that the islands are in the process of disappearing, both figuratively and physically, thanks to rising sea levels, unsustainable economies, toxic urban poverty, and sheer neglect. Their plight should act as a wake-up call to the rest of the world, but it is in danger of being accepted instead as a fait accompli. 'Out of sight, out of mind' seems an appropriate phrase, and I have noticed drop-down menus on various websites that simply omit their names. Whilst there have been efforts to preserve the islands' cultural dimensions and sustainable skills, the truth is that they are in the midst of a struggle for survival, which is now being focused on four pillars – wealth, peace and security, infrastructure, and governance.

My own introduction to these islands, as I've noted, came through reading Arthur Grimble's book, but their biggest claim to fame stems from the Battle of Tarawa, which took place in 1943 and during which the Japanese were driven out by Allied troops. The most recent census figures for 2017 show that the population has more than doubled to just over 110,000 inhabitants, compared to the early 1960s when it was slightly less than 50,000.

It seemed to me that Britain's interest in this remote colony would only be sustained so long as it could deliver a healthy income from exploitation of its natural resources. Money earned from wages of copra producers and corporate sales of phosphate, mined on Ocean and Christmas Islands, was channelled through local supply stores, or Cooperative Wholesale Societies, into a few social development projects. These include the establishment and management of schools such as the Bikenibeu-based KGV School and Elaine Bernacchi School (EBS) for girls, inaugurated on 25 June 1960. EBS marked a milestone for the education of girls in the colony and was to become my main teaching post during my stay on the island of Tarawa from October 1964 to late August 1965.

Bonhomie

The government motor launch, carrying me in towards the shore, alternately raced ahead or proceeded very slowly. I thought the helmsman was drunk, since our course meandered alarmingly. At one stage I studied our wake as we executed an almost perfect figure of eight. The tide was out, and groups of islanders in the shallows were collecting some kind of seafood. As the depth reduced, I could see that the cause of our strange route was the large number of rusting American landing craft, lying in wait for the unwary helmsman. They were relics of the Battle of Tarawa that had raged here two decades earlier, in November 1943, when American forces recaptured Tarawa from the Japanese: one of the bloodiest and most notorious battles of the war in the Pacific.

Later on that first day, I walked along the coral road around the island and discovered a small coral cross in memory of the Europeans executed by the Japanese in 1941. A small laconic inscription brought a lump to my throat. Did it really happen? It seemed like a page from a war novel, read in the comfort of a fireside chair. I turned away and reflected on the high price that was paid for our freedom.

Further on, where the point of land jutted out towards the ocean breakers, stood an enormous gun, its barrel almost wide enough for me to climb inside. It seemed so out of place among the gently swaying palm trees creaking in the breeze and reef herons searching for food around its base. There was something odd about this gun. It was the only shore-based gun on this side of the island, and it pointed far out to sea, towards an empty horizon, perhaps aimed at American ships coming to wrest back control of the island in November 1943. But the Americans had attacked from the other side, via the lagoon passage, as their numerous wrecked landing craft so poignantly attested. I pondered for days about the gun, but it was several weeks before the mystery was solved and a year before I put the whole saga to rest.

It happened quite unexpectedly, 30 kilometres away, at the other end of the atoll, where fellow volunteer Tony Fleetwood-Wilson and I were visiting in a Gilbertese outrigger canoe. Upon arrival, we gratefully accepted the hospitality of the local pastor in his lovely lagoonside house and slept through the heat of the afternoon. Later, after joining the ritual early-evening swim in the lagoon, we changed our clothes and walked to the house of the *Uni Mane* (headman) of the village. His house was much like the others: a floor made from stiff midribs of coconut palms, raised a metre above ground level by corner posts made from pandanus trunks that also supported a roof of thatched palm fronds. There were no walls: if he needed privacy he could roll down side screens, also made from woven palm fronds. Hanging from the middle of the ceiling was a large white mosquito net. Close to one edge of the floor stood a large wooden chest in which he kept all his possessions. The Uni Mane himself was sitting on the edge of the floor, facing the lagoonside road. He glanced up as we approached and, grinning widely, beckoned us to join him.

He was about sixty, but his withered, sunburnt physique told tales of hardship. He had lost his right arm, whose short stump protruded from his shoulder and shot up when he became excited. His grin revealed an almost complete lack of teeth, creating a somewhat alarming appearance, but one that was immediately countermanded by an openness and warmth so typical of the rural Gilbertese. As the oldest member of the community, he was its headman, respected by all the villagers for his greater experience and wise judgement. As we talked, he pulled out a rusty tin and extracted a large fish hook and a few chicken feathers, tying them together in a convincing lure that would prove its worth on his next fishing trip, catching a tuna big enough to feed the village. It was an adept operation, carried out with the hook sometimes in his mouth, sometimes in his only hand.

I asked him how life had changed over the past fifty years. It was an invitation for him to tell us his life story, and, liking nothing more than a good yarning session, he insisted that we each have a drink of the delicious juice of young coconuts before he began. Then we sat back and listened.

His name, he told us, was Tevenai, which means 'bright sky'. The year preceding his birth had been a very dry one. Palms had shed their leaves, and islanders had lost the shade that made it possible to endure fierce sunshine. Coconuts were soon used up, well water became unbearably brackish, and the men lost the will to launch their canoes. The village, known throughout the atoll for its fine choir, band, and dancers, was silent. No one gathered in the evenings for a sing-song and gossip in the *maneaba* (meeting house). Most houses had invalids in need of nursing.

Tevenai's mother's pregnancy must have been very worrying. There were none of the customary celebrations whilst the mother suffered her pains. Tevenai's father had been collecting water for many weeks, filtering it through a coral-filled strainer to make it palatable. He hid this in the bush and, before dawn on the morning of the hottest day for weeks, sneaked off to recover it when his wife was close to giving birth. As he did so he felt raindrops on his forehead and ran back to tell his wife the good news. By the time he arrived, a son had been born and rain was falling steadily.

'Tevenai. Tevenai. Tevenai,' the villagers shouted for joy as they were wakened by pattering raindrops falling harder as the dawn sky brightened. Tevenai was a lucky baby, and the villagers never forgot the good fortune he had brought them. As he reflected on island life, he reached out for another coconut, opening it with a deft strike of his machete, tipping it back and loudly gurgling its juice. 'Each one is tastier than the one before,' he told me. 'Much better than your beer or lemonade.' A slight drawl came into his accent when he mentioned the two drinks.

'Where did you try the lemonade and beer?' I asked him.

'The Japanese gave me the beer, and the Americans gave me lemonade.'

'Did you work for the Americans?' I asked.

'No, but I worked for the Japanese for a while. Have you seen the big gun on the beach at Betio, on the south side?'

'Yes, but why do you ask?'

'Well, I helped them to rig that enormous monster. Sixty of us worked for two weeks to finish the job. Another group worked through the night. When we finished it, the Japanese gave us a party, and that is where I tasted my first beer.'

He laughed as he recalled the scene: the Gilbertese had not tasted beer before and so drank it like water, not noticing its effects. They were filled with bonhomie and told the Japanese of their own secret drink: fermented coconut sap, more potent than beer. Before long, many of the Japanese were also in high spirits, and the party escalated into a grand feast. Chickens and pigs were stolen from the army's pen, which was fair game, since the army had initially stolen them from the villagers. In any case, some Japanese soldiers attended the feast.

Tevenai's eyes glowed as he remembered his younger days, and he spoke of the Japanese without malice. I asked him if they had treated him badly. 'Certainly not,' he answered. 'Both the Americans and the

Japanese were kind to us. They gave us medical treatment and usually respected our customs. The Japanese had strict instructions to respect our women, but they did pinch some of our property. The Americans were very friendly but much wilder, and many of our women were taken by them. It was not cruel, though, since many of the women loved the men with whiter skin. I grew to like both Japanese and Americans.' This new insight into the Japanese occupation and the liberation of Tarawa by America diverted my attention, and I almost forgot to ask him about the gun.

'Why does the gun point out towards the ocean instead of over the lagoon?' I asked.

'I told you that it took a great deal of work to erect the gun; well, the truth is that it was never completely finished. The soldiers could only move it slowly, so they decided to point it in the most likely direction of the expected American assault. Japanese command believed their coastal guns would protect the approaches into the lagoon, so an attack on the island was anticipated to come from the open waters of the western or southern beaches. But the Americans came ashore through the lagoon. It was the biggest military force they had ever mounted in the Pacific, with nearly 150 ships carrying about 35,000 troops. The Japanese were outgunned and tricked into leaving the lagoon inadequately defended. They bombarded the fleet, but their main guns were soon disabled by an American counter-attack using weapons twice as big as those of the Japanese. Your cannon never fired a shot.'

I pictured Japanese soldiers desperately trying to turn the gun towards their enemy.

The story received its postscript almost a year later, when I was back in the UK preparing to attend university. At our local sailing club I received a warm welcome home. Many of the members had heard about my travels and wanted to have a few words. But the conversations were brief and repetitive, lacking in much insight, and I was feeling irritable, pining for my Gilbertese girlfriend, dreaming of the sun-kissed islands, imagining, as best I could, that I was back there. It was a warm, cosy illusion until the spell was broken by another 'Did you have a good time?' Reluctantly I dragged my mind back from a walk along the shore, hand in hand with Tafua, digging our toes in the soft coral sand and playing 'catch as catch can'.

My latest questioner seemed satisfied by my polite 'Ah yes, it was wonderful.' He returned to his drink at the bar, and I returned to my reverie. Now I was sailing across the lagoon with Tony. We were on a fast reach, causing a solid spray to shower our faces as the knife-edged bow cut through the wavelets. The evening sunlight created a rainbow under the outrigger. I hung on to the stay as we careered towards the shore, almost out of control. Tony was singing loudly, out of tune, for the sheer joy of living.

'Did you have a nice time?'

I was back in the sailing club. 'Ah yes, thank you. I had a very nice time.' The short sunburnt man was staring intently at me, holding his beer glass. I slipped into my usual Gilbert Islands conversation, half hoping he would leave me alone so I could return to my sailing.

'Were you on Tarawa?' he asked.

'Why, yes. I'm surprised that you remember the name – hardly anyone that I speak to has heard of the Gilbert Islands, let alone Tarawa.'

'I was there,' he said, almost causing me to spill my beer.

'Good Lord. When were you there?'

'During the war. I was on an American ship at the Battle of Tarawa.'

His words brought back memories of my meeting with Tevenai and the strategic deception involved in that horrendous conflict.

'And it's a bloody good job their big gun wasn't working,' he said.

I bought him a fresh beer and we retired to a quieter place next to the fire. He told me his incredible story.

'We knew the Japs were expecting our attack, so we purposely appeared on the ocean side of the island on the evening before. That must have been when the lookouts spotted us. We figured that they would train their heavy armaments in that direction in preparation for a morning attack. But then we crept around to the lagoon passage on the opposite side and attacked from there. The plan worked well until our landing craft were about two hundred yards from shore, when they touched bottom. Someone, somewhere, had miscalculated the tides, and those poor soldiers were paying for it with their lives as the "Nips" fired on them from the cover of pillboxes and dug-out trenches. Our ships were hurling everything they had at the island, and it's a good job your friend Tevenai wasn't around, for he would definitely have copped it. It was one of the bloodiest battles of the whole Pacific, and when we finally captured the island, there was not one palm tree left standing. Tell me,' he added, 'you didn't actually enjoy yourself in that sweltering hellhole, did you?'

'Of course I did, and so would you if you went back there today. It is peaceful, and they're the friendliest people you could meet anywhere.'

He finished his beer and started to make his way back to the bar. I felt sorry he could not see the peace he had helped to create.

'I wouldn't go back there if you paid me,' he said. 'It's the hottest, filthiest place I've ever seen. Some of the guys used to plead insanity when they heard they had been posted to the Pacific.'

He looked quite happy at the bar, and I decided that perhaps Tarawa is only attractive to those, like me, who have no experience of war.

Betio Youth Club

The island of Betio, the epicentre of the battle, had never fully recovered from the devastation it suffered, even twenty years later. My arrival in the crowded urban conurbation provided the greatest shock of my journey up to that point. Whilst my fellow volunteers Gary and Ben set off for Tevenai's island, Buariki, at the other end of the atoll, from where they would direct structural development projects such as building an airport and causeways, Mr Weeks, the district commissioner, took me under his wing. He explained the proposed programme for my activities in the coming year – which boiled down to community development work focused on young people in Betio.

According to Mr Weeks, I was scheduled to replace a previous VSO volunteer who, given the circumstances, had done a great job. The task I faced was daunting and quite far from my dreams of living in paradise. The youth club building, located in the midst of a high-density urbanised population, had the reputation of being a brothel. Most of the attending members had the same social issues that I had grown accustomed to seeing among deprived sections of Liverpool's youth scene: local gangs, drink, drugs, and rampant boredom, combined with a disaffection for organised society. The only difference was the setting – Liverpool lacked the palm trees and tropical beaches. Betio did have beaches, although they were littered with the destructive debris of a relatively recent bloody battle that Betio and its people preferred to forget. It was really a waterside slum in which Gilbertese families were struggling with the loss of traditional and cultural values. How would I set about creating the enthusiasm, skills, and commitment that these youngsters – all about my own age – needed in order to combat their loss of self-worth and, in many cases, their slide towards criminality?

The club did have a committee, and soon after I had settled in, I called a meeting. Instead of the club nights being an endless scene of western dancing (the Twist), cards, and bingo, I suggested that we create groups for activities such as photography, dressmaking, mat-weaving, carpentry, boxing, volleyball, basketball, hairdressing, singing, music, sailing, swimming, dramatics, traditional formation dancing, and so on. The plan received an enthusiastic response from the youngsters.

Bikenibeu

Behind the scenes there were debates about whether this was the best use of my skills, and the district commissioner lost the argument. Two weeks later I left the urban chaos of Betio to become a schoolteacher. I travelled across the Tarawa lagoon by a small launch to the government administration island of Bairiki, and from there by Land Rover to the village of Bikenibeu, which was the site of two government schools: the King George V School for boys (KGV) and the Elaine Bernacchi School for girls (EBS). The journey gave me my first view of unspoilt parts of the atoll. The land was low and flat, hardly rising more than three metres above high tide level, and cannot have been more than a hundred metres at its widest part. The road we travelled followed the shore of the lagoon, but one still caught glimpses of the ocean with its crashing breakers. Every mile or so we passed through small villages, their houses gathered on either side, with a mandatory church and large maneaba or meeting house. We passed several islanders on bicycles with strings of coconuts draped over their crossbars, or their fish catches hanging from poles balanced on their shoulders. Out in the lagoon I could see several Gilbertese sailing canoes and was impressed by their speed in such light winds.

Local men wore shorts and colourful shirts or just brightly coloured cloths wrapped around their waists, covering most of their legs. These *lava-lava* or *sulus* were worn by both sexes. Women also often wore blouses. I later learned how useful the lava-lava can be, serving well as a garment, as protection when sitting on the ground, as a towel, as cover for the head, or as a kind of container.

The journey carried me across two narrow causeways bridging the gap between adjacent islands of the atoll. Each was about 300 metres long and was created by building up piles of coral blocks. Gary and Ben, my fellow VSO volunteers, were to be engaged for the whole year in constructing similar causeways in the northern part of the island, hence I was interested in their construction but breathed a sigh of relief that it was not me doing it. The road at this point ran close to the lagoon shore, and houses were in neat rows on both sides. Instead of the traditional house with raised floor, thatched roof, and no walls, these houses were built from sheets of hardboard and boasted shining corrugated roofs. Although they were by no means as attractive as the traditional houses, and gave the village the appearance of a refugee camp, these semi-European houses were more comfortable and provided better protection from the elements.

This first row of houses stretched for about a hundred metres, broken by a junction with a track leading to the Colony Central Hospital. Opposite the junction, on the lagoon side, was a massive maneaba that provided accommodation for patients and their relatives. The Land Rover slowed down just short of a large prefabricated building, the village store, and then turned across the atoll towards the ocean side, where my new home was situated.

The house was a grand affair. Located at the edge of the ocean, well within the 'roar zone', it was on a slight promontory which gave a perfect view across the two adjacent bays and out to the white-tipped breakers marking the edge of the ocean shelf. It was unexpectedly large and luxurious, constructed from coral blocks with a European layout and a thatched palm-leaf roof. Inside were three bedrooms, only one of which was occupied, by me, since Tony, a fellow teacher, lived in a homemade mini-house in the garden, constructed entirely from palm tree components. After my luggage had been deposited in the main house and I had thanked the driver, I walked back into the garden and admired the little palm house. The door swung open and out came a fair-haired young man of about twenty-five. His cool attire contrasted with my formal government 'uniform' of shorts and white shirt. He wore swimming trunks and a red bula shirt from Hawaii.

'Hi there. You must be Pete. Well, I'm Tony,' he announced as we shook hands at the start of what would be a long friendship. Tony was also a volunteer teacher, had already been there for a year, and had built the palm hut himself. 'When the tide is high it covers my floor, but at least it reminds me I'm in the Pacific. Most expats forget that in their lush houses,' he mused.

I used one of the spare bedrooms as an office, and in addition there was a bathroom, a shower-cum-toilet, a kitchen fitted with a large fridge and electric stove, and a spacious sitting room. It was well furnished with a varnished dining table, chairs, and desks. Instead of glass in the window openings, we had wooden shutters that were permanently propped open, except when it rained. We actually suggested to the administration section that they could give us a smaller residence, but it suited them to hang on to the big 'volunteers house'. Our garden had bright red hibiscus flowers and several coconut palms that provided shade, coconut meat, toddy, and husks for the fire. We were provided with a cook, Teatou, and a housekeeper, Taoati. Teatou was also the village songwriter and was an adept (and frequently inebriated) toddy-maker, using sap from the coconut tree in our garden. That first evening he prepared a welcome meal of fried tuna, fried breadfruit, and papaya.

Once a week Tony or I would venture down the road to the Wholesale Society Store that sold just about everything the islanders might need, from razor blades to champagne, but that lacked a few of my own requirements, such as Cadbury's chocolate and Kodak film. Here we would buy a box full of tins, perhaps a little fresh fruit (expensive) and some frozen meat (very expensive). Teatou would then surprise us at every meal with what he could make from such a restricted array of ingredients. Meat pies, fruit pies, cakes, scones, and even ice cream were regular offerings. Ice cream appeared at every meal without fail. Teatou would also catch, harvest, or purchase fresh fish and breadfruit. He arrived at the house each morning with fresh bread to be toasted. Meanwhile, Taoati kept us on our toes, cleaning, washing, and ensuring that everything ran smoothly.

Schools

Thanks to a dire lack of staff, my positions included house master of Kennedy House in KGV and head science master. If only the reality matched the veneer. This emperor truly had no clothes. I was even remunerated for my volunteer services: £30 a month for food and £3 a week pocket money.

'*Memento praeterita, nova aude*' ('Respect the old, dare the new') was the EBS motto, and I was determined to do my best to live up to it. The only saving grace was that the school had few if any options – there were no qualified teachers available at such a remote location. In a foreword to the school's magazine, which I edited and produced in 1965, the headmistress Ms Winfred Courtney wrote:

> This, the School Motto, sums up all I would wish for the School – that it should be a place of learning, not by rote, but by understanding: that the girls should leave with open, informed and inquiring minds, capable of distinguishing between the good and the bad of the old ways and the new ways.

I travelled between classes and home on a bicycle donated by the school. The morning was divided into seven 45-minute periods, and school finished at 1 p.m. There were five Europeans and three Gilbertese on the staff of KGV, where I began my teaching under headmaster Alan Law. Other teachers, apart from Tony and me, included John Harris and Mary Llewellyn. None of us had a clear sight of the massive changes that the 'new ways' would bring, nor of the crushing defeat of the 'old ways' as the victim of modernity. But I did get introduced to some of the old customs, thanks to the very traditional upbringing of our pupils. Belief in ghosts was still strong and was part of a spiritual existence that missionaries tapped into to spread their own supernatural-based religions. However, EBS and KGV were non-religious schools, leaving plenty of space to practise traditional ways that had evolved as part of the islanders' sustainable lives, and the girls and boys of both schools followed their hearts as often as their heads.

This led to some surprises for a young man straight out of the science-based rules of 'civilised' UK. I was intrigued at the urgent notes that would be tucked into the saddle of my bicycle. 'Please Sir, forgive me for laughing in class. I did not mean to upset you' would be fairly typical of the tone and content. The girls would do their best to keep their slate clean with numerous written apologies. Their real fear was not that I was unhappy with them but that I might release a ghost to deal with the issue.

Teaching

'Have you done any teaching before?' asked the thin white man with the posh English accent and delicate manners.

'Actually, no, sir,' I said, desperately trying to think of something that would compensate for my appalling lack of experience.

'I see that you've done maths at GCE O level.'

I thought of the stuffy exam room back at Calday Grange Grammar School, where I had almost ripped up the paper but just managed to scrape through on this and all my other subjects.

'Well, yes, but that was quite a long time ago, and I've forgotten most of it now,' I replied, trying not to show too much negativity to his unspoken suggestion.

'I last studied maths seventeen years ago but am teaching it to the upper forms at present,' he countered. I was surprised by this, since I knew he was a history graduate. I left the room holding a note to the effect that I was now head teacher for maths and science throughout the school and was also to teach history to first and second years, geography to second years, and English to the first, third, and fourth forms. As I accepted the note, he added an afterthought which I read later, having been scared to stay longer in his company. He had written just three letters that changed my life: EBS.

'Don't tell me,' said Tony when we met at lunchtime. 'You're teaching all the maths and science and a load of other things that you know nothing about.'

I nodded weakly and realised that not only was I in trouble, but so were hundreds of students and the school itself. I felt like the Mad Hatter.

Classes began at 7.30 a.m. and, due to staff shortages, it was hard going. With one typewriter shared among the staff, and teachers expected to duplicate their own exam papers, there was not much room for complacency. 'I have just made a rough calculation,' I wrote to my parents. 'I reckon I have marked 360 exam papers and have 30 still to mark.'

At the beginning of the second term, in January 1965, I was assigned to more teaching. This included all top forms in health science and maths at EBS, in addition to classes at KGV – exhausting but satisfying. It was an uphill battle to motivate the students, especially among the boys, who felt there was little point studying since there were no jobs. Furthermore, any government vacancies were dished out to applicants before the exam results were known. Day-to-day life at the school was quite different from anything you might encounter in the UK. They held competitions to see who could cut the most toddy and who could produce the fattest pig. Every Sunday one of the school pigs was slaughtered by the boys, who then set about cleaning and cooking it.

Teaching maths was a particular challenge, especially at the girls' school, where my lessons usually ended up with everyone collapsing into fits of hysteria. Despite this unorthodoxy they learnt the subject better than in the past. The formula of a joke, a sum, and a story seemed to work wonders, but alarm bells rang when I heard that a promised replacement for maths teacher was not going to materialise. I emphasised my short-comings to Alan Law, and serious efforts were put in place to recruit a qualified maths teacher. Finally the jokes ended.

Arrival of the qualified maths teacher made a big difference to my own teaching schedule. It basically shifted most of my teaching over to EBS, where I taught at all levels, up to leavers who were the same age as myself. Health science was popular with the students, and they achieved very high results in the matriculation exams. They were quite giggly at times, not helped by the fact that my first lesson with them was on mammalian reproduction. All seemed to go well until I asked for any questions. A hand shot up, and, not realising that I was heading straight into a trap, I gave the student the floor. 'Why do only married women have babies?' she asked me. The class broke down into hilarity and uproar, and I was unable to persuade any of them to offer anything approaching a sensible answer. I returned to the simple explanation of fertilisation. That was followed by lessons on the human skeleton, for which I arranged a visit to the local hospital so they could see the real thing.

The new maths teacher also took over physics, so, in addition to health science, I was left to teach chemistry and biology as core subjects, together with first- and second-year history. My first reaction on seeing the history syllabus was to tell the headmaster that it was, in my opinion, an embarrassment in terms of relevancy, focusing on the UK's story and ignoring the region where our students lived. He agreed with me and put in place arrangements to change the syllabus for the younger students.

Apart from teaching, I became involved in a few extracurricular activities, including a school play, the debating society, and a school magazine. The latter, published in 1965, serves as a time capsule, reminding me of how my days were filled with the school's activities all those years ago. Our 'Canoe Debate', for example, provided an opportunity for some of the best orators from KGV and EBS to lock horns on the thorny issue of who dies and who is saved in a drifting canoe. The idea was that four famous people, John Lennon, Queen Elizabeth II, Florence Nightingale, and the president of the USA, were cast adrift. In order for the food to last and for the canoe to stay afloat, it was necessary to convince the others in the canoe (and the judges) that their contribution to human survival was the most significant. John Lennon came to a very wet end at an early stage despite a brilliant and moving speech by Otinelu Tafia from KGV. Meanwhile Nikinam Teitei defended HM the Queen who, sad to relate, was thrown to the sharks soon after Mr Lennon. Verbal battle then raged between the usually calm and gentle Florence Nightingale (Nui Founouki) and the political genius of the US president, represented by Silinga Kofe. At the final count, the US president managed to pull through and Ms Nightingale took her last plunge.

The Drama and Music Club, for which I wrote a script and directed performances, stretched my limited artistic talents even further. The play was entitled 'His Honour Commands' and was a satirical take-off of the British colonial administration and the endless paper trail that it creates. A Fishing Club and Girl Guides completed the mix of pursuits followed by the pupils at EBS, along with the usual sporting activities.

School Holidays

One of my students' essays on school holidays ruminated on the destruction to local society being wreaked by alcohol:

> One night we went to see the dance at the maneaba. All the men were drunk and they danced with the women. A Solomon man was dancing with a little girl, and a little boy who was drunk was throwing stones at smaller children. A policeman came and took him to prison. Next morning two women were fighting near the store and all the people came to watch them.

Concerns over the safety of girls living on densely populated Betio meant that many of the students were happy when holidays were over and they could return to the relative safety of their school at Bikenibeu: 'I could not see the cinema nor go anywhere by myself, because the cinema was too far away and it was not safe to go by myself.' But some were thrilled to be on holiday: 'I was very happy there. On my last night I went to see a film about cowboys, and at the end of the film everyone went home with happy hearts, but my heart was sad, because I had to go back to EBS.' One of their regular gripes was the chores they had to complete at home: 'Now I am back at EBS I can have a rest from all that housework,' wrote one happy schoolgirl.

A Science Lesson

I am reminded of my science teaching by an article that appeared in the first school magazine. Written by Tiritake Teanako from Form IV, it was called: "'Honesty is the Best Policy", or "Think Before You Act'":

> One bright afternoon quite recently the five Form IV girls had their extra lesson with Mr Vine in the laboratory down at KGV school. Things were still very new to them as they had been there only a month, and they were quite fascinated by the amazing things to be found in the laboratory. When the teacher went outside for something, these girls looked around the laboratory in search of mischief. One of them suddenly set eyes on something interesting: it was a box of 'Glass Wool'. Thinking that this is the wool for cleaning a mirror, she pointed out her amazing discovery to a classmate. The other girl agreed with her so they quickly opened the box and pocketed two large pieces of the wool. Their pockets bulged and their minds could not stop thinking about the precious thing they had found.
>
> Unfortunately for these two poor girls, the mirror cleaner began to bite their legs, where their pockets were resting. After a long period of great discomfort one of the girls started to look for the word 'itching' in the dictionary and at that moment the teacher returned to the room, and immediately set eyes on the girl reading the dictionary. 'What on earth are you doing?' asked the teacher. 'Sir, I am looking for a word to describe me itching in the dictionary,' replied the pupil. 'Why? Are you itching?' asked the teacher. 'Yes Sir I am itching very badly after touching the glass wool,' she said, pointing to it.
>
> Instead of being angry the teacher just laughed, and explained that it was not wool to clean glass but wool made out of glass. 'It is just like cutting yourself with many fine pieces of glass,' he added.
>
> So you see, it is really true that honesty is the best policy

for the girl was dishonest to pinch the glass wool, and had to continue to suffer afterwards because she did not tell the master the whole truth.

Rain Starts Play

About a month after I arrived in Tarawa, it rained. It was none too soon, and the heavy downpour coincided with an official notification of drought. Cool, refreshing rain brought with it jubilation and the long-prayed-for chance to wash in fresh water after five months without a drop. Villagers grabbed their bars of soap and stood outside wherever they could get the wettest. Once the rain stopped, it was back to normal, with unrelenting sunshine from six in the morning to sunset at 6 p.m., with only the 'mad dogs and Englishmen' venturing far outside in the middle of the day.

Traditional Values

Living in close proximity on a tiny remote island meant that the locals had to find ways to exist harmoniously, avoiding tensions, arguments, or jealousies. One of these ways was the *bubusee*. It meant that you did not admire another person's belongings, since the owner would then feel compelled to give the item to the admirer. Another was to avoid showing off. A canoe race would often end with the leading boat waiting for others, so they crossed the finish together, with no declared winners or losers, despite the fact that they all knew who had sailed the fastest.

Respect for each other was paramount, especially for the older members of society, who were akin to tribal leaders. Whilst walking near others, it was customary to bow one's head rather than marching past without acknowledging each other. And the customs associated with meeting on paths away from the village were quite rigid:

Ko na Maury (Hello) greets the first person; *Ko na Maury* is the response.

'Where are you going?' asks the first.

'I am going that way.'

'And where do you come from?'

'I come from there,' answers the second, pointing in the direction from which he or she has come. Such exchanges take time to complete before either party is able to extract or impart any real news.

Trouble in Paradise

Alcohol was a major curse to social stability. Expatriates regularly exceeded the limit, and islanders, well used to drinking toddy, found it hard to hold themselves back when it came to beer and whisky on tap. It sometimes felt as if we were living in the wild west. One social gathering I attended a couple of months after my arrival was hosted by a Fijian surgeon and held out hopes of being a less frantic affair. Halfway through the night, not everyone was drunk, and we were hoping that we could get to the end without the usual mayhem. Unfortunately it was not to be, and the inevitable fight broke out between two drunk Gilbertese, one of whom landed in the lap of the girl I was talking to. Naturally upset, she encouraged me to remove the gentleman, which I did, helped by several others, in the most gentle way possible. After all, we would no doubt be meeting each other the next day, and losing face was considered bad karma.

Drunken behaviour usually resulted in painful heads the next day, without too much collateral damage, but this was not always so. Three incidents come to mind. First, the director of education driving the department Land Rover halfway up a sloping palm tree before it rolled off, landing upside down just outside his office in a corner of the school-yard. Second, the female bar manager of the Bairiki Club carrying a legless senior district officer to his regular crash-out bed behind the bar. Finally, and tragically, a jeep crash in which a nurse from the colony hospital was killed and a primary teacher seriously injured.

This last incident is etched in my memory. I had been sitting in the house, typing copy for the school magazine, when Tony raced in and told me to come quickly. As he drove us at great speed up the atoll, he explained that there had been a terrible accident. An expatriate we both knew, Bruce McKenzie, had crashed a Land Rover into a coconut tree. Seven people were in the car, and all were injured. Tony had been first to arrive at the scene, two minutes after it happened. It was a devastating sight. Bruce was trapped inside the vehicle but possibly one of the least injured. People were lying all over the ground, and Tony was shocked to see his Gilbertese friend Anetiba groaning in pain; his neck was severely cut, and his trachea had a big hole in it through which came a mixture of air and blood.

They were all rushed to the hospital, about a mile back along the bumpy single-track lagoon road. By now everyone knew about the accident – word travels fast in such places – and a deathly hush spread over the village, broken only by the sombre voices of toddy cutters harvesting their day's bottle full of coconut nectar. By 8 p.m. news came that one of the nurses from the car had died and that Anetiba was severely injured. The resident commissioner radioed an American base north of Tarawa, begging for a mercy mission to pick up Anetiba and take him to a suitably equipped medical facility. Their plane touched down at 11 a.m. the next day, greatly improving his chances of survival.

The accident had been influenced by heavy drinking, and the police, government, and local people were determined that a legal case would be heard, making it clear that they would no longer tolerate the dichotomy of rules that existed in the colony – one rule for the expats and another for the indigenous population. *Imatang* (white man) scandal was never far away. In June 1965, the manager of the Wholesale Society ran off with a large amount of stolen cash. It was the sixth incident of imatangs setting a really bad example since I had arrived. We were rapidly losing ground in the eyes of the locals, and I learnt to disassociate myself from these antics by disclaiming the *imatang* title and claiming instead to be a white Gilbertese: 'I te Kiribati mainena.'

Harry Duesbury

I regularly went to stay at Harry's house in Bairiki to soak up the party atmosphere that he created so well, with the help of a number of Gilbertese girls around my own age. Harry himself was about twenty years older than us but revelled in being part of a young crowd. I can still hear his teasing, giggling laughter as he translated the bawdy comments of the party girls while we three volunteers enjoyed the welcoming embraces of these vivacious island women.

It was Harry who helped me break the ice with Gilbertese girls. He invited me to accompany him to the village's Sunday evening film show. Intrigued that such a thing should exist in such a tiny village, I agreed at once and we walked from his house to the large maneaba. It was 7 p.m. and dusk was just giving way to moonlight. From the shadows of the village a steady stream of excited islanders gushed along the moonlit path. Many were arriving straight from church and wore their traditional Sunday best, consisting of white vests and white lava-lavas wrapped around their waists like we would wear towels after swimming. Many, like ourselves, were carrying chairs, but the majority had woven sleeping mats rolled under their arms, and they simply spread these on the maneaba floor, forming a large communal carpet.

Already many had heard my name, and shouts of 'Ko na maury, Peter' came from all directions. Harry, it seemed, had things organised in advance, for after some adept juggling with chairs I found myself cut off from him and surrounded by Gilbertese girls. Their giggles of embarrass-ment brought forth an encouraging wink from Harry, but before I was able to ask him for protocol instructions, the screen lit up with the seventh episode of a twenty-year-old Hollywood thriller. A scream of surprise rose from the audience at the sight of a plane plunging towards the ground, and sheer bewilderment took over when a flashback of the pilot's mind pictured him kissing his wife goodbye. Any incomprehensible stretches of English dialogue provided opportunities for outbursts of gossip, which soon took over from the film as the main source of entertainment.

Harry's official position was manager of the Public Works Department, and as such he had access to the colony launch that we borrowed on numerous occasions to go diving for clams or underwater sightseeing in the ocean pass. Whilst writing this account, I wondered what had become of him and turned to Google to see if I could trace him. After a false start caused by the wrong spelling of his name, I landed on a page that brought shock and horror. Harry, I knew, had married a local woman after I left Kiribati, and he had at least one son. He made his new home in Belize and loved it there – no doubt diving and sailing as he had on Tarawa, and perhaps also creating a strong rapport with that country's young people as he had done on Tarawa. But to my utter shock I learned that he had been murdered in his sleep at his home in San Andres village, Corozal district of Belize, in June 2007. The youngest of the three arrested suspects was a fifteen-year-old who was known to Harry as someone he had befriended and helped, like so many others. Harry, who was stabbed sixteen times, was eighty-one years old. The three accused were released after three years in prison and a legal review that indicated mishandling of the case by local police. I shall always be grateful to him for teaching me the rudiments of scuba diving and for his warm hospitality.

My notes from those times bring back much happier stories of Harry. 16 January 1965:

> It is now Saturday evening and I have just arrived at Harry Duesbury's house in Bairiki where I spend most of my week-ends. It makes a relaxing change from the educational hub of Bikenibeu and it is easier to make friends here since people do not regard me as a school teacher. Gary has also come down from Nuatabu where he has been having great difficulty in making one particular village work on its causeway. Tomorrow we will forget all our problems as we pay a visit to Oscar the Grouper at the Fairway Buoy on the far side of the lagoon.

Harry's house was rapidly becoming both a refuge and meeting venue, and it was here that I met Tafua, who was to become my girlfriend.

Tafua

I first met Tafua at one of Harry's parties before Christmas 1964. We rapidly became an item and remained one when I left the Gilberts in August 1965 and for some time after that, until separation by thousands of kilometres and an agreement to face up to the impossibility of a long-term relationship brought us to a reluctant separation of our ways. Tafua returned to her family in the Ellice Islands, and we eventually lost touch. While in Tarawa, our time together, mostly at weekends, was full of fun, laughter, music, friends, drinking, and feasting. Though her English was basic and my Gilbertese was rudimentary, we had a lovely understanding and appreciation of each other.

Since our relationship was played out in real time, it did not involve a written record, and it was only after we had parted company, me to

Swansea and Tafua to Funafuti, that we wrote to each other. One letter from that time survives. It is full of the passion that we felt for each other and is enveloped with the innocence of youth that gift-wrapped our love-filled lives. It brings back many happy memories, and I hope that Tafua went on to have a healthy and successful life. I have no idea what became of her, and Internet searches have proved fruitless.

'Darling, I bati n tangiriko [I love you very much], I wish you could be with me all nights and all days and forever,' she wrote to me in October 1965, when I was finding my feet at university. It was not to be.

School Magazine and School Play

'Last week I was working from midday to midnight on it until, on Thursday night, I fell asleep at the typewriter and fell off my chair,' I wrote in my journal. The creation of a school magazine at EBS proved to be a big undertaking, since everything was left to me: editorial tasks, typing copy, arranging layout, printing, binding, and sponsorship.

The school play was a 20-minute affair for Open Day on the last day of term. As director I was blessed with one talented actress, who took the role of the head pirate in an adapted play called 'Commissioner Commands'. The original story, 'Elizabeth Commands', was set during the rule of Elizabeth I, whereas our play portrayed fictional events in 1950 in which pirates occupied Tarawa lagoon. I recall one line: 'It's as easy as lying under a coconut tree with sweet toddy pouring into your mouth', convincingly delivered by our lead actress. The Queen's Court was replaced by the government secretariat on Bairiki, and instead of ladies-in-waiting we had the all too familiar horde of government secretaries. The hero of the story was one Captain Teitei, who happened to be the colony's only qualified sea captain.

After the play's performance to wild applause, I was called in to the office of the headmistress, Wynn Courtney, to be embarrassed by enthusiastic thanks for both magazine and play. She told me she was going to request that the resident commissioner express his thanks by giving me a week of extra travel time in Fiji on my way home in August.

Sports Day

1 August 1965 was Inter-School Sports Day, and I was in charge. Schools from all over Tarawa competed, and the Bikenibeu Sports Ground was thronged with spectators and competitors. Following an official opening, attended by the resident commissioner, all went well until the last event of the morning: the over-seventeens 220-yards girls' running race. Only four girls were competing, and it was a very fast race. As they crossed the finishing line one girl collapsed, and as I rushed to her aid she stood up, seeming to recover. Then her friend collapsed. I carried her about 50 yards through a massive crowd of people, to get her out of the sun. Fortunately some young nurses were present and they administered first aid. About 500 people from the crowd rushed to see her, and I had to physically fight to give the girl space.

Diving

I had learnt to dive from Hans Hass and Jacques Cousteau. Their tele-vised adventures and books made it all so exciting and seem so easy. They were my idols, along with James Bond and Elvis Presley. By the time the Beatles came along I had living proof that a kid from the streets of Hoylake could conquer the world. Sure, wasn't Cynthia Lennon living just down the road, and didn't the Beatles get their first big break at the Empire Theatre in nearby Liverpool? Name the game, I was your man. Fortunately I did not push it on the musical front, since my brother was following that path and it would not have taken long for me to be found out. But emulating Hass and Cousteau was another story. When the established divers of Tarawa asked if I knew how to dive, there was only one answer to give. Sure I did – just let me get my hands on a scuba tank, and I would see them down below. And so it was, one weekend, that Tony and Harry Duesbury cast their watchful eyes over me as I made, unbeknown to them, my first ever descent.

The first bit was a doddle. Using a twin-hose early-design regulator made popular by Cousteau and his team, I swam down towards the seabed about 9 metres beneath the surface. My short-sightedness ensured that I missed seeing a shark, giant clams, and pretty much everything else. At 3 metres' depth I was in mounting agony with ears that didn't know how to equalise, and the game was up. I resurfaced and was accompanied by Tony, who by now had realised that I was worse than a diving novice: I was a diving virgin. Embarrassed by the crass stupidity I had displayed, I determined to take instructions and try again. Next time the ears cleared, I was on my way, and I stayed close to my buddy, copying his pathway through the water.

'To be able to float around among the coral formations and to chase little coral fish in their own environment is an experience that I find quite indescribable,' I enthused in my first dive log. 'After slight initial difficulty in clearing my ears it was all very simple,' I lied to my parents. 'I went down to thirty feet and spent about an hour at that depth. I carried out routine safety checks such as mask clearing and putting on air supply underwater without any trouble at all.'

I thus made up the fourth member of Tarawa's diving team: Harry Duesbury, government engineer Ron Summers, my fellow volunteer teacher Tony, and me. Their personalised dive 'training' comprised instructions to clear my ears at least three times a day to get them accustomed to popping, and to stay calm underwater. That is how I learnt to dive – the rest was practice and plenty of reading, together with absorption of knowledge from my much more experienced colleagues. For any reader who is mistakenly impressed by this sorry tale, I am tempted to add, *Don't try this at home.* There are quicker ways to meet one's demise but few less certain.

In Tarawa there were basically three ways to dive: boat dives in open water, generally in the lagoon or in a passageway between the open sea and the lagoon; oceanside shore dives; and lagoonside shore dives. Of these, the most exhilarating was the oceanside shore dive, which generally involved harnessing wave power to carry one out through the breakers and over deep water. Our house was perched at the edge of the ocean, so all we needed to do was kit up in the back garden, next to Teatou's toddy palm, and wade out towards the line of breakers that formed a dazzling-white roaring barrier between the beach and deep water. The breaking waves could be just a few metres high or considerably more, depending on the wind. Providing one mastered the rhythmic pattern of surges, in and out, using their power to push one offshore, it was feasible to pass through the breaker zone to reach the relative calm beyond.

Here's how it worked. With the water at waist height and the line of breakers about 25 metres in front of us, we lay down and took a firm grip of a dead coral boulder or crevice. Within seconds a wave would crash over us. Holding firmly onto the rock, we resisted the drag of water threatening to deliver us back to the beach. Then the current slackened and reversed direction. As that water washed back out to sea, we released our grip and went with it, doing our best to protect our bodies from being scratched on the sharp corals. Then the outward flow would cease, and another incoming wave crashed over us. We held on tight again, the rushing waters attempting to drag us back across the reef platform. A brief lull, and that wave's heavy load would wash back out to sea, with us riding its current, taking us about 10 metres forward and through the breakers. For the last ride, we usually held our breath, dived down under the incoming wave, and then took a last exhilarating ride into the clear calm water off the oceanside shore. We switched our breathing to compressed air and dived down to spend an hour or so exploring the colourful exotic marine life that inhabited this neighbouring, mysterious, underwater world.

Giant Clams

Most of our open-water dives would be from a hired or borrowed government launch. More often than not we were playing at being hunters, with giant clam shells (*Tridacna gigas*) as our prey. In those days, 1964–65, we had no idea that giant clams were one of the most endangered clam shells in the world, listed by the International Union for Conservation of Nature as vulnerable to extinction – a situation that may have since changed due to successful captive breeding programmes at Harbour Branch Foundation in Florida and at James Cook University of North Queensland. Island fishermen had learnt of their value in markets such as Fiji and were earning good money from this trade, but there were virtually no Gilbertese trained in scuba diving, and our methods were more efficient, threatening local populations of giant clams.

These are seriously big animals, often weighing almost a quarter of a ton (200+ kilograms) and living from the intertidal down to 20 metres or so. Their shells are well over a metre in length, and they live for more than a hundred years. A formidable creature by any measure, and one that earned our deepest respect, but unfortunately not our protection. As I look out of my study window in Ireland, reaching back over the years to write this memoir, my eyes fall on a shell of one of the giant clams we lifted from Tarawa lagoon. How many houses around the world sport these magnificent shells as garden plant pots or fountain bowls?

Giant clams are relatively easy to identify underwater, since they are the only clams unable to completely close their shells. Even when shut as far as possible, there are fleshy parts of the mantle clearly visible, and these, like corals, have symbiotic algae, zooxanthellae, that lend iridescent green and blue colours to the flesh. Our own clam diving trips funded the purchase of some diving gear, including a Calypsophot, forerunner of the Nikonos underwater camera. But the clams almost took their revenge on me. This is how it happened.

Abandoned

A small tug took us out to the clam grounds, and once we were in the area, two of us would don our scuba gear whilst the other two prepared to use their snorkels. The two scuba divers hung on to a large board that was towed behind the tug on a long line. Their arms were strapped to the board, and they had handles to grasp. By tilting the board this way and that, the divers could wend their way between coral outcrops in search of clams, and since there was no swimming involved, their air lasted longer than usual. The two snorkel divers hung on to ropes tied to each side of the stern, and they carried out their search from the surface. As soon as a clam was sighted, they let go of the rope, and a new rope was handed to the scuba divers to tie onto the clam shell. The clam was then hauled aboard by the crew, who set about cutting out the innards and eating the raw meat.

You may have read the story of Australian divers being abandoned by their dive boat on the Great Barrier Reef in 1998. Back in 1965 I gained a unique insight into how it must feel. I had been riding the line for about half an hour, when I was delighted to observe a giant among giant clams. I quickly let go, raised my arm, and waited for the boat to come back to me. Keen to be sure that I didn't lose the clam, I kept my head down and waited . . . and waited . . . and waited, as the sound of our tow-boat's engine slowly diminished. Finally I looked up to take a sighting of the launch. It was nowhere to be seen. I was alone in the ocean, about 20 kilometres from shore and without any other craft on the horizon.

My pulse raced. Just a few moments earlier I had been elated by the sheer beauty of the reef below. Now it felt dark, dangerous, and menacing. How could they have missed me dropping off the line? Where were they? How long before they realised I was not on board? I noticed an extra-shallow bit of reef and swam towards it. Stinging corals reached up just below the surface, but I ignored the pain and climbed onto the knoll, hoping that this would enable me to see my dive boat. Standing upright, not feeling the coral cuts and stings that were releasing blood into the water, I finally saw the boat, about a mile away and apparently stationary, presumably working at lifting another clam shell.

I waved madly for what seemed like five minutes, but there were no signs that they had seen me. I was worried about the blood in the water and the setting sun that would soon cause the boat to head for home. I decided to swim, as fast as I could, to the clam boat. I doubt that I have ever swum so fast since, and when I was within about a hundred metres of the boat, a cheery wave from the skipper finally acknowledged my existence, as if I was on a pleasure swim around his vessel. Hardly anything was said as I boarded, but I carried with me some vivid, nightmarish dreams that haunt me to this day.

Bikenibeu Youth Club

Apart from teaching and school-related activities, my other role in Bikenibeu was to assist in running the local youth club. This club, it was said at the time, was 'the greatest thing to hit social life here for years'. It was a claim that Betio's elders would have loved to make for their struggling community. Once the Bikenibeu club had completed construction of its own maneaba, more and more young people turned up to the activities that were held there. One aspect that was particularly pleasing was how the club provided a catalyst for greater integration of village people with children from the primary school.

Sailing Outrigger Canoe

Up at dawn, we crept though the awakening village, past the thatch-roofed church, along the rough coral road with the dogs and chickens warming themselves in the morning's sunshine, and to the lagoonside house of Matang, the canoe builder. As we approached his house we heard the rustling of his sleeping mats as he prepared to convert his bed mat into a couch. The crunch of our feet on the coral woke his wife, who hastily covered herself and rolled up the matting walls to welcome in a reluctant sun. Already we had doubts about the wisdom of our venture, for the ominous dark clouds that obscured the tropic sunrise and the wavelets in the lagoon seemed angrier than usual.

'Ko na mauri, Matang.' We gave the traditional Gilbertese greeting in unison, and I hoped my face did not betray the fear I was beginning to feel. 'How's the wind?' asked Tony, and Matang turned his half-awake face to the turbulent lagoon. 'It's no wind for white men,' he replied as he fetched the sails. A greater compliment I could not imagine. At last he was treating us as islanders and was prepared to trust us with his precious canoe. I smiled to myself, realising that now there could be no turning back, and I caught a glimpse of Tony casting a last look at the village we were about to leave behind.

We were planning to sail across the lagoon to Nuatabu, much to the fascination of the local people who had gathered around the canoe at Matang's house. We intended to stay there for a weekend but travelled light; the canoe was really fine-hulled and sank visibly deeper with every pound added. My own kit amounted to a toothbrush in my top pocket and a lava-lava. We were under pressure to make a smooth departure. This was a tall order, since these canoes are notoriously difficult to rig, let alone sail. Everything is tied to the masts, which must be raised in one smooth motion until the single stay to the tip of the outrigger carries the weight of both spars and sails. Then it is a balancing act, with the weight of the rig countered by the force of the wind. There is no turning around in these fascinating craft. You simply lift the forward spa to a balance point halfway along the narrow hull, and then, in another smooth movement, you move it to the opposite end so that what had been the stern now becomes the bow. Then you sail off on a new tack, always keeping the outrigger to windward.

Tony pushed up one leg of the mast while I kept the canoe into the wind, holding the other leg of the mast in its step and letting out the one and only stay, which has to support the masts as they are raised. This time, at least, everything went according to plan, and the crowd on the shore seemed impressed. As we trimmed sails to the force 4 wind, a farewell cry of *Tia kabo* went up from the crowd. It was a fantastic sail. At times I was perched on the very end of the outrigger, looking down on the knife-shaped hull as it cut through the short waves of the lagoon. We were the fastest sailing vessel for hundreds of kilometres, and you should have seen the looks of sheer amazement on the faces of fishermen as we sped past their almost stationary canoes.

Spray came in solid cascades, and Tony, clutching desperately at the steering oar, was lost from vision for minutes at a time. I knew that his eyes must be stinging terribly from salt and was pleased that he continued to force the canoe through the waves. To anyone but an experienced islander, my position must have seemed most precarious, as I flew through the air on the end of the bucking outrigger. The village had now sunk beneath the horizon, and I could just distinguish the tops of the coconut palms as they too were merging with the sky. Shortly a headland should appear ahead, and once around that it would only be 14 more kilometres along the mangrove-lined coast before we reached the village of Nuatabu. There an eager band of islanders would clutch at the delicate canoe and carry it, like a ceremonial throne, to the centre of the village for all to see. An hour later, still on a flying float, I saw the distant roof of a church, and we flew in to the palm-fringed shore.

It took us exactly two hours to reach Nuatabu, an average speed of 10 knots, and we touched close to 20 knots in our fastest moments. 'Who sail?' asked the children who swam out to us. 'Who sail?' asked the he-men carrying it ashore. 'Who sail?' asked the band of laughing girls on the beach, and the old man in the house where we were given coconuts to drink. 'We did,' we replied for the tenth time, before finally realising that this was too improbable for them to grasp. 'Teanti,' (ghosts) said Tony, and they seemed satisfied. 'Welcome,' said the old man. 'Welcome,' said the children, and with uncanny shrewdness, Tony whispered, 'We've arrived.'

On our last evening in Nuatabu we were invited to a farewell feast organised by our respective *bangiangas* (girlfriends). It was a really beautiful evening, so we sat under the stars and ate roast pig, roast chicken, fried breadfruit, babai, coconut meat, and bananas, which we washed down with delicious coconut water, *moi-moto*. After the food, we talked to some of the Uni mane, the old men, who told us about life in the Gilberts before many white men were present. They told us of old customs long forgotten, and of the ghost-worshipping which was still a feature of their daily lives, albeit a secret one. They even related tales of ancient battles that they learned from their own parents, passed on from generation to generation.

We were fascinated by all these stories, and it was not until someone enquired about the time that we realised we had been sitting and talking for four hours. The girls began to complain that they wanted to dance the Twist. We were quickly brought back to the present-day 1965, where ghosts and battles had been replaced by pop music. As the orange light of dawn began to flood the sky, we heard the happy laughter of villagers returning to their homes, and we walked together along the rough coral road, stepping over the dogs and chickens stretched out in lazy defiance of another day in paradise.

Disaster Waiting to Happen

In late January we suffered the westerlies, more accurately described as the season of bloody gales and pouring rain. Despite the intensity of the weather, there was a certain predictability that somehow gave comfort. Bright sunny mornings with fresh breezes, clouding over soon after midday to produce heavy downpours. Temperatures, although feeling a bit cool in the rain, never dropped below 24°C. Gales and bad weather brought their fair share of excitement.

One afternoon we were due to go diving. Tony and I arrived at Harry's house at around 2 p.m., only to discover that neither Harry nor Gary were present and the canoe was missing. There was no note to explain their absence – most unusual. We searched the lagoon, straining our eyes, and were concerned that the wind was picking up into a force 6 or 7, raising steep and dangerous waves, especially for such a small canoe.

Hoping they had found shelter somewhere on the island, we made our way back to Bikenibeu and waited for news. Three rescue boats were on the water for the afternoon and evening, but they failed to find the pair. It was looking pretty grim.

Next day I received a telegram from Harry, who described what must have been a hair-raising experience. They had reached the island safely, had a short snorkel dive and then headed back to the main island. The storm struck suddenly, quickly swamping the canoe, which half sank in the water, retaining just enough buoyancy to provide a handhold for the two men. They put on their flippers and started to swim with the canoe towards the shore. Neither wind nor tide were in their favour, and it was an exhausting and frightening slog, especially after sunset, when sharks were known to be hunting their food. Six hours and a lot of swearing later, they reached the shore and staggered back to Harry's house, where many anxious friends were consuming Harry's ale. The canoe was forgotten, drifted away, and broke up on the reef.

Not all such tales have happy endings, especially out where there are thousands of square kilometres without even the smallest speck of land. There are many stories of offshore fishermen missing Tarawa due to wind, waves, or currents, and being left on this great ocean without water, food, or engine. Some do survive, but many perish.

During my own time in Tarawa there was an ongoing saga that was mentioned at every church service, with prayers offered for the safe return of islanders who had gone fishing in a small boat. If they were lucky they could have drifted westwards, hitting Nauru 700 kilometres away, or else perhaps the Solomons lying about 1,900 kilometres towards Australia. We have no idea what happened to them, and they were never heard of again. Harry and Gary's fate could easily have been similar, had it not been for their determined effort with their flippers and their resolve to remain with their waterlogged canoe.

Causeway Conflict

Fellow teachers such as Holland Panapa, the woodwork teacher, and Amasoni, a junior schoolteacher, proved to be sensitive guides to local customs, helping to ensure I did not offend too many people from sheer ignorance of rules that were embedded in their society. The rules had evolved over centuries, and I had some idea of what they involved through reading *A Pattern of Islands* by Sir Arthur Grimble, a previous and long-serving civil administrator in the colony who eventually became resident commissioner, and who was still remembered and apparently loved and revered by the islanders. Prior to travelling to the Gilberts, I had also attended a training course at which previous volunteers told us of their experiences. One message shone through all these presentations – that we should listen to what we were told by local people and should not have the arrogance to think that we could teach them about how to live in their own unique communities. Some practices may seem strange to us, we were told, but we were not missionaries, passing judgement. We were simply there to help when that help was requested and agreed.

True to character, it was not long before I found myself stretching the limits of established cultural boundaries, trying my best to advise the villagers of Nuatabu on something that was crucial to their future well-being, or so I thought. During our visit we were bowled over by their kindness and hospitality, which extended to making floral dresses and lava-lavas for our welcoming party, fanning our food as we gorged on the roast pig that they had killed in our honour, and dancing across the island, serenading us with guitars and local songs that drifted with us out to sea, where a group of strong men carried our canoe to deep water, in readiness to be sailed back to Bikenibeu. I immediately determined to help in the construction of a link that would join their small island in the northern chain to its neighbouring islets, thus making the land journey along the ribbon of coral reefs less arduous.

Joining us for this official visit to the village was Harry Duesbury, wearing his director of public works hat. He was particularly important, since he controlled the only suitable or available government dumper truck, which would greatly lighten the load. Harry's only condition was that the road over the passage would be constructed by a bridge and short causeways, so that the flow of water from ocean to lagoon would be maintained. The headman of the village stood in the maneaba and rejected this approach, preferring to build a solid causeway. Harry dug in his heels, and I was asked to explain the importance of maintaining the seawater exchange. They listened politely, said little more, and bade us, in their inimitable, friendly manner, farewell.

There would be no truck to help the villagers, and we expected that there would be little progress in the weeks and months ahead. Two weeks later we were on the Public Works Department launch heading towards the northern part of the lagoon, not far from Nuatabu. To our astonishment, the causeway was built – solidly. Fait accompli. We kept an eye on the project over the coming months, during our giant clam expeditions throughout the lagoon. It was more substantial each time we visited. I had, hopefully, learned a valuable lesson.

Visit to Buariki

Buariki is the northernmost village on Tarawa, and the local population looked forward to visitors, who were few and far between, especially imatangs (white men). Traditional practices had hardly changed here, despite the influence of the church. We had not been expected but were accommodated at the pastor's house. There was one lagoonside road, and the houses, on legs, were grouped on either side of it. Each family had two houses, one for sleeping and one for eating. Privacy was almost non-existent, as the houses lacked walls and toilets were just open platforms, community-owned, over the lagoon. The residents had few inhibitions: bare breasts were the norm, and breastfeeding was standard practice, including in church – a fact that I find it strange to have remarked upon in my diary of the time, but which clearly reflected the restraints that still influenced our thinking, even as recently as the early 1960s.

That evening we attended a big feast with a roasted pig as the centrepiece and palm-woven dishes laid out on the ground with other delicious local foods. There was enough to feed the whole village, which was just as well, since the whole village was in attendance. Flower-garlanded girls sat opposite us to fan flies away from the food. After eating, it was time to dance in the local maneaba. First we had to find our correct places. After a spirited debate, it was decided that we were 'sharks' and therefore should sit in the middle of the audience, towards the front line. Music began and girls took to the floor, waving their arms and shaking their hips – a modification, it seemed to us, of the Twist. The band leader was also the choreographer, and as the dance progressed he became increasingly animated, issuing more and more explicit directions: *Shake those breasts and sway those hips*, he urged his followers.

The terrible moment came when we had to contribute to the evening. First a line of girls slowly extended across the floor, twisting rhythmically to the music. It took them about five minutes to arrive enticingly at our feet, clearly inviting a response. There was no escape, so I stood and danced with the closest girl, wishing I was Chubby Checker or Elvis Presley and embarrassed by the hundreds of eyes locked only on me. After about five minutes of this agony, a new girl took her turn, encouraging me to up my game and offering me closer encounters with her voluptuous, bare, swinging breasts. The pattern was repeated a few minutes later, when an even more energetic young islander determined to break down my British reserve and make me soak up the pulsating music from my head to my feet. The crowd loved it and sang louder, laughed more infectiously, and eventually rose to their feet to join in the fun. Finally I was engulfed by grass skirts, flower garlands, and the urgent erotic beat of the drums.

After about half an hour of this excitement we sat down, thinking that we had done our bit, but we were not to be let off quite so lightly. The girls told us they had entertained us with all their hearts and that now we must do the same. How could we follow that? We sang a few songs – 'Frère Jacques' was called upon for some group chanting – and then, brilliant idea, we told them that the 'Twist' with which they had been regaling us was really out of fashion in the 'outside world'. The latest dance was called 'the Shake', we announced. 'Show us,' they begged, and so I was back on my feet, demonstrating. The only problem was that they could not grasp the concept of free movement. Their whole dancing lives had been dominated by a choreographer who orchestrated synchronous moves among his disciplined dancers. As I shook my head to the left, so did about thirty young girls, a second out of synch to the rhythm. Head to the right, followed a split second later by a similar movement. A flick of my wrist brought cries from my dance troupe that they would never be able to learn such a complicated dance, not realising that the next time I contorted to the Shake, the moves would be completely different.

Visit to Northern Islands on Colony Ship MV *Nivanga*

During the school holidays, I was lucky to join an administration voyage on one of the colony's ships, MV *Nivanga*. I recall standing on the foredeck as she crept between the submerged coral heads, avoiding the light blue shallow patches of water and slowly advancing towards the long narrow band of white coral sand. I promised myself that this island visit would be a more immersive experience than some of the other stopovers we had made in the last few days. Here I would not storm ashore and shoot off a roll of film like an American tourist on a first visit to the Eiffel Tower. No, this time I would make my way quietly ashore to soak up the atmosphere. For several days we had repeated the task of sailing in through narrow lagoon entrances, across dangerous uncharted reefs, and, after anchoring as close to shore as possible, boats would be put out and copra collected and loaded aboard. Then we would sail away to the next island.

Each island looked much like the next. The difference between them had only occurred to me after saying farewell to another island on the previous day – people singing, old men nimbly transporting their purchases ashore, girls dancing on the beach, sad farewells between new passengers and their relatives or friends left behind. These human gatherings defined the very character of each island that we visited. This time I resolved to get to know the people a bit better than I had been doing.

The thud of the diesel engines slowed to bring the ship to a halt, and a cooling breeze faded away. On the two hatch covers, the crew went about their tasks in silence, not heeding the wailing woman who sat cross-legged at the top of the ladder to the foredeck. Was she crying through pain or was it the uncontrolled notes of someone who was ecstatically happy? Nobody seemed sure, but they had heard the sound many times before and were seemingly indifferent to its cause. An angry yell rose from one of the older crew members, who had tripped over another woman's basket of live chickens that she was hiding in one of the work boats. The captain on the bridge was talking quietly through a voice pipe to his mechanic in the engine room. After a signal that I missed, the mate on the foredeck released the anchor, which dragged down fathoms of chain into the deeper water. The metallic rattle of running chain set off a renewed energy in the wailing woman's cry.

Almost as soon as the chain had ceased its noisy run, and the woman had stopped her plaintive wail, there came the clatter of wood against the metallic sides of the ship, and a rope ladder was lowered to receive the island magistrate. For Captain Ward, this was a mildly aggravating formality, whilst for the magistrate it was a great occasion. The island may not have a similar visit for a whole year or even longer. By that time the islanders may have elected a new magistrate, and the unique opportunity for his elevated status to be formally displayed would be lost. The magistrate stepped onto the deck with a great show of dignity, and the captain played his part in the ceremony, giving a slight bow and inviting the excited official to his cabin for the traditional glass of whisky before the signing of papers that recorded the cargo of copra that was being collected. Once the pair had disappeared aloft, work could begin in earnest and the workboats were lowered over the side. I climbed down into the first of these and sat as inconspicuously as possible between the huge, golden-tanned muscle-men. Each of us took hold of a long oar, and we rowed clear of the ship before turning and heading for the line of breakers marking the transition between the dark depths of the ocean and the turquoise shallows of the inner reef.

A low morning sun cast shadows on the undulating, well-defined muscles of the island's boatmen as they strained against the reef's backwash that was threatening to impede our access to the shore. A rhythmic chant of *NaaaGo . . . Wirriup* delivered by the bowman ensured coordination, especially at more difficult points where we surged through foaming waters on the tip of a curling wave crest. The cry quickened, and we rowed faster as the wave started to break. Then, at the bowman's bidding, we rested our oars and enjoyed some exhilarating seconds being carried on top of the mountain of water, before being finally dumped broadside on, in the calmer waters inside the reef. Quickly, the men took up their sweeps and rowed wildly for several strokes to pull us clear before the next wave came crashing in. No expression showed on their faces. They were used to their battle with the sea, which was repeated almost daily and had engaged their skills for as long as they could remember.

At the top of the beach, a group of islanders was sitting on the sand in the shade of a pandanus tree, and I gave them the traditional greeting of *Kam na Maury.* The village to which they belonged lay stretched along the lagoon side of the narrow atoll – typical of other islands I had visited in the Northern Gilberts. A string of palm-roofed houses was elevated above the ground on tree trunks. At one end there was a Catholic church with an enormous meeting house, and a smaller meeting house for the London Missionary Society.

A short walk across the island brought me to the ocean side – devoid of houses, since this was believed to be the domain of ghosts. It was heavy with atmosphere, and I could almost imagine meeting my own ancestors in such a place. I sat on a large mound of dead coral and soaked it all in. A breeze cooled my face, and the rustling leaves of the coconut palms played a symphony with the tuneful breakers. Down at the water's edge, a cat which must have belonged to one of the islanders was supplementing its diet with a squirming eel captured from the retreating waves as they flung their load onto the coral sand. Hermit crabs beneath my seat scuttled for safety, and a reef heron glided over to a clump of trees that provided a useful vantage point for picking out fish in the channel.

Tamnei, tamnei. Ahh te Imtang. Imatang, Imatang. I was woken from my daydreaming by the familiar cries of Gilbertese children begging to have their photographs taken, and then their shocked realisation that they were shouting at a white man – and a resting white man at that. They all ran away.

Fishing

Holland Panapa had been encouraging me to go fishing for some time. We eventually chose a day with no wind, when it was easy to paddle out through the breakers and to fish along the oceanside, between my house and the school. We launched the Ellice Islands canoe – basically a hollowed-out tree trunk with a stabilising outrigger and no sail – taking up a position about 50 metres beyond the breakers, where our hooks dangled over the coral about 20 metres below us. The water was so calm that we could see the coral reef face quite clearly and could even see fish taking our hooks.

As twilight merged into darkness we continued trolling along the reef, maintaining the right distance from the breakers by listening to the gentle swell breaking, not letting it become too loud. Now the fish really began to take the hooks, and we were pulling them in at a steady rate. On two occasions we disturbed large turtles that were resting at the surface. After about two hours of this night fishing, we approached one of the other canoes that was out fishing for flying fish. They did this by hanging a Tilley lamp from a pole and catching the flying fish with hand nets. The canoe that we approached was manned by a single elderly man with weather-beaten features and no hair, sitting cross-legged and watching the surface intently. After exchanging greetings, we asked him how he was doing, and he showed us a bag containing about fifty flying fish. He gave us one of these, and we cut it up to use as bait for bigger fish.

Staying close to the pool of light thrown by his Tilley lamp, we lowered strong lines down to about 30 or 40 metres and gently jogged the bait up and down. I had grave doubts about the efficacy of this method but was quickly reassured by a sharp tug on the canoe. Holland had hooked a whopper and was frantically letting out his line as much as possible. For over an hour we played the fish, gaining deep respect for its strength and fighting spirit. Once we had it by the side of the canoe, we used a club and knife to stun it to be able to drag it aboard before sharks took their fill. It was about 2 metres long and provided us and everyone in the neighbourhood with fish for about a week. It tasted so much better having caught it ourselves.

A feast and dancing extended well into that night, and just as I was dreaming of a good night's rest there came a clamour from outside the fisherman's hut. *Te nivou, te nivou*, and all the dancers rushed into the night. I grabbed at Kabururo, the old man, just as he too was leaving in haste, and he sought to deliver instant enlightenment by muttering *te nivou*. My Gilbertese was far from good, and I followed as he ran across the island to the ocean shore.

The wind had died and the full moon was hanging behind the silhouetted palms. A pale yellow light shone on the rippling waters, casting eerie reflections. The air was filled with the rhythmic music of the coast: rustling of palm fronds, the dull thud of breakers as they crashed on the reef, the shrill cries of lonely waders. A small group of us kept close to Kabururo, paddling through the shallows, staring intently at a small area on the sand illuminated by the burning palm frond which Kabururo had magicked on our way. A hermit crab scuttled out of the light, pulling its heavy burden of a cone shell. A group of small, bright blue fish darted from under a coral rock in search of darker places. And we moved on.

Again we stopped, Kabururo pointing to a slight depression in the sand. I saw nothing but sensed that Kabururo had discovered the object of our search. His whole body tensed, and for several seconds he remained motionless; then suddenly his arm shot out and he grabbed at the head of an octopus before it retreated to its hole. The shallow water boiled and I saw a thin tentacle creep around his arm, attaching its powerful tentacles to his skin. He rose from his stoop, smiling, displaying an octopus of about 80 centimetres in length, which squirmed vigorously in his unyielding grip. Placing his free hand around the top of the tentacles, he slid his grip down them so that all tentacles were held together. The animal fell limp as he took a small bite from the back of its head.

For three hours we walked along in the shallows, gathering octopus in Kabururo's woven basket, just like English children collect mushrooms. I plucked up courage to perform the operation myself, but being quite unable to see or catch one, I accepted Kabururo's offer of one of his victims. He handed me the squirming animal as if it was a cigarette. As I held it in my mouth, several tentacles escaped my grip and slid over my face, fastening slimy suckers to my skin. As I gasped for breath, a sucker clamped on to my right eyelid. In a half-conscious daze I heard Kabururo laughing. 'Bite it,' he instructed as I took a determined mouthful of the greasy flesh, and then another, and another, until finally the grip of the suckers relaxed and I was able to survey my victim – now beheaded. 'It's easy,' I told Tony, but he declined my suggestion to give it a try.

Farewell Party or Not

I returned from a diving trip on St Valentine's Day, to join Tafua and other members of our group at Harry's house. It had been a long day of productive clam diving, and I was feeling the effects of sleep deprivation and dehydration. Apparently I did not seem my normal jovial self, and Tafua asked if something was wrong. Without thinking, I falsely claimed, 'Yes, I have been recalled to the UK and have to leave you all.' There were murmurs of regret, and soon after this the girls all left the house. I had no idea of the repercussions I had so unintentionally triggered.

On Wednesday 17 February I received an invitation to a party to be held in Bairiki on 20 February. It was to be for one of the locals, who was not named. On the next Saturday I arrived at Harry's house at 7.30 p.m. and the news broke. It was *my* farewell party. This was no joke. It was clear that people had gone to some effort to prepare the going-home party which, in all innocence, I had assumed was for someone else who was actually leaving. It called for some quick thinking to save face and minimise embarrassment. I announced to the gathering that I was fighting the decision and hoped to get it reversed. I would know through mail that would be delivered in a week's time, on the next plane. Tafua gave me a big hug and wiped tears from her eyes, and the party resumed at a high pitch for all. Then came the killer shot: If I was allowed to stay, the girls told me, there would be another party to celebrate. The latter was to be organised – surprise, surprise – by Harry and myself. Thanks to Harry's generous hospitality, it too went off with a bang.

That should have been the end of the story, but there was more humiliation to be suffered. I reached Harry's house after a day of diving on the following Sunday to discover the 'Bairiki girls' waiting for me. Tafua, wearing flowers in her hair and a big necklace of hibiscus, presented me with a parcel that turned out to contain four beautifully embroidered pillowcases – all handmade by herself and friends as farewell presents. I had already explained that I would definitely be staying until August, but they insisted I keep the gifts. I shall always treasure them as souvenirs of my year in paradise.

Letter to Home Near End of VSO

On 10 August 1965 I was in reflective mood – feeling that my days in paradise were numbered. I described some of my feelings in a typed letter to my parents, who had been vicarious partners in my year away, sharing my experiences via weekly letters.

> Next Saturday there is to be one joint farewell feast for Tony and I, from EBS and KGV, and it looks as if this will be

a pretty massive affair as elaborate arrangements are being made; in secret of course. I am trying to learn a farewell speech in Gilbertese but will probably be in tears on the night so what's the use? Leaving so many friends and having to say so many final goodbyes is very difficult, as I have already discovered. A great friend of mine, Holland Panapa, who was on the staff of KGV has just left for his home island in the Ellice group and I shall never see him again. Tony and I took him down to his ship in Betio, in our dilapidated truck. I went with him on board and we were both in tears when it came to parting. A companionship built over months was broken in seconds by circumstances beyond our control. I have also had to say goodbye to Harry and Villi who have both gone to the Line Islands (about the most remote part of the world).

Exactly two weeks today I shall be boarding a plane that will whisk me, in a matter of hours, back to 'civilisation'. Within days my whole year here will seem like one enormous dream and I will have to touch physical proof of my visit to persuade myself that it really did happen.

Whilst I am still here and the Gilberts are still part of my life I have several things that I feel I must write. I know that when I get home I will not be able to muster up the words so here goes. I know that it was not exactly easy for you to let me go to such a far corner of the world immediately after leaving school and that there have been many doubts and prejudices in your minds that you have had to overcome. I really appreciate your help and encouragement without which I could never have stayed here. To say that I suffered from homesickness sounds pretty weak from a son who has been half way around the world, but the truth is that I have had strong pangs of homesickness since I arrived here and your cheerful letters have greatly helped to keep my spirits high. . . .

I suppose that the greatest problem about my coming out here is that of my education – both academic and financial.

Well it would be stupid of me to make any promises, but I am keen to qualify in marine biology (probably more so than a year ago) and I will do my level best to do so. But whether or not I qualify I believe this has been a very worthwhile experience. I have learnt a lot about life. . . . Disraeli said 'Life is too short for little things' and I agree. . . .

All added together this amounts to one big 'thank you' so THANK YOU.

Farewell Letter from a Student

17 August 1965

Dear Loving Teacher,

I should like to say sorry for what I have been doing to you. . . . I am awfully very sorry for my rudeness to you. I do not mean to be rude to you, but I can't help it because I am so fond of reading. Do you remember when I read my Annual during Health Science? That is what I mean for my rudeness and if you have something else that you think is not good about my behaviour I am sorry indeed. I hope you will forgive me for that. Please do forgive me sir.

I should also like to say goodbye in this letter to you as I have heard from the girls that they will go to Bonriki to say goodbye to you there. I can't come so it is better for me to write to you instead of not saying anything. Well you have been so kind to me and the others and I really enjoy your teaching and everything you do to us. I think you are an excellent teacher. I really want to say goodbye to you at Bonriki but you know the result will not be good as it will make everything even more sad and because I want you to enjoy your journey home. I'd better not come. If the others think carefully they will think the same thing as I do and won't go to Bonriki at all.

Thank you very much indeed for everything. I wish you a safe journey home and every success in your future career.

I hope you will be happy to see your beloved parents again and I send my love to them. Will you do that for me and I think the whole form as well? It is so bad that we are all to be separated when we are getting very fond of you and I hope you like us as well even if we were so naughty to you. We will all miss you very much indeed, but I do hope we will see you again. I had better stop here because I have talked a lot and I must say goodbye and God be with you always. I will try to write letters to you as often as I can because I think it is my duty to you.
Your pupil,
Teaketai

Love and Marriage in Paradise

Not long after Holland left Tarawa to return to his home in Funafuti, he wrote to me with his news. He had married a fellow Ellice Islander and was in seventh heaven with her. 'She is fat and beautiful and I am so lucky,' he told me. I was so happy for him but could not help reflecting on how western society has so many differences from indigenous cultures. I hope Holland's new wife was as happy as he was. I was confident that she would be, because he was such a strong, decent person, but this was not something to take for granted – particularly in Micronesia and Polynesia, where marriage was ruled by traditions, especially back in the 1960s. The pressure on young girls to get married to older partners chosen by their parents or their extended families could be overbearing. A letter from one of my ex-students, written to me almost a year after I left the Gilberts, illustrates what they faced.

> . . . I think it better to become a nun than staying with my people. If I do remain as a nurse then there is no future for me as it will be a 'future everlasting'. The trouble is that when I go back to my home island I will get married very soon which is very disgusting to think of. You see our customs are very different from yours. Even when you have not met the boy before, his parents will just come over to the girl's family

and tell them they want their son to become engaged to the girl. If they agree there is nothing the girl can do about that . . . but sometimes the girls go into the bush and hang themselves. Don't you ever think I will marry anyone because marriage is out of the question . . . One funny thing when I first entered EBS and my brother was at KGV, he told me that he will not hear one word that I have a boy-friend because we are intermediate brother and sister. I obeyed him because he obeyed me as well when I told him to break off his engagement. You may think it is stupid but I often feel afraid of the girl he was going to marry as I didn't know her attitude when he marries him.

I love nursing very much but above all is becoming a nun. Lots and lots of love from your pupil . . .

6 Swansea University

Fame at Last – New Genera *Vinearia* and *Anomalorbis*

Whilst studying for my B.Sc. degree in Swansea, I fell under the spell of my Professor, E. W. Knight-Jones. He was the guy who had approved my postponement of the course for a year so that I could go on VSO to teach in the Gilbert and Ellice Islands. He was the guy who later accepted me to join an expedition of more senior biologists to the Greek island of Chios. He was the guy who supported my application for a research scholarship at James Cook University of North Queensland and later advised me to return to Swansea to prepare a Ph.D. thesis from the work I had carried out in the Red Sea and Pacific. He was the guy who arranged a postdoctoral fellowship for me to work at what was then University College Galway. He was my inspiration and mentor throughout my academic career.

Prof. Knight-Jones was also the guy who introduced me to the tiny spiralled tube worms of his own research, the spirorbids. I remember thinking at the time what an esoteric topic it was. What possible good could come from studying the minute differences between these tiny worms? I would certainly never follow such a useless path. Suffice it to admit that the title of my Ph.D. thesis was 'Studies on the Biology and Zoogeography of Spirorbinae'. I gained the doctorate in 1972.

What I learnt from Knight-Jones and this study went far beyond the immediate topic, which in itself brought some extraordinary results. It led to me describing around a dozen species that were new to science and one that was the type for a new genus, *Anomalorbis*, that challenged the established rules used by taxonomists to differentiate between the spiralling spirorbids and their wavering, long-tubed cousins, the serpulids. It also led to the naming of a new genus, *Vinearia*, by Prof. Knight-Jones's wife and fellow taxonomist, Phyllis, in 1984.

Needless to say, it was easy to get carried away by such name-dropping success. Who would have ever imagined they would gain distinction for having a worm genus named after them? But it was the zoogeographical part of this study that was the most interesting to me. There was a lot to learn from a knowledge of where each species was present, and of which other species shared its habitat. In any set area of shallow seabed or seashore there was likely to be a dozen or so different species of spirorbids, each adapted to a particular niche. It felt like forensic science when I unravelled the tube worm communities. Identifying localised assemblages of species provided clues to the ecological influences at play, especially with regard to ocean currents and marine bio-transportation. It felt as if I was solving a biological code revealing the ecological conditions likely to characterise each faunal community. But the taxonomy (i.e., species description and identification) was key to this process and formed the bulk of my research. As I sorted through Petri dishes of tiny tube worms, with the aid of a binocular microscope, I quietly chanted ditties like 'Hello, *Anomalorbis*, my old friend'. Perhaps the time had come to move on.

Chios, August 1967

There are many stories about Professor Knight-Jones, who was like a second father to me, always interested in what I was doing and quintessentially pragmatic and kind. The fact that he gained a D.Sc. speaks volumes for his research, and he was incredibly generous with his knowledge. His invitation for me, a first-year honours student, to join the department's expedition to Greece in August 1967 was typical of how he created opportunities for those of us willing to grasp the nettle. Rather than fly to Athens, I helped the senior laboratory technician, Alan Osborne, and his wife, Shirley, together with baby Hamish, to drive the department's van to Greece.

Our route took us through France, across the Alps, and over the scorching, desolate, corrugated, concrete-slab roads of what was then Yugoslavia. We slept at roadside lay-bys, under star-sparkled skies, serenaded by howling wolves prowling among the nearby cliffs. We skirted around Pristina and Skopje in northern Macedonia and left Albania far to our right whilst racing southwards and into northern Greece. We celebrated our arrival near Thessalonica, in the land of ancient gods, by bathing in a roadside fountain, removing the grime of the 3,000 or so kilometres that we had just driven. Heading down to Athens, catching regular glimpses of an azure Aegean, we could hardly contain our excitement at approaching our destination. We headed straight for the bustling port of Piraeus and a large ferry that took us 300 kilometres across the Aegean to the historic island of Chios – a place etched in my memory for more reasons than one. It was the beginning of an eventful expedition.

Among my scariest stories of that summer spent at Chios's southernmost settlement, Emborios, is the time that I almost disappeared without trace, within a stone's throw of a traditional stone farmhouse and a field full of tents. We had pitched these around the perimeter of a Greek farmer's rubble-strewn field that was covered with just enough scrubland to support the resident donkey. Whilst the perimeter of the field was well trodden, the centre was quite overgrown. Making my way across the field, I ventured through the long grass with snakes on my mind and suddenly fell down a deep, hidden well without time or breath to let out a single sound. As the ground literally disappeared beneath my feet and I flailed my arms in a futile gesture of alarm, the thought flashed through my mind that nobody had witnessed my impressive disappearing act. In the dark I felt an agonising stab of pain. My right arm had snagged a spiky wooden branch, about three metres below the surface. My fall had been arrested and I was now spreadeagled across the void. Not being much of a climber, and with absolutely no head for heights, I controlled my breathing and slowly pulled myself to the well's vertical stony side before catching my breath and climbing out, heart in mouth. Once safely back on firm ground, I looked around. All was calm among our team of happy campers. Nobody had seen a thing. I still shudder to think what would have happened if my arm had not caught on the wooden stake.

My biological study on Chios was a survey of sponges, a topic of great interest to the local people and our sponsor. It became the project for my B.Sc. Hons. degree and hooked me on the field of underwater ecological surveys using scuba. At that time, in 1967, we were transitioning from the old traditional methods of studying marine life to ones that depended on putting researchers underwater, rather than have them hanging over the side of a boat dangling instruments in the sea.

In what was probably the first such scientific study of Chios's surrounding seabed, Prof. K-J joined technician Paul Llewellyn and me to mount a survey of commercial sponges around the island. The methodology was simple. We headed off in our department's Zodiac dinghy, laden with full scuba tanks, sleeping bags, and cooking equipment, and took turns to shout 'stop'. The randomly selected stops became data points on our map, and one of us then dived down and made a quick count of visible commercial sponges at depths averaging about 15 metres. We surveyed twenty-five sites around the island, comparing the abundance of two commercial sponges, *Hippospongia communis* and *Euspongia officianalis*. Interestingly, the greatest concentrations were found on the steep, south-facing reef faces at Cape Mesta and Cape Mastikho, both affected by tidal currents. I postulated at the time that helmet divers from Kalymnos, who visited once a year to harvest the sponges, found it harder to dive at these sites but that the introduction of scuba diving for sponge collecting would lead to overfishing.

At times we would dive as deep as 60 metres through very cold clear water. Our wetsuits in those days were rudimentary and inefficient. When Prof. K-J dived alone it was always a worry, since he hardly consumed any air, making his bottle last twice as long as Paul and I did. Multiple deep dives and inadequate clothing led to the need to take overnight breaks on remote shores, cooking up meals on beach grills and crashing out under the stars. We were worried that the physical strain was becoming too much for Prof. K-J, who was fifty-one years old at that time, and we kept a close eye on him. He seemed to be OK, but I did notice he fell asleep as soon as his head hit the sand.

One particular morning, the sun woke Paul and me, forcing us out of our sleeping bags. We brewed coffee, prepared some fruit, and started reloading the boat. Prof. K-J remained fast asleep. We drank our coffee, ate our fruit, and finished the tidy-up, expecting the professor to stir at any moment, but he didn't move. Finally, I began to worry and drew Paul's attention to the possibility that he had stopped breathing. Leaning over him I placed my ear near his mouth. Not a sound. Then I lay down so that I could line his chest up along the horizon. It didn't move at all. I got up and signalled to Paul that we had a problem. By now, Paul had completed reloading the boat, with the exception of the professor's belongings.

'We'll have to make room for him,' I told Paul, and we returned to the dinghy to rearrange space for a corpse. As we did so, the supine body slowly raised itself up and the professor let out a murmur which I interpreted as appreciation for the beautiful natural bay and his solid night's sleep. Ten minutes later we were back on our course around the island, and it was my turn to shout 'stop'.

Bon Voyage

Departures are never easy, and emotions were running high when it came time to leave Chios. On that memorable morning, my eyes opened slowly and painfully, knowing that the sun was already high. I rolled over and focused on the gently lapping wavelets, several yards away, and on the two headlands that stood guard over the little bay that had become my home. The morning's heat was already driving me out of my sleeping bag in search of a refreshing breeze, and I walked, precariously unbalanced, on the loose black pebbles, down to the welcoming sea. It was six o'clock on Monday morning. That it was six I knew from the sun. That it was Monday I can only say now by looking at my diary.

During the past month, days of the week had meant nothing to me. As I lay in my sleeping bag each night, gazing at the stars, I pondered an unwritten to-do list, and I woke each morning with a clear vision of what lay before me. After work, in the evenings, I sat at the local café and chatted with my new-found friends. But this morning was different. I waded into the warm Aegean, took a deep breath, and dived in. I had left my diving equipment at the main camp, but I could still open my eyes underwater and see fish and seaweeds merging into a vague blue horizon. With the renewed pleasure of swimming in such paradisiac surroundings, I almost forgot why I had woken so reluctantly. Today, I reminded myself, was my last day on Chios and our expedition was drawing to a close.

Chios had not disappointed us, and I said a silent prayer of thanks to the Greek cultural ambassador in London, who had proposed the study and facilitated many of our needs.

Had it not been for this Mr Argenti, I doubt that I would ever have heard of Chios, an island in the eastern Aegean whose importance to Greece in years gone by can hardly be overemphasised. It was home for many of the great Greek philosophers, including Aristotle, who lived for a while in the north of the island. It is even thought that Homer's wanderings, recounted in the *Iliad*, brought him to Emborios, where our base had been established. To me the island had become far more than a place of historical, economic, or biological importance. It introduced me to challenging, exciting, and rewarding work that created the basis for what was to become a varied career in marine biology and a life associated with the sea.

We spent most of that last day packing and tidying the campsite, but first I had promised my friend Christina that we would enjoy the next few hours in one last adventure together. After my swim I carried my sleeping bag to her house, where I usually left my bedding, and waited for her to wake. Our goal was to walk up to the monastery on top of the mountain behind the camp. We were late already, and if we did not start soon it would be too hot to attempt the climb. She must have heard my feet on the loose gravel path, for she was ready in minutes and we set off.

We were both exhilarated at the thought of the early-morning climb and walked quickly, laughing and joking in French (our only mutual language) on the way up. At the summit we had a wonderful view of the coastline. At the bottom of the mountain lay the village of Emborios, where we had made our base, and where the now familiar beer café stood. The wharf looked tiny from up there, with just a few sardine boats tied up. Cutting the placid mirror of deep blue sea, like jewels on blue velvet, came the fishing fleet returning from a night's fishing to the south of the island. Bay after bay stretched out so clearly that we could pick out our favourite swimming spots, almost to the exact stone. My black pebble bay lay deserted now, and when I looked at it I was reminded that I was about to depart its comforting embrace, probably forever. Christina sat on the edge of a newly built well, and she too looked sad that such an idyllic vacation was about to end. Time passed too quickly up there, and we had to run down the side of the mountain, leaping from boulder to boulder, so that the packing would be finished in time for the ferry.

Four of us, Alan, Shirley, baby Hamish, and I, were to travel home in the twelve-seater minibus loaded with equipment, towing a boat trailer and carrying the boat on top of the car. Our experience on the way out had shown that the trailer was not strong enough to carry the boat's weight over hundreds of kilometres of cart-track roads in Yugoslavia. After a hard morning's work of packing our gear and taking expedition members to the ferry, I determined to have one last luxurious swim with Christina and enjoy a freshwater shower before resigning myself to the rigours of the homeward journey. When I eventually returned to the camp, pandemonium had broken out. The short road running along the bay was packed with Greeks coming to say their farewells. Alan was losing all hope of ever catching the ship in Chios, since he had just been told that it would leave at 7 p.m. instead of 8 p.m. Christina, her mother, and her grandmother had all come to say goodbye. I shook their hands and turned to the minibus.

At the back of the crowd stood Old Sam. It was he who had welcomed us to Emborios and later accused us of being Turkish spies. He had spent much of his life in the rat race of New York and had recently returned to Chios. Now he was suffering from a nervous disorder and almost crippled. I pushed my way through to him and shook his hand. 'You fellahs come back one day, eh?' My eyes were wet, and I could not put into words my thanks for all his kindness. He leant on his walking stick and shook my hand. I told him that, if ever I had the chance, I would return to Emborios, and that I would never forget the place, or my Greek friends who lived there. 'You good fellas,' he said and walked away.

I made my way back to the minibus and climbed in. Christina and her relatives were standing at the back of the crowd. There were dozens of faces that I knew, and I wanted to say goodbye to each of them. An old and immaculately tailored gentleman approached the open window and shook my hand, wishing me 'Bon voyage'. Alan pressed the horn, the crowd in front parted, we all waved out the windows, and we were on our way. It was like tearing a plaster off a wound. We started slow and painfully, but it became so difficult to tear ourselves away from the village that finally Alan put his foot down and we left in a cloud of dust, not daring to think of all the unsaid farewells. That marked the beginning of our long drive home. We started in silence but before long a new threat to our timely arrival at the ferry loomed. I was soon to reflect on the sailors' old saying that 'Bon voyage' said before a long journey brings bad luck instead of good.

Somewhere underneath the huge pile of equipment and clothes which had been jammed into the back of the minibus was a leaking bottle of formaldehyde. Fumes were rapidly pervading the air, making our eyes stream with tears, baby Hamish cry, and Alan's driving become frantic and erratic. There was no question of stopping even for one minute. I reached beneath the jumble and pulled out a bottle, which I threw out of the window as fast as I could. But there must have been more hidden among the baggage, since acrid fumes continued to strangle our eyes and throats. They were too much to tolerate, so I leant out of the window and vomited. Every bend presented a challenge in concentration. The rocky, dusty road gradually improved, and we knew that Chios port was only another eight kilometres, encouraging us to keep going. My head was buzzing, my eyes were streaming, and I was vomiting incessantly. We had to stop soon or there would be four corpses to transport to the UK. Chios town appeared. Coughing and spluttering, we groaned our relief.

The quay was packed with happy, gaily dressed Greeks who had come to say goodbye to their friends, or simply to enjoy the evening spectacle. We forced our way through them and positioned the minibus under one of the ship's derricks, but it looked as if we were too late. We almost fell from the vehicle, eyes streaming and sweat dripping from our foreheads. To the Greeks on shore, and the ship's crew, we appeared to be experiencing intense emotions at missing the boat. The skipper took pity on us and found a space on the foredeck to stow the minibus. We drove her onto the slings that they had laid on the ground, and a ship's officer approached us to ask about our weight. We admitted to probably being about twice the permitted load for the crane, but the minibus was by now poised above the ship's deck with onlookers gathered around its designated space. We said some silent prayers, and the vehicle was lowered into place.

We ran up the gangplank just before it was lifted, and we gazed back at the quay. There was George, who had insisted we visit Turkey in his boat, and there was the young yacht skipper who had been so keen to try out our scuba tanks. They waved as the ship slipped away from the harbour wall. I stared longingly at the island and town of Chios – home to 50,000 proud Greeks, dozens of whom had become my friends. A new moon had just risen above the mountainous coast, helping us discern the island's skyline as the ship made its way southwards, parallel to its shores. Occasional clusters of lights marked tiny villages or isolated settlements. It was hard to imagine Emborios with all my friends sitting at the café, supping their beer and talking in heated tones about a wide range of subjects, from fishing to politics.

I leant on the ship's rail, dreaming about the wonderful days I had spent on Chios. We were rapidly approaching the southern tip of the island from where we would steer straight across the Aegean to Athens. That final cluster of lights must be Emborios. There was the café and the lights from Christina's house. Then I blinked deliberately and looked again. Each end of the village was suddenly illuminated by flames that reached higher just as we were passing. I could clearly see the outlines of houses lit up by the fires and remembered Christina's last words to me: 'Remember to say goodbye to Emborios when you pass in the ship.' This was their way of saying goodbye. Flames of friendship. I could almost feel the fire's warmth. Slowly the flames died down, and I attempted a response with the car's headlights.

We rounded the southern tip of the island, Cape Mastiqua, and set course for the mainland. Chios was behind us now, but 3,900 kilometres of driving lay ahead. I prayed that nobody else would shake my hand and wish me bon voyage.

Professor E.W. Knight-Jones

Prof. K-J was constantly solving scientific puzzles, always on the lookout for detailed facts that could inform the larger picture of life on earth. He loved life and, having survived WWII as a gunnery officer, was devoted to the preservation and study of nature in all its forms. Students used to love walking with him at low tide along beaches and rocky shores. He had an endearing way of communicating his fascination with all animals and plants, inspiring all of us.

One special interest of his was a healthy diet. He decided to apply experimental data from fruit fly (*Drosophila*) studies to his own dietary regime. We now know that he was not far off the mark, since dietary restriction has been shown to extend lifespan in many species, including yeast, worms, flies, rodents, and primates. 'Starved fruit flies live longer, Pete – why should that not also apply to humans?' I took it as a mildly amusing quirk of our much-loved professor, but I had no idea at the time how close his ideas were to one of the key influencers of the ageing process. *Drosophila*'s genetic code is fully sequenced, and more than 50 per cent of its genes have homologues – identical structures – to those found in humans. Meanwhile, more than 75 per cent of known human disease genes, covering a broad range of disorders, have fruit fly homologues. These directly comparable features make *Drosophila* an ideal model organism for studying the mechanisms of ageing and for developing effective ageing interventions, which are relevant to research on ageing in humans.

The research on ageing would have continued to fascinate the professor right up to his death. He did indeed minimise his diet, was very thin, and kept up high energy levels, both physically and mentally. He would no doubt have been amused by the related finding that sex-starved fruit flies die younger than their satiated cousins.

In his later years, Prof. K-J suffered from osteoporosis – presumably triggered by low calcium levels, which are often associated with dietary restriction in humans and winglessness in fruit flies. It was a cruel fate for a true pioneer who was ready to turn his own body into a human laboratory, testing hypotheses to the very end and always generous with his time and attention. My wife, Paula, and I like to remember the professor bringing us tea in bed in the morning, while staying with him and Phyllis in their house near Rhossili. He had a wry grin on his face, as if to say, 'Well done, old boy.'

VOLUNTARY SERVICE OVERSEAS.
3 HANOVER STREET,
LONDON. W.I.

Telephone: HYDe Park 0501

ERC/C.2072   25th June 1964.

Peter Vine, Esq.,
70 Alderley Road,
Hoylake,
Wirral,
Cheshire.

Dear Peter,

      I am glad to inform you that your services have been
accepted in the Gilbert and Ellice Islands where you will be
assisting with youth welfare work and general administrative
duties under the District Commissioner, mostly in urban communities.

      I suggest you get in touch with one of the volunteers
who was in the Gilbert and Ellice Islands in 1962-63, who will
be able to give you some useful information about local conditions,
etc.   His name and address is:-

                Martin Hayden,
                17 Drayton Lane,
                Drayton,
                Portsmouth,   Hants.

If you can arrange to meet Martin, so much the better.   We are
enclosing a list of clothing requirements which has been compiled
from returned volunteers' reports, but Martin should be able to
help you on this point.

      We are awaiting details about transport from the Resident
Commissioner of the Gilbert and Ellice Islands; until we get this
we will not be able to tell you anything definite, but it is unlikely
that you will be going before late September, or even October.

          Yours sincerely

          (for) E.R. Chadwick
          Assistant Director

TOP Sir Arthur Grimble wrote *A Pattern of Islands* based on his time (1914–33) in the Gilbert and Ellice Islands. His book was an inspiration for me to learn about the people of these enchanting islands, now known as Kiribati (pronounced 'kiribas').   © Alamy

ABOVE 'Blackbirding' was the name given to the capture, imprisonment, and forced migration of islanders to work in the Australian sugar plantations and on American farms. Our crew member James had been one such slave, separated from his family when he was about eleven years old. The picture illustrates seizure of the blackbirding schooner *Daphne* and its human cargo by *HMS Rosario* in 1869. Australian law struggled with the question of whether this was slavery, recruiting, or indentured labour.   © Alamy

TOP Over just four days in November 1943, the now famous Battle of Tarawa took place on and around Betio in the south-west of Tarawa. The atoll held great strategic importance for the US, and this battle was part of the US invasion of the Gilberts, known as Operation Galvanic. While the US Marine Corps were ultimately victorious, they lost over 1,000 of their troops, and double that number were wounded. Of the 4,500 Japanese defenders and Korean labourers, it is estimated that about 97% were killed, or committed suicide rather than submit to surrender.   © Alamy

LEFT Abandoned by the Japanese, this gun has a larger story, as I learnt from chance meetings in the islands and later at my local sailing club in Hoylake. When the Japanese finished installing the gun, helped by some pressed labour from locals, they held a party.   © Alamy

RIGHT An Ellice Island canoeist, sculling with a single paddle, visits our ship to sell fresh fruit and eggs.

TOP I arrived in the Gilbert Islands by sea and left by air, following construction of Bonriki International Airport: a project assisted by my two VSO colleagues, Ben and Gary.

MID The thatched hut served as both arrivals and departures lounge for the weekly Fiji Airways flight.

ABOVE Arrivals and departures were invariably accompanied by music, song, and dance. These pupils from Elaine Bernacchi School were practising for a traditional performance.

TOP The original plan had been for me to lead the administration of Betio Youth Club and other youth ventures, but plans soon changed and I was assigned to teach at two secondary schools on Bikenibeu.

MID A youth club girl making a coconut mat. The club made a strong social impact on Bikenibeu's community.

ABOVE Youth in a northern village. 'Tamnei! Tamnei!' ('Take my picture! Take my picture!').

TOP Women re-enacting a storm at sea in a song created by the local composer. Gilbertese song and dance traditions were still an integral part of daily life during my time on Tarawa in 1964–65.

ABOVE Kiribati folk music is generally played sitting down, but Te Kaimatoa and Te Buki were performed by standing dancers. Traditional songs were often about love and romance, but many songs and dances were based on the drama of daily living, epic adventures at sea, or legendary battles between rival factions. I made a number of tape recordings which are quite unique, since many such traditions were being eroded by modern music. Our arrival in a village was usually taken as an opportunity for feasting, singing, and dancing by young and old.

TOP Boxing match on National Sports Day.

MID Football on the pitch constructed from mangrove lagoon mud.

ABOVE Our tyre 'shop', where human labour replaced tools and machinery to repair and change truck tyres. The truck was employed in making a football pitch for the school by carrying lagoon mud from the shore to the rubble-strewn pitch.

TOP Wyn Courtney, headmistress at Elaine Bernacchi School, teaches Form 4.
She was a dedicated teacher and highly respected by her pupils.

ABOVE In Elaine Bernacchi School library.

TOP   With fellow teacher Mary Llewellyn.

ABOVE   In traditional, formal Gilbertese dress.

TOP Outside our house, on the ocean side of the atoll.

RIGHT Dancing the twist with Tafua.

ABOVE The solid causeway at Nuatabu that behaved like a dam and reduced water exchange with the lagoon. The locals wanted the solid structure to help in their fishing and were resistant to the biological arguments we made for a bridge that would allow tidal currents to flow.

ABOVE The giant clam, *Tridacna gigas*, is one of the most endangered clam species. It can weigh more than 200 kilograms (440 lb), measure as much as 120 cm (47 in.) across, and has an average lifespan of over a hundred years.
Unfortunately, populations are rapidly declining, and the giant clam has become extinct in many areas where it was once common. Like corals, it cultivates algae called zooxanthellae in its tissues. Back in 1964, when we dived for these amazing shells, we were unaware of their vulnerability.
We searched the lagoon for giant clams, towed behind the government tugboat.

TOP   Fishing at night for crayfish. Part of the night's catch.

ABOVE   After a hard night's fishing. Tape recorder on table.

TOP The island bus that took me to Bairiki at weekends.

ABOVE Loading copra at one of the outer islands of Kiribati.
Copra, the sun-dried kernel of coconuts, was collected by individual farmers.
In 1964 the Gilberts produced 5,442 tons, worth A£411,302.

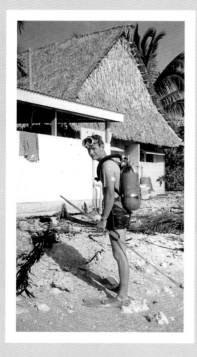

TOP The house that Tony built from local coconut and pandanus trees.

LEFT Tony, kitted for diving in front of our house.

RIGHT Teatou, our cook, tending his coconut toddy tree in the garden. Teatou was also the village songwriter.

Central Colony Hospital,
Bikenibeu,
Tarawa,
Western Pacific.
6th May, 1966.

Dearest Peter J. Vine,

Thanks a lot for your most welcome letter which I received in todays mail. I am very happy that you find my letter interesting so am I. Once again thanks so much for helping me with with my decisions. I find myself unable to answer what you have thought I can answer, but I think it is better to become a Nun rather than staying with my people. If I do remain as a nurse then there is no future for as it will be a future everlasting. The trouble when I go back to my home island is that I will get married very soon which is very disgusting to think of. You see our customes are very different from yours. Even when you have not met the boy before his family will just come over to the girls family and too I . . . . . That they want their son to be engaged to the girl if they agree, there is nothing the girl can do, but sometimes the girls went into the bush and hang themselves. Dont you ever think that I will marry anybody because marriage is out of the question as you said in your letter that there are things to consider well I can consider other things but not this one. One funny thing when I first enter ERS. and my brother was at Whit School he told me that he will not hear one word that I have got a boy friend and because we are intermediate brother and

TOP Correspondence with an ex-student, then working as a nurse but fearing a forced marriage.

TOP RIGHT Trying to climb the coconut palm tree in our garden – harder than it looks.

ABOVE Tony's sailing canoe was capable of speeds approaching 20 knots.

RIGHT Gilbertese sailing canoes were constructed from local woods tied together by string spun from coconut tree fibres. The canoes were a key form of inter-island transport.

TOP   Making flower garlands with Tafua.

ABOVE   Finally back in the UK in 1965. The gifts that I treasured from friends on Tarawa recalled the excitement and adventures of my 'year in paradise'. One clam shell finished up in the Zoology Museum at Swansea University, while the other half sits outside my study window in Ireland – a constant reminder of the sea's incredible productivity and vulnerability.

7 Pacific Bound

Back in Swansea, news that I had been granted a Rotary International Scholarship could not have been delivered at a better time. The award letter was dated 12 September 1967, over a year before I would set off on another round-the-world trip – this time in support of an M.Sc. degree at James Cook University of North Queensland, Australia. With my VSO travels behind me and expeditions like the trip to Chios fresh in my mind, I determined to make the most of this incredible opportunity. It is a reflection of the time that news arrived first via telegram.

On 17 December 1968, a particularly cold and blustery midwinter's day, I arrived at Heathrow Airport as a passenger in Tony Fleetwood-Wilson's car. My journey to Townsville, Australia, was to include stopovers in Trinidad, Jamaica, Mexico, Tahiti, and New Zealand. I could not help recalling the flights I had made as a VSO recruit, almost missing the ferry in Fiji. I had planned this to be a much more leisurely affair, taking two months rather than two days to reach Sydney. The VC10 in which I was travelling climbed above a cold grey London, and my spirits were soon lifted by the bright blue sky above the clouds. I was excited by this first taste of the sunshine year ahead.

An exceptionally strong Atlantic gale caused an unscheduled stopover in Bermuda. From the air, this historic semi-tropical island presented a depressing picture of humankind's insistence on overdevelopment at the expense of the very features that made initial development desirable. At least nobody could take away that salty sea breeze nor the warm blue sea.

Things were different in those days. Security was lax, to say the least. Whilst my fellow passengers busied themselves at some tourist shops, I wandered down to the beach, adjacent to the airstrip. It was the first time in three and a half years that I had stood on a coral reef, and it felt good to be back. I bent down and turned over some stones, immediately finding samples of local spirorbid tube worms that were the subject of my M.Sc. research. If I had been armed with preserving jars, I could have started my research right there and then.

Trinidad

I planned to spend a week or so in Trinidad, and after landing at Port of Spain I was met by Leo Seebarin, whom I had known at Swansea

University. He had known only the date of my arrival, so he had spent 12 hours waiting for my plane to arrive. Leo introduced me to Peter Newhouse, whose father I had met while he was convalescing at a Leonard Cheshire Home in North Wales. I had been leading a volunteer group of teenagers, painting the hospice home. I had promised Peter's terminally ill, bed-bound father that I would deliver a large teddy bear to his young grandson. Peter invited me to stay with him for a few days and offered to introduce me to what was known as Carnival Island. It was an apt description for this most colourful of islands. Colourful in scenery with green coconut palms, bright flowers, verdant mountain slopes, blue seas, and white beaches; colourful in birdlife, too, with brilliantly hued hummingbirds to be admired any morning as they sucked nectar from garden flowers; and colourful in its infinite mixture of races blended more harmoniously here than anywhere else I had visited.

I soon learned that all Trinidadians love colours, and what might otherwise be drab urban streets are brought to life by ever-changing patterns of bustling, gaily dressed crowds. It was clearly an optimistic community built on the 'she'll be right, mate' school of philosophy that I had already experienced among Australians I had met. I was joined the next day by my brother, Andy, who had just arrived from Canada and was planning to crew on a local yacht built by Trinidadian Harold La Borde. Hosted by local Rotarian Jonny Rooks and wife, Jessie, we spent a Christmas full of parties, music, drink, and good cheer – all in the name of fostering international relations. Our circle soon became so big that we could not walk down the street without exchanging greetings with new-found friends.

After the festivities of Christmas, I determined to get down to some underwater research, so we made our way to the north coast of Trinidad. This is about the only possible diving region, since the west coast is severely affected by run-off from the Orinoco River, in neighbouring Venezuela, whilst the east coast is exposed to Atlantic breakers. We drove over the precipitous northern mountain range, along a tortuous narrow road which, after climbing over the mountains, provides an exquisite view of the north coast with its white sand beaches lined with coconut palms, edged by mangroves and bamboo trees wherever they could find fresh water. There, at Las Cuevas, I took Andy for his first ever scuba dive in shallow but murky and turbulent water. Beneath the surface, the wave current was so strong that we had to cling on to lumps of brain coral to avoid being swept against the rocks. Here, for the first time on my travels, I collected *Spirorbis* tube worms and preserved them in bottles of formalin.

We were generously hosted by a number of locals, including Buster Anderson's family and Sonny Paul, who was commodore of San Fernando Yacht Club. Sonny loaned us his Shearwater catamaran. A plan for Andy and I to sail 'cats' along the west coast of Trinidad, as far as Port of Spain, nearly ended in disaster.

Andy and I set off for this new adventure in blissful ignorance of local winds. Just visible in the far distance was the mountain at the back of Port of Spain. As long as no squalls blocked our vision, we could use this to guide our route. Sonny, much more experienced in these waters, wisely stowed a compass and plenty of water to prevent us becoming dehydrated. As we sailed out past the oil jetties, our weather floats lifted and we hauled on our wind. Andy helmed the other cat while I helmed Sonny's cat, pleased to have him on the float.

A 'close reach' in sailing terms means that one can simply aim at one's ultimate destination by sailing close to the wind. We settled down to an exhilarating close-reach race, with each boat taking advantage of wind shifts and clawing its way to windward of the other before racing downwind in an overtaking tactic that saw the floats take off and the boats almost take wing. So engrossed did we become in our competition that we hardly noticed the high-pitched whining of the wind in our shrouds reach a crescendo as the gusts strengthened. Eventually, the strain on our rigging became so great that we were forced to slacken off, but not soon enough. As we loosened our sheets a loud crack announced that one of Andy's shrouds had snapped. We looked back to see his mast and sails topple into the choppy waters.

There was little we could do except sail around Andy's catamaran until a rescue boat arrived. They grappled desperately to retrieve mast and sails, and we were eventually taken in tow. When we turned to continue on our way to Port of Spain, we were met by the full force of a vicious squall. Shivering, our bodies lashed by giant raindrops, we steered by compass, with sails flapping to spill the wind, towards Port of Spain. Bedraggled but in high spirits, we reached the yacht club and warmed our insides at the bar. Andy met Harold and Kwailan La Borde, owners of *Hummingbird III*, bound for the Panama Canal and beyond. The proud ketch lying at anchor off the Club was a monument to the tremendous effort the couple had made to build her and set off on their second round-the-world voyage.

Tobago

Thanks to the generosity of Port of Spain Rotary Club, I found myself on a flight to nearby Tobago. Just 20 minutes in the air, the hop and skip brought me to a jewel of an island populated by some cool, sea-loving people. Local diving guide Dellarosa took me out to Fly Reef, so named because the current is so strong all you can do is 'fly' with it on exhilarating drift dives. As I did so, I admired rich coral growths and plentiful fish life. Reefs on the Atlantic side tend to have more soft corals than their Pacific counterparts. They were nonetheless colourful and enticing. The water was obligingly warm and clear, and I wanted to stay down forever, marvelling at the teeming life. Before my air expired, I collected some tube worm substrates, and later, beneath the shade of a coconut palm, I sorted my collection, picking out the white spiralling tube worms.

Jamaica

A five-and-a-half hour journey in a small plane took me from Trinidad to Jamaica, with refuelling stops at Barbados, Antigua, and Puerto Rico. I was met at the airport by research student Pete Reason, who drove me in the Zoology Department's minibus to the Marine Laboratory at Port Royal. Within an hour of arriving in Jamaica, I had my dive gear on and was collecting spirorbids.

Jamaica was a thriving tourist location but not one that I could afford. Fortunately the university provided facilities for my one-week stay, and I was able to further my research. First off, I explored the nearby historic capital city, Port Royal, much of which lay underwater. The bits above water revealed a rather desolate arm of the larger harbour that suggested a long history of destruction rather than development. There were no boats anchored at the location, and only one or two houses survived at the notorious site. Divers had recently discovered remains of the fortress, and the seabed was littered with timbers of old ships, crockery, and ancient grog bottles from privateering and pirating days. The site was protected from looting and was clearly suited to become a centre for marine archaeological research and tourism development, in the form of an interpretation centre or museum. It was a fascinating place, calling out to have its story told.

I dived many times around the south coast of Jamaica with Jeremy Woodley, who kindly put me up at his home. Jeremy was spearheading marine archaeological excavations of the fortress and educating Jamaica's growing number of scuba divers to preserve the island's prolific marine life. After several days in the south, the Zoological Department lent me a Mini Moke to travel through the Blue Mountains to the north of the island, where Prof. Tom Goreau, the distinguished coral physiologist, was based. My Moke provided a rather precarious transport system. Its open top invited hurled missiles from Black Power Jamaicans, who hurled nothing more offensive than verbal abuse at occupants of closed-in cars. In addition, I was travelling with an amusingly bald offside front tyre and a spare in the boot that was no better. I was quite certain it would burst and had resigned myself to the adventure of becoming isolated at 1,200 metres in the Blue Mountains, or being forced to spend the night in the company of crocodiles and mosquitoes in the mangrove swamps along the coast.

There were stretches of road 30 or 40 kilometres long without a house or garage where I might seek help. I had already planned the opening paragraph of the article I was going to write for *Blackwoods Magazine* in the style of its most prolific author, Leslie Gardner, describing the incredible adventures which befell me when I suffered a blowout on Jamaica's lonely roads. Instead of a bang – a good start to any adventure – my tyre sizzled down and I limped to a halt without any close escapes from death to report. I had been travelling through desolate swampland, it was approaching nightfall, and there was not a house to be seen. I comforted myself with the certainty of a night to write home about. I set off on foot along the road to see what lay ahead. Around the first bend, about 50 yards from the Moke, stood a large yellow sign announcing a Shell Service Centre. All notions of adventure vanished, and I meekly admitted my plight to the mechanic, who had me on four wheels again in half an hour – along with a new pair of tyres that had been impossible to buy in the city.

The marine laboratory at Discovery Bay to the east of Montego Bay was superbly located for underwater research and scuba diving. Around this section of the coastline the water is usually crystal clear, and there were many rich coral reefs. One of the highlights for me was diving in Tom's Cave, which Prof. Goreau had made famous as a habitat for several new species of sponges. A deep ravine in the base of the reef opens out at around 35 metres into a narrow cave. I entered at this point and slowly made my way back towards the surface within the shady grottoes, dramatically illuminated by my diving torch. The effect of trapped bubbles escaping through cracks in the coral, combined with torch beams capturing the brilliant colours normally filtered into a monochromatic ocean blue, was so fascinating that I almost forgot to make a spirorbid collection.

I loved Jamaica for its wonderful views from high mountains, its rugged coastline studded with jewel-like bays, its climate, and its colourfulness. I did not, however, enjoy feeling the discomfort that my skin colour bestowed upon me. The Jamaicans were heartily sick of the whites with their superior airs and money-buys-anything attitudes. They had discovered a pride in being black. Stokely Carmichael was their man of the hour, and white people didn't count any more. In some ways I was not sorry to see the tables so dramatically turned – it helped me to understand the degradation that black people had suffered and were still suffering. But for that reason alone, I was not sorry to say goodbye to this island in the sun. On my last morning, I drove into the mountains to savour more of the interior. Encountering a particularly steep hill, I stopped to give an elderly gentleman a lift. He told me his name was Alan Beckford, and he seemed well educated and well travelled. His son was working in Britain, and he invited me to his mountain home to meet his wife and join them for lunch.

This welcoming magnanimity was in sharp contrast to the politics of racial hatred and division that were so prevalent at the time. After lunch, Alan acted as my guide as we drove through cloud-covered peaks to the uniquely positioned army camp at Newcastle. As we ascended, hairpin bend after hairpin bend, Alan and I exchanged views on the racial tension that was tearing his country, and the world, apart. I eventually bade him farewell and made my way back to the airport to catch a flight to Mexico City.

Mexico

On the plane, I sat next to two girls from the UK experiencing their own round-the-world trip: Kirsty McLachlan and Georgina Fraser. For that first night in Mexico City we joined forces, finding a reasonably priced hotel in the heart of town, Hotel Emporio, and enjoying an evening of folk singing in the hotel bar. My own flight to Acapulco was due to take off at 8 a.m., so rather than make for our rooms when the bar closed, we allowed ourselves to be persuaded by Mexican Antonio to join him in a pre-dawn tour of 'the city that never sleeps'. Despite the time, many of the shops were lit up, and it was fun to drive through deserted streets that in an hour or so would again be taken over by the blaring chaos of rush-hour traffic. At 5 a.m. we walked around the walls of the cathedral and finally made for our beds. Two hours later I was rushing off to the airport to catch my Aeronaves de Mexicana flight to Acapulco, where we had all promised to meet up again.

Acapulco was expensive, sunny, and packed with holiday-makers. It was also a little unfriendly, revoltingly commercialised, and spectacularly fascinating. I could not find a beach with clear water, or a comfortable sandy one that was not the haunt of dozens of persistent vendors, most of whom should have been at school. Telling myself it was all part of the job, I lay in the sun on Paradise Beach and gaped at the incessant activity. Could that really be called a *bi*kini?

And 'No', I did not want to buy a hammock, nor a string of shells, nor a bottle of coconut oil, nor a hat, nor candyfloss . . . 'but try that man over there. Yes, the pale one with the red swimming trunks. The one chatting to the bikini-clad girl.' The stage moves, and I resume my place in the audience. I listen as the young tourist makes slick remarks designed to impress his giggling girlfriend. Oh, yes, sure, she would love a shell necklace. The persistent seller recognises enthusiasm on the girl's face and instantly ups his prices in negotiation with Mr Red Trunks. Out in the speedboat-cluttered bay, a water skier creams by, twisting in and out of moored boats. Up above, looking for all the world like some Mesozoic flying reptile, is a young bronzed guy strapped into a kite being towed by another speedboat. Red Trunks agrees to the exorbitant price, the girl giggles again, and the Mexican seller smiles rather cheekily before winking at me and continuing on his profitable way.

I turn over and look in the other direction. The scene is much the same, and I begin to wonder how long I could enjoy such a hedonistic life. I knew Acapulco had more to offer than this, and my scientific collection needed to at least look as if spirorbids were the reason for my exotic travels. Back at my hotel I took a dip in the seawater pool, where I soon noticed some tube worms growing on dead seashells. Out came the scalpel and formalin jar, and hey presto, another species record entered my growing, increasingly individualistic collection.

Tahiti, Moorea, and Tuamotus

Tahiti had been calling me for longer than any of the other countries I had visited. This is the island of Rodgers and Hammerstein's *South Pacific* fame, where one steps off the plane to be greeted with a garland of hibiscus and frangipani flowers and a kiss on each cheek from a grass-skirted young wahine. Who could not like it? But things weren't quite working out as planned. I staggered bewildered and exhausted from the plane at 5 a.m., cleared customs, and dragged my luggage to the arrivals lounge in anticipation of some cultural titillation. I was approached by what I had the temerity to consider an old man (he was sixty-five). He kissed me on each cheek in French style, and handed me a jar of Polynesian Fragrance. My disappointment was short-lived, however, for I soon learned that Achille Drollet was better than any enticing Tahitian bouquet.

Rotarian Achille was a practical man with interests similar to my own. He rushed me to his home for breakfast, introduced me to his family, and whisked me to the south of the island to take part in a fishing expedition. I spent the rest of the day admiring the rugged skyline of the lush green island with its cascading waterfalls, expansive valleys, and long white sand beaches. We caught no fish, but this hardly mattered. Fellow Rotarian Michel Vilar invited me to stay at *Kon-Tiki* sailor Bengt Danielson's lagoonside house, complete with library. For several days I enjoyed an idyllic, peaceful existence, canoeing in the lagoon around Bengt's house, fishing, and aiming my camera at the legendary beckoning island of Moorea.

For the remainder of my time in Tahiti I stayed with Michel Prevot, a French architect living there. He was also owner of a fast speedboat in which, together with Kirsty and Georgina, last seen in Mexico, we surrendered to Moorea's magnetic attractions. It was breathtakingly exciting to be speeding across the 17 kilometres of placid ocean separating Tahiti and Moorea. The distant rugged mountains gradually changed from a misty blue to green, and when the lagoon surrounding Moorea's coastline appeared, it revealed an exquisite, unspoilt chain of coral sand bays and steep, palm-clad mountain slopes. It seemed only right that lunch on board should be iced champagne and caviar. I could get used to this.

But again my work called me to even more exciting adventures. Jean Pellissier, who, like Bengt Danielsson, had arrived on Tahiti by raft, had established a technical marine company with eyes on both commercial and tourism-related underwater ventures in French Polynesia. Jean's company, Études et Travail Sous Marin Pacific (ETSMP), had been contracted for work in connection with France's nuclear testing programme and was now suffering due to a pull-back of that programme. He hoped to replace nuclear testing with tourism and invited me to join him on a try-out excursion to Rangiroa, famous for sharks, other fish schools, and marine life in general.

As the *Marc Joly* sliced through the glassy Pacific, I lazed on deck and chatted with the crew, gradually learning how to pronounce their Tahitian names. Our visit to Rangiroa was tied up with making a movie to show customers just how fantastic the diving is around its perimeter and in its notorious ocean passage. We all gathered on the bridge to gaze at a setting sun and feel the freshness of the sea breeze after the dry heat of Papeete. Over on the starboard bows, a school of tuna made the sea boil as they in turn were attacked by frigate birds and Pacific terns. A dense patch of baitfish was at the root of the commotion, and the crew quickly abandoned their leisurely postures to make their lines ready. The captain, as happy as any of us to stock his larder, swung the boat sharply to the right, heading for the centre of the screaming birds and leaping fish. Within minutes we were hauling in metre-long little tuna, triggering even louder protests from the agitated birds.

The following day, as we steamed over an ocean whose surface was broken only by our wake and that of the flying fish that we disturbed, Jean Loup, business manager of ETSMP, set forth his plans to attract visitors from the United States, New Zealand, and Australia, flying them straight into Rangiroa and picking up the *Marc Joly* for some memorable diving and Polynesian living. He looked on me as a try-out tourist, and that was fine with me.

Next morning the *Marc Joly* steamed through the picturesque pass and tied up at the wharf in the tiny village of Manihi at 5 a.m. We were expected, and within minutes the whole village had assembled at the waterfront to greet us. It was a warm welcome, since the boat and crew were well known to the villagers. Before breakfast I walked around the cluster of palm-thatched bungalows with their well-kept gardens and coconut and breadfruit trees begging to give up their fruits. At each lagoonside house an outrigger canoe was tied up, while fishing nets were hung from palm fronds. Chickens scrambled from my path on the coral gravel road, and small naked Tuamotu children followed me curiously, offering smiles guaranteed to engage any film director.

Later that morning I took a snorkel dive towards the pass, where we were greeted by two pygmy devil rays, *Mobula diabolus*. They 'flew' like giant albatrosses, directly towards us, surprising us with their lack of fear. It was a moment to remain motionless, and as they glided around us our cameras attempted to capture the breathless excitement that consumed us. When they finally grew bored with these human intruders, heading off for deeper waters, Jean caught my eye with a wide grin. This was some of the finest diving I had encountered, anywhere – fish and corals in abundance – healthy reefs that were a delight to behold. On coral reefs inside the lagoon, in the pass, and outside, where ocean rollers crashed incessantly against this living barrier, the waters teemed with fish of hues that Kodak itself could not exaggerate. Diving was comfortable and exciting. A Boston Whaler placed us over the reef, and we worked for an hour underwater without wetsuits and without feeling cold.

Sharks provided the climax of the experience. Crewmen Tiko and Alain baited the reef with speared fish, whilst cameramen positioned themselves on each side, waiting for sharks to appear. Everyone was armed with a harpoon, and lead divers even had explosive heads at the end of their spears. It was not something that I would advocate today, but those were early days for diving with sharks, and we had less understanding of how to do so in relative safety. Predictably, the most inquisitive sharks were the white-tip reef sharks that came in fast, grabbed the bait, and retreated to a safe distance. Jean Loup used his power head to kill the first shark, scaring others away, and effectively ending our shark filming for a while.

We drank champagne (the French in Polynesia drank it like water) under the friendly shade of a giant breadfruit tree at the water's edge. We yarned with each other about diving and with the locals about fishing and what it is like to live on Rangiroa. As the cool of late evening approached, we played volleyball against the village team and were like schoolchildren challenging an Olympic squad. As the sun set, guitars were brought out and soft Polynesian music accompanied our evening feast.

This famous and well-preserved wall painting, entitled *Fisherman*, was found at
the western house in the prehistoric town of Akrotiri on Santorini. It is one of
the most important wall paintings of the Aegean Minoan era. I am particularly
interested in this fresco, since the fish being held by the ancient fisherman are
identifiable as dolphin fish, dorado, mahi mahi, or *Coryphaena hippurus*.
While managing Charter Aquaculture, I helped to set up trial farming of this
fast-growing species. This facsimile of the original was given to me by Sheikh
Ossama Zainy during his visit to Greece in 1972.   © Alamy

Dead coconut stumps provide a depressing outlook for a Gilbertese woman who can recall when these magnificent trees flourished, before rapid climate change caused the salt water table to rise. Today, thanks to global warming, the island of Tarawa is in a battle to survive.   © Getty Images

P.P.S.
Happy birthday
Dad!
[X flag — INTERNATIONAL CRUISES]
PPPS

P.S. Sorry about infrequent letters, but they can only be posted from the town of Chios — 20 km from Emborios, + we will pass thro' tomorrow on my way to the N for our extended exped æ sponges. I.S.S. Carina

Hope all are fit — love to Sue + John + Hilary.

Wednesday, August 14th. (1967)

Dear Mum + Dad,
                    I was most surprised last night to be accosted at a festival in the nearby town of Pyrgi, at 2·0am to be told that there was a letter waiting for me in the village Post Office. The chap went to get the key + presented me with your letter. Thus the address I gave you is O.K.
                    The last week has been very active + most enjoyable. During upto 2x a day and sorting collections at odd times. I still find time to have a beer with my Greek friends in the evenings + last night I took a party of exped members to Pyrgi for the above mentioned festival. It was really marvellous. The town is unique — architectural style, + their is a "Tom Jones" atmosphere about the place. Cretin peasants sitting on curb stones watching their wealthier countrymen dance gaily. The contrast is staggering. I danced with a Greek girl — Christina — who is quite a wow y + also a millionaire's daughter! She speaks no English but we manage via French.
                    Work is going quite well. I have now produced a map of a big cave (under-water) close to where we are camping, + have done 3 of a series of 8 vertical transects to show change of habitat ecologically with respect to light intensity + wave-action. This has been going along at the same time as a general survey of sponges over Chios. Tomorrow I set off on an extended tour of the island to investigate the potential commercial sponge fishery. This seems to be about the one practical contribution we can give the island. We shall be taken upto the N of the island by minibus + will spend several days returning — diving in many spots to record sponge frequencies. Prof, myself + a technician — Paul Llewellyn are going. It should see the light of print in something like the Times or Observer.
                    So far as returning is concerned there is no question of me not driving home. I would not swop my place for the luxury cruise despite the hardship involved. It is a fantastic opportunity to see out of the way places — like Skopje bazaar, the Yugoslavian coast, + poss Florence etc. Also there is a sense of achievement + excitement about it. Don't worry, I look forward to another interesting journey. See you on Sept 12th.
                                                            Love, Pete

TOP The Zoology Department Commer 'dormobile' proved to be remarkably resilient on some very rough roads in what was then Yugoslavia. The boat trailer was much less so, and we had to carry the expedition boat on the vehicle's roof. Alan, Shirley, one-year-old Hamish, and I travelled 3,500 km, from Athens to Swansea, without anything more serious than a flat tyre.

ABOVE The Commer van being lifted onto the ferry after a dramatic drive from our campsite on Chios.

TOP The cave at Emborios, on Chios, which I mapped for invertebrates.

ABOVE On my last day at Emborios, before catching the ferry back to Athens.

TOP The commercial bath sponge, *Spongia officinalis*, was much sought after in Greek waters. We dived at many locations in order to study their distribution around Chios.   © Alamy

ABOVE Black pebble beach at Emborios. Instead of sleeping at the expedition campsite, I slept here, within a few feet of the water and under the stars.   © Alamy

SEYCHELLES BULLETIN   August 11, 1971

Marine life exhibition attracts many

YOUNG and old have been filling up a small room in the Victoria Museum in a constant stream to see a small exhibition of fish and other living animals found in Seychelles waters.

Since the Cambridge Coral Conservation group opened its exhibition on Monday afternoon, over a thousand people have seen it so far, and such has been the interest that the exhibits are now on view all day long instead of 3—6 p.m. as was originally planned.

Poison harpoons

The exhibits include two giant sea anemones which are found in tropical waters only. This primitive animal without brain or heart is reported to kill any small fish which approaches it with minute poison harpoons in its tentacles. The only exception seems to be the Clown Fish—in the same tank as the anemone — and, according to the Cambridge group, no scientist has ever found out why they are unaffected.

Another specimen on view is the red and white banded coral shrimp. These, according to the group, are very plentiful here, but are not the painted prawns which prey on the Crown of Thorns starfish. These coral shrimps are the "doctors" of the sea, eating parasites from other sea-dwellers.

The Crown of Thorns starfish, also exhibited, is killed by a blue, brown and white type of prawn which has not so far been found here.

Unique Angel Fish

Altogether about 25 different specimens are on show and the Cambridge group will be adding more, including a type of Angel Fish unique to Seychelles.

The specimens were collected by members of the expedition around Port Launay, Cap Ternay and in the proposed marine park, using hands and seine nets.

The aquariums themselves are made from strong glass and an especially strong rubber sealant to withstand the pressure of the water. (The pressure in a three-foot tank is over two hundredweight!). The glass tanks are filled with sea water from the reef aerated by a small vibrator pump to simulate the movement of the sea.

A visit to the exhibition is a must for swimmers and non-swimmers alike for though small, it shows the beauty of the many coral inhabitants of our reefs.

The brilliant emperor angelfish *Pomacanthus imperator* was quite common in the Seychelles and one of the most popular fish in the aquarium.   © Alamy

TOP Seychelles Governor, Sir Bruce Greatbach; Chief Minister, Sir James Mancham, and team at the opening of our public aquarium. Members shown are myself, Miguel Nadal, Roger Lubbock, Nicholas Polunin, Peter Etherington-Smith, and Alastair Birtles.

ABOVE Myself, Nimo Jivan Shah, Kantilal Jivan Shah, and Paula on a visit in 2005.

OPPOSITE Dr John Casey feeding fish during a Seychelles sailing cruise. When he stopped, the fish turned their attention to my bare skin, causing me to leap at the ladder.

IN THE HIGH COURT OF JUSTICE   1990 -M- No 33

QUEEN'S BENCH DIVISION

B E T W E E N :

SIR JAMES MANCHAM KBE

Plaintiff

- and -

(1)   PETER VINE
(2)   IMMEL PUBLISHING LIMITED

Defendants

To the Defendants PETER VINE of Ely House, 37 Dover Street,
London W1X 3RB and IMMEL PUBLISHING LIMITED whose registered
office is situate at 1 Gresham Street, London EC2V 7BU.

This Writ of Summons has been issued against you by the
above-named Plaintiff is respect of the claim set out on the
back.

Within 14 days after the service of this Writ on you, counting
the day of service, you must either satisfy the claim or return
to the Court Office mentioned below the accompanying
Acknowledgment of Service stating therein whether you intend to
contest these proceedings.

If you fail to satisfy the claim or to return the
Acknowledgment within the time stated, or if you return the
Acknowledgment without stating therein an intention to contest
the proceedings, the Plaintiff may proceed with the action and
judgment may be entered against you forthwith without further
notice.

Issued from the Central Office
of the High Court this 3 day of January 1990.

NOTE:-   This Writ may not be served later than 12 calender
          months beginning with that date unless renewed by
          order of the Court

                    I M P O R T A N T

Directions for Acknowledgment of Service are given with the
accompanying form.

Legal writ from the solicitors of ex-President Sir James Mancham, claiming
I had libelled him.

AQUALINK
FAUL · CLIFDEN · CO. GALWAY · IRELAND

Patrick Berlouis,
Director General of Information,
Seychelles Government.

8.1.90

Dear Patrick,

Further to our telephone conversation of today I note that the Seychelles Government is not willing at this stage to promise any financial support to me in regard to negotiating a settlement with Mancham's lawyers, but that they will consider the position following settlement.

I have pointed out to you that the Seychelles Government has left us in a very weak position with regard to any negotiations. I have stated that I am personally quite upset by this since I checked the veracity of my written statement in Seychelles and that everyone I spoke to confirmed it was correct. In particular, Patrick Nanty, acting in his role as DG of Information, confirmed it was correct. In the light of this, our lawyer has informed me that we would be in a much better position to negotiate, and to possibly keep the case out of Court, if we could have in our hands some written statements signed by people in Seychelles to say that they have read the wording on this subject in my book, and that it is a true comment on what was happenning at that time. Christopher Winder from Biddle & Co may elaborate a little more on what is needed. THE MAIN POINT IS THAT WITH SOME WRITTEN STATEMENTS FROM PEOPLE IN SEYCHELLES TO SUPPORT THE STATEMENT IN MY BOOK WE WILL BE IN A MUCH BETTER POSITION TO NEGOTIATE A SETTLEMENT. Without it, we have very little to support us in negotiating an acceptable settlement.

I cannot see that getting some such statements from people in Seychelles, whether they are members of the present Government, or private individuals, should prove too difficult, and it would help us enormously. You must remember that I did not write that he had published his intentions, merely that he had declared them. I did not write that he did this in public. If this happened, as I have been told it did, surely someone is willing to confirm in writing that it is correct.

As always, best regards,

Peter Vine

One of the letters that I sent to the Seychelles government asking them to support my legal defence. In the end we had to settle, but our legal costs were reimbursed.

Blue tang *Paracanthurus hepatus* were the crème de la crème for aquariums.
I discovered a small concentration of them on the Great Barrier Reef and helped
Ian Croll capture some specimens for Magnetic Island's Marine Gardens.   © Alamy

ROTARY INTERNATIONAL

Service Above Self – He Profits Most Who Serves Best

1600 RIDGE AVENUE · EVANSTON, ILLINOIS 60201, U.S.A.

Air Mail   12 September, 1967

Peter James Vine, Esq.
70 Alderley Road
Hoylake, Wirral, Cheshire,
England

Dear Mr. Vine:

It is a pleasure to advise you that the trustees of The Rotary Foundation have awarded you a Rotary Foundation Graduate Fellowship for study
during the academic year 1968-69.

The school at which your Graduate Fellowship has been made tenable and
the conditions under which your award has been granted are outlined in
an agreement form, two copies of which are enclosed. To signify your
acceptance of the award, please sign and return one copy of the agreement form to Rotary International as soon as possible.

As a Rotary Foundation Graduate Fellow you will have many person-to-
person opportunities to promote international understanding while advancing your academic career. Those of us who work with the Graduate
Fellowships program are looking forward to a close and mutually rewarding association with you in the months and years ahead.

In the meantime, we anticipate receiving from you by return mail your
signed agreement form, indicating your acceptance of the award.

Congratulations and best wishes.

Sincerely,

George R. Means
General Secretary

After my VSO year (1964–65) in the Gilbert and Ellice Islands, I spent three years
based at Swansea, studying for my B.Sc. Hons. in zoology and was awarded a Rotary
Foundation Fellowship to study for a master's degree at James Cook University of
North Queensland.

TOP   Hammond Rock Lighthouse is one of Australia's most northerly lighthouses.

MID   Tony Ayling and Roger Grace with black coral.

ABOVE   Tony Ayling with cleaner wrasse at the Poor Knights Islands, New Zealand.

TOP   New Guinea tribesman in Goroko.   © Alamy

ABOVE   Grave of Aborigine girl on Great Barrier Reef island.

TOP   Wewak's meandering river, where a flying doctor with whom I dined had just landed to treat a young boy for a potentially lethal snake bite.

ABOVE   After the storm at Rabaul. I was underwater when the cyclone hit and didn't realise it had occurred until I found trees blown over, blocking our drive back to town.

8 New Zealand

My journey to begin work in Australia continued, and Thursday 6 February 1969 was a lost day to me. I rose, exhausted and hungover, staggered to Papeete Airport, made farewell gestures to my disgustingly cheerful and fresh-looking Tahitian friends, and, thanks to the International Date Line, flew straight into Friday. I was departing the island on a particularly grey and overcast morning but flew into Auckland on a bright afternoon with everyone getting ready for the weekend. But the weather had not really settled down. A tropical cyclone had just passed through, and my optimism was dampened on Saturday morning when I awoke from my slumbers at Goat Island Marine Laboratory to more grey skies, sleeting rain, and strong winds. For the next two weeks New Zealand suffered the worst February weather on record. I was quickly consoled, however, by finding myself among like-minded souls at one of the most attractive marine laboratories I had ever visited.

Set above a cliff, the laboratory had a wonderful view of the sea, Goat Island, and the long sweeping bay named after it. Between rain spells, I discovered that the beach here encompasses several fascinating habitats with a rich assemblage of animals and sea weeds. Guided by fellow researchers, I strolled the water's edge as high rolling seas crashed against the rocks, making diving impossible. However, all was by no means lost on the scientific front. I collected spirorbids which eventually became the subjects of a paper published by the New Zealand Oceanographic Institute.[1] The sixty-eight-page monograph described twenty-four species in eight genera with nine new species and was to become the largest publication dedicated to NZ spirorbids published up to that time. Whilst the descriptive taxonomy was a laboratory-based, time-consuming effort, the collecting of specimens was a much easier activity. I only needed to pick up a stone, or a piece of Sargassum weed thrown onto the strand line, to find them speckled with the tiny white tube worms.

My guide to New Zealand shores and its unique pubs was Mike Barker, a student at the university who, after spending a day collecting and working at the laboratory, followed by an evening drinking and chatting, would, after I was unconscious to the world, return to the beach to observe limpets whose rhythmic movements he was studying. He also introduced me to the well-known diving partnership of Roger Grace and Tony Ayling, and between us we started to plan some exciting diving.

On Tuesday 18 February, eleven days after the 'wet' had set in, a slit appeared in the cloud-covered sky. Rays of sunshine were at last fighting their way through. The ground started to dry, the sea abated somewhat, and it was clear that prospects were improving fast. It was as if someone had pressed a magic button, and I pondered this further when, at 11 a.m., just after the day really brightened up, an unexpected camera crew from New Zealand Television appeared on the scene, complete with interviewer. Grasping at this chance for my first dive in New Zealand, I persuaded Tony and Roger to take me on a dive in the channel – to collect spirorbids, of course.

Fully rigged for the dive, we awaited instructions from the TV team. The laboratory is set close to the top of a cliff overlooking Goat Island Channel, and a Jacob's ladder provides access to the bottom of the cliff from the garden. Sweating in our wetsuits and weighed down by our equipment, we climbed and reclimbed the ladder until the cameras had captured the whole sequence, then we made for the water. A large swell still crashed regularly on the rocks. We waited for a lull in the intensity of the waves and then plunged in. Under the swirling water, icy cold to one more used to diving in the tropics, brown fronds of kelp lashed backwards and forwards in time with the waves. The dark form of a pair of flippers, about a metre away, was all I could see of the others. After swimming away from the turbulent zone, we regrouped and decided on the best area to focus our dive. There was no great depth, and we could not escape the problems of wave action unless we moved outside the comparative shelter of the channel.

We stayed in the channel and battled with the surging force of the waves as they threatened to tear us from our hand holds and crash us against the rocks. I found that by bracing knees and elbows against the sides of surge channels, I had two free hands to collect the substrates that were covered with tube worms. Less than a metre visibility was not a huge hindrance, since all I could do was collect rocks and weeds or other settlement surfaces. I would study them later under a binocular microscope. When we returned to the shore, we found that the camera crew were pleased with what they had managed to film of our efforts, despite their camera being doused by one big wave. This first impression of diving in NZ shattered my belief somewhat, but it was quickly restored by Tony and Roger, who told me they were the worst conditions they had ever encountered. They took seriously their responsibility to convince me of NZ's superb diving.

That night Roger and I turned the kitchen at the laboratory upside down in our efforts to make our own concoction of 'extra-rich creamy chocolate fudge'. After testing frantically for the 'soft ball stage', it was 1 a.m. when Roger looked up from his sampling spoon, wagged it in my direction, and announced, 'Let's go to the Poor Knights.' Notwithstanding the eccentricity of making fudge in the early hours of the morning, I thought Roger had lost it. 'What the hell are the Poor Knights?' I asked. Roger looked askance at me. Could it be that they had omitted to tell me about the Poor Knights? The possibility seemed quite preposterous, but he eventually cooled down enough to give me the whole story.

New Zealand divers kept a special place in their hearts for the Poor Knights. They were widely accepted as the best diving that the country offered. Their rugged cliffs and barren aspect gave no clue to the tremendous richness of marine life beneath the surface of their crystal blue waters. There and then we began planning a four-day trip to the Knights, forgetting the fudge in the pan, which finished up burnt into treacle, way past the soft ball stage.

We had five objectives:
1. Collect spirorbids.
2. Take close-up photographs of black coral at around 60 metres.
3. Find, film, observe, and collect cleaner fish that had not been previously recorded in New Zealand.
4. Collect sponges at all dive sites.
5. Make general collections of fish and marine invertebrates, noting their behaviour and habitats.

For a four-day expedition it was a tall order, and it was only thanks to Roger the scientific leader, Gerry Hunter, skipper of the trimaran *Clansman*, the technical diving expertise of Roger and Tony, together with their knowledge of sublittoral ecology and systematics and the support of John Hale, that we would be able to achieve all our objectives. While we were making plans for the Poor Knights trip, I continued to mix earning my keep around the laboratory with diving nearby in the improved conditions. Visibility in the channel eventually exceeded 10 metres, and I was able to see some of the fish and invertebrates that Tony, Roger, and Mike had described to me.

We had fun feeding some fish by hand. I had done this before, in Tuomotu island and in the Gilbert and Ellice Islands, but I had never seen fish so fearless as the small leatherjackets and blue cod which abounded in those days around Leigh, where the marine laboratory was situated. While Mike and I were making collections at 15 metres off the south-east tip of Goat Island, I broke open a sea urchin and fed the gonads to the multitude of fish that surrounded me. A leatherjacket became so bold that I easily caught it by hand. When I released it there was no effort to escape; it just kept on eating.

At last we were experiencing the New Zealand summer weather that I had been promised: long sunny days with gentle breezes casting delicate ripple patterns on an otherwise tranquil sea. The intensity of the sun's rays was greater than anything I had experienced in the tropics, even when living right on the equator. Exquisite splashes of colour across evening skies promised more of the same on following days. Around this rather isolated region of north-east New Zealand there were only a few people on the beaches during the week, and at weekends those that came were dedicated divers, surfers, and sailors – all good company.

On one of the long sunny afternoons before our Poor Knights trip, Roger and I set off in search of crayfish. Rather than hunting them for food, we were intent on removing spirorbids from their carapaces. We snorkelled around the southern side of the laboratory, just outside the channel. Experienced cray divers are fascinating to watch. They know at a glance whether a hole is worthy of close attention, and their lungs seem immune to any strain when the scent is hot. I had dived in England with one such character, whose ability to stay down in a cray hole was quite legendary. He would come up from ground already picked over, with arms full of crays. Roger was another such character, adept at staying down for ages whilst he teased crays out of their holes before grabbing them with a deft dart of his hand. Sadly, crays in Europe have been overfished to the brink of extinction, and such prolificacy is a thing of the past.

On this occasion we were fishing an area that was earmarked for protection, and we needed only a few spirorbids preserved from this habitat. We had started rather late in the afternoon, and light conditions underwater were rapidly worsening when Roger surfaced with a cray in each hand. Gripping them firmly by their heads, he pointed one of them down to the hole from which he had just emerged. I dived down to inspect under the ledge that he had indicated. At first I looked at the bottom of the ledge, towards the back, and could see nothing of special interest, but quite suddenly, as I was starting to go back to the surface, I looked at the roof. There were so many crays hanging there, like bats in a cave, that I almost gulped in water. By the time I had surfaced Roger had placed his two crays in the boat and was on his way down for more. This time I dived down to watch his technique.

With one hand braced firmly against the ceiling of the cave, he waved his hands gently in front of the tentacles of a large cray. Instead of retreating, the male cray advanced slowly and inquisitively towards Roger's hands. Before the cray or I had a chance to realise what was happening, Roger's hand had shot forward to grab it. Back on board the dinghy, I searched the crays for spirorbids, scraping off several healthy-looking specimens and placing them straight into a glass specimen tube containing a preservative solution (10 per cent formalin). Then we returned these magnificent crustaceans to the sea, hoping that they would not fall foul of any more aggressive hunters.

Our plans for the Poor Knights expedition had by this stage been finalised. The director of the Marine Biology Laboratory, Dr Bill Ballantine, agreed to add his sponsorship to the effort, which resulted in our gaining some financial assistance. Gerry Hunter, skipper of the yacht *Clansman*, agreed to take us out to the islands, and on the following Sunday, Tony, Roger, John, and I made our way in three cars, piled high with diving gear and food, to Whangarei Harbour. After we offloaded twenty-two 70-cubic-foot scuba tanks onto the wharf, Gerry climbed

ashore to survey the heavy cargo. His expression switched from scepti-
cism to optimism, and with a shrug of the shoulders he began stowing
the gear aboard.

We steamed out of the harbour under engine and headed for the
'Hen and Chicks' islands, en route for the Poor Knights. Roger set the
tone by heaving a bucket overboard to sample the water temperature.
After overnighting in the shelter of Whatapuke Island, we finally arrived
at the Poor Knights, and I was excited to see what all the fuss was about.
We anchored in the lee of the islands, close to an enormous cave that the
boys called Southern Cave and which I later learned was Rikoriko cave,
the largest cave in the world by volume, with an opening large enough
for small tour boats to enter. I am quite sure that Gerry could have sailed
right into the cave, and there are many subsequent examples of quite
large boats doing just that. But these were early days of investigating the
islands' underwater terrain, and we preferred to play it safe.

As I swam down towards the base of the island's rugged cliffs, which
level off at around 60 metres, only my myopic vision limited my observation. This was not too much of a problem, since lots of the action was
big and in my face. I was immediately struck by the large shoals of what
could only be described as good-sized fish. Equally thrilling as the sheer
number of fish was their colourfulness and lack of fear. I could almost
reach out and stroke the blue maomao as they schooled all around us.

I swam into the cave and began examining the fascinating sessile
fauna and flora that choose to settle in the special conditions that such
submarine caves provide. The reduced light soon obliterates dense algal
growth, leaving spaces for invertebrates to settle. Also, the extreme
shelter in a cave is comparable to conditions at much greater depths. The
inner recesses of such caves have physical habitats that may be compared
with those occurring at thousands of metres' depth, far beyond the reach
of us scuba divers. I considered it a privileged window into the relatively
unexplored depths. The walls of Rikoriko were dramatic in their variety
and richness. A mat of a green polyzoa was so thick and prominent that
even the least observant diver could not miss it. And yet the species
responsible for this carnival of colour had not yet received a scientific
name or description. At the back of the cave we found a solitary cup

coral. Previous records for the species were limited to depths below 600 metres. In the cave it existed in a dense band at only 10 metres.

The cave was so huge that a dozen divers could be working in there on separate projects, hardly noticing each other's presence. Indeed, as I was collecting spirorbids, Tony and Roger were engaged in an altogether different pursuit. They were studying and photographing the first cleaner fish to be recorded in New Zealand. They worked as a team, Roger with his camera and Tony with his harpoon, and we ticked off the third objective of our expedition.

Once we arrived back at the lab with five-day beards and salt-caked bodies, I frantically sorted my spirorbid collection, and less than 24 hours later I was supping coffee with Roger at Auckland International Airport. Steeped in discussions about what was to come next, in both New Zealand and Australia, we did not hear the first boarding call. A final call sent me rocketing through the gate with my 70 pounds of neatly disguised hand baggage and mouthing a quick farewell to Roger before boarding my flight to Sydney.

9 Australia

I eventually arrived in Townsville, North Queensland, where I was based until March 1970 to study for an M.Sc. degree. It was the start of another phase of my academic life and a whole host of new adventures.

Townsville

I soon settled into the Australian way of life in this tropical Queensland town. My Holden FC saloon car, bought at a dodgy car dealer's for about $50 in today's money, leaked both oil and water and had weak brakes and smooth, gripless tyres. Nevertheless, it enabled me to explore the intriguing, drought-stricken bushland. Kookaburras, hawks, wild cockatoos, kangaroos, wallabies, and giant anthills reminded me that, despite the relatively effortless travel made possible by jet-age living, I was in the land explored only two centuries ago by Europeans led by Captain Cook. It was a land so old in geological terms that all the mountains that once climbed proudly into southern skies had been replaced by arid, worn-down hills and parched deserts.

Whilst my research continued, at that time mostly involving sorting of collections made in New Zealand, I was active in other areas, most notably sailing, diving, and socialising. My love of dinghy racing was soon satisfied, with the help of a child psychiatrist from the hospital who had recently purchased a sailing dinghy and was looking for a helmsman. May Leatch and I struggled to come to terms with *Belmont*'s quirks and idiosyncrasies, especially her oversize spinnaker that had a mind of its own. We practised in the waters between Magnetic Island and the mainland whenever May had time off work, and gradually we got the knack of it.

I was a highly competitive, some would say aggressive, helmsman. I recall my first club race here in Australia, when I rewarded the kindness shown by various members, who helped us to rig the boat, with a heart-stopping, screaming, starboard tack along the starting line, forcing several boats to retire before the fleet had really taken off. By Easter we were a force to be reckoned with and were selected for the Townsville Team in the Queensland Championships. Near-gale-force winds lashed Cleveland Bay, and the three days of sailing were memorable for some dramatic capsizes and thrilling planes down mountainous waves. We focused on just keeping afloat and completing the course. To our utter amazement we were placed fifth and awarded a prize.

The Great Barrier Reef beckoned, however, and *Spirorbis* would provide a legitimate excuse to travel 1,050 kilometres south from Townsville to the coastal city of Gladstone and a ferry out to the reef.

> Four coral heads climb tall.
> Millions of fish hang loose.
> Giant mantas rest cool.
> Excited cleaners dance gay.

This was how my buddy Ross described his favourite underwater location. It was, he said, a diver's heaven. I could not believe my luck in being accepted to stay at the island's marine laboratory and pinched myself on a number of occasions.

I ambled along the white coral sand beach, admiring the darkening red glow as the sun rested on the horizon. I gazed seaward as flight after flight of noddy terns returned, squawking, from a day's fishing and searched excitedly for comfortable roosting perches among the *Pisonia* trees. The next day, I would visit the area that Ross had described, but for now I was content to dig my toes in the sand and forget the mad pace of mainland life. I was on Heron Island.

Any diver visiting the Great Barrier Reef at that time was drawn to Heron Island as if by some mysterious magnetism. From the boom town of Gladstone, halfway up the east coast of Australia, it lies 80 kilometres offshore and is accessible by boat or helicopter. I arrived by launch and returned by chopper. For ten days I stayed at the marine laboratory, and again I silently thanked *Spirorbis* for landing me in paradise. I recalled how as a schoolboy in England I had often dreamed of diving the Great Barrier Reef. Dreams were now becoming reality. I donned my gear in the small boat, slipped under the surface, and made for the coral bommie that Ross had said 'climbs tall'. 'Bommie' is an Australian term for vertically projecting, isolated coral heads. They often attract schools of reef fish.

I caught my breath as an 80-centimetre-long remora swam inquisitively close, presumably checking me out as a potential host. Its sleek elegance seemed superfluous for such a lazy fish, but as it relentlessly pursued me I realised that speed and agility would be necessary to hitch a ride on a shark's belly. I was fascinated to find that around the base of the bommies, in narrow channels and overhangs, there were hundreds of dazed fish hovering as if a stalled movie film had frozen the action. Working my way closer, I realised that there was more going on than immediately met my eyes. Coral cod, up to 20 kilograms in weight, were poised with fins extended and mouths agape, all tended by dancing striped cleaner fish. The cod rolled their eyes in apparent shows of ecstasy while the cleaners picked at parasites on their scales or bits of food stuck in their gills or between their teeth.

I watched, fascinated, while one coral grouper had its teeth methodically cleaned. At times the cleaner fish were completely lost from sight while they worked inside the grouper's mouth. The scene was so mesmerising that for half an hour I simply sat and watched one small area. Then I swam up a bit and surveyed a larger section of this busy cleaning station. There were hundreds of cleaner fish and thousands of clients waiting for attention. Every now and then a fish would give a flick of its tail and disappear into deeper water, apparently satisfied with the service it had received. Gazing into the darker waters, I saw several groupers scatter from the cleaner fish and pause a few metres back from the cleaning hotspot. Intrigued to know what had alarmed them, I swam down towards the vacated station. I was quickly rewarded with the sight of several mimic cleaners busily attacking the groupers from behind, biting off bits of flesh in a manner clearly disapproved of by the larger fish that had been so patiently awaiting a once-over by the true cleaners.

This con-fish poses as a cleaner until the last moment, when a bite into the flesh betrays its true motives. It was easiest to identify the mimics by their behaviour, but on close inspection it was clear that they were not great replicas. Smaller than the true cleaners, they also had different patterning along their bodies, but the overall effect of a long stripe was clearly enough to trigger a passive response in fish approaching the cleaning station. The mimics also lacked the characteristic rocking dance and tended to approach their targeted fish from the blind spot behind their head. I had often wondered how the cleaners themselves kept clean and free from parasites and was pondering the question when I saw two cleaner wrasse approach each other, rocking their bodies back and forth. As one of the wrasse hung vertically in the water column, the other delicately picked over its body, removing parasites. Later I watched cleaners from the same school engaged in mating. They did so by swimming upwards, rubbing their bodies together as they spiralled around each other. It was reminiscent of the start of a cleaning ritual until the purpose of the dance switched from general maintenance to reproduction. It did seem, however, that there may have been some evolutionary connection between these two types of behaviour.

The bommies were so tremendous that I returned there for many more dives. They were always inhabited by big fish and shoals of smaller ones, hanging loose, waiting to be cleaned. On one of these dives, as I sat in a hole on top of the deepest bommie, engrossed in collecting spirorbids, I looked up to be rewarded with a close-up view of a metre-long barracuda, stationary, fins extended, mouth wide open, enjoying the attentions of several cleaners. As it posed there, in an apparent state of ecstasy, I could have touched it. Finally, with a flick of its tail the magical moment was lost and the magnificent fish was gone.

There are few sharks around Heron Island, and those that I did see were relatively shy reef sharks. But on one occasion, as I was sucking the last dregs of air from a tank that had sustained me on a long collecting dive at the bommies, I was treated to an action-packed shark scene. Six white-tipped sharks approached the bommies. As I stared at them I noticed two gigantic fins following them. I sat quietly on the bottom and waited. The fins belonged to the largest giant manta ray that I had ever seen. As this harmless monster gracefully glided in, it was met by a whole army of enthusiastic cleaner fish which had abandoned faithful clients in favour of the main meal of the day – an ocean-wandering manta that could keep the cleaning brigade busy for hours. After a minute or so, resting over the hole that I had been sitting in earlier, the manta raised itself with flaps of its 'wing' tips, circled around the bommie, and returned to a slightly different location, once more inundated with cleaners. All this time, the sharks were in standby mode, patiently waiting for the manta to get its fix so it could rejoin them on their reef swim-about. My own air cut out before the scene ended, and I returned to the boat.

In late afternoon I ambled around the island, quietly observing the stealthy, statuesque reef herons as they darted their necks forward in uncannily accurate displays of how to fill their bellies. A dark cloud in the water, under a cloudless sky, announced the presence of shoaling pilchard. Often these were herded inshore by larger fish or small sharks. Noddy terns dived excitedly for the waste left by the voracious attacking fish. I walked through the shoals in knee-deep water and hardly disturbed the scene. Little pilchard scattered only inches from my legs, large mullet streaked by, and noddies dive-bombed my wake. After sunset, Heron Island releases a blundering brigade of comic mutton birds. They found their way into every conceivable situation, including, on my first evening there, the kitchen, the toilet, under my bed, and in the hotel bar. Years later, Paula and I visited Heron during the turtle breeding season: a wonderful experience in its own right, and one that helps to secure the unique island as one of my favourite wildlife venues, and a place to which I would most like to return.

Northern Great Barrier Reef

Back in Townsville, I sought ways to visit the northern Great Barrier Reef and struck gold. On 17 July I flew to Cairns and stopped there for a night before catching an early morning flight to Thursday Island, just north of Cape York, the most northerly part of the Australian mainland. As we flew over Cookstown, I thought of Captain Cook, who had sailed these waters and rebuilt his ship there. More recently, Captain Bligh hit this coast after the historic mutiny and named Restoration Island, which we could see from the air. The terrain may have been difficult for Europeans, but it was home to Aborigines who had mastered the skills of surviving there over thousands of years.

Thursday Island lies in the Torres Straits, 160 kilometres south of New Guinea. As we approached the runway I could see pearling luggers at anchor off Port Kennedy and pearl culture rafts moored close to Horn Island. Hundreds of islands and reefs make navigation through the straits a complex task. Names record the progress of explorers' boats fighting fickle and powerful currents together with light winds: Monday Island, Tuesday Island, Wednesday, Thursday, and Friday Islands.

With one day to spare at Thursday Island, before the MV *Cape Moreton* arrived to take me on an epic collecting expedition, I arranged with Eddie Foulkes of the Aucher Pearling Company to visit the pearl farm at Horn Island. Australian companies had joined up with knowledgeable Japanese companies to cultivate pearls in these waters. On the island, I was introduced to a Japanese student of marine biology, Harada, who was the technical manager on this farm. While I collected spirorbids among eel grass beds, Harada stood guard in the dinghy, keeping a sharp eye out for sharks. One of his men had been attacked at this location in the previous year. I was always afraid of unpredictable shark attacks but fought an inner battle to overcome these fears. Whilst snorkelling on the *Cape Moreton* trip I encountered a tiger shark that was following my scent into water so shallow that half its body was exposed. I stood on a reef top bommie to escape its attentions. But more often than not my encounters with sharks had been calm and lacking in obvious threats. I did my best to use reason to counter fear.

Later, Harada demonstrated the delicate operation necessary to extract cultured pearls from implanted shells without killing the molluscs. As each pearl was carefully extracted, it was placed in a polythene bag bearing the name of the operator who made the original insertion of a plastic nucleus. After careful scrutiny, the pearls were sent to the nearest market, in Sydney. Seldom does a perfect pearl result from such pearl culture, but Harada told me about one such pearl, produced in the previous year, that fetched over US$15,000 in today's money.

Thursday Island and other islands of the Torres Straits in the late 1960s were peopled, as far as I could tell, by brown-skinned, well-built, attractive, and good-natured folk who exuded enthusiasm and good humour in a similar manner to the Polynesians. Since many of the men had travelled to Australian cities for work, there was a surplus of women and a high preponderance of venereal diseases. Combined with rampant alcoholism, it was clear that western ways were bringing about a rapid decline in the stature of these once proud islanders. It was a pattern playing itself out across many of the Pacific islands and a trend that was giving rise to a repugnance towards insensitive developments led by Europeans who were ignorant of, or uninterested in, the long-held traditions and cultures that were the bedrock of the sustainability that had been maintained for centuries.

The lighthouse ship, *Cape Moreton*, arrived at Thursday Island on Friday 18 July 1969, and I boarded her along with my scuba-diving bottles and enough preserving jars to house every spirorbid from here back to Cairns, or so it seemed. I slept on board, and the following morning found the ship steaming out of the Straits towards our first navigational marks. In the following days we stopped to maintain beacons, reef marks, lights, and buoys at Young Reef, Horn Island, Farmer Island, Booky Island, Round Island, Moody Reef, Waterwich Reef, Goods Island, Eel Reef, Restoration Rock, Hannah Island, Fahey Reef, and Chapman Island. Each name conjures up memories of tropical scenery and fascinating dives at remote, unspoilt coral reefs.

On Farmer Island, an uninhabited strip of coral gravel with stunted bushes eking out an existence, we found a grave. A simple cross made from driftwood marked the site, and a note inside a tin can explained that it belonged to a young Aboriginal girl. The gravedigger had inserted 60 cents to 'pay her way to heaven'. No name. No clue as to how she arrived at this desolate spot, just a pile of stones and an old wooden cross. As I cleared the grave of weeds, I wondered who had last visited this lonely place. Perhaps no one since the girl died.

On Fahey Reef I waded between coral heads as a swift current flooded the reef flat. It was a glorious, calm, sunny afternoon. MV *Cape Moreton* lay at anchor half a mile away, and I was alone, standing on a coral boulder, watching and listening as the whole reef sprang to life. From pools that had not dried out at low water, thousands of fish emerged, excitedly investigating their rapidly expanding environment. Vivid green parrotfish flapped their pectoral fins clownishly as they circled newly submerged coral heads. Giant clams squirted water almost a metre high as their valves clamped closed. Shoals of tiny reef fish speckled the surface as they skidded in and out of staghorn mazes. The sleek motion of two reef sharks in the shallows was marked by their dorsal fins slicing the surface. At Restoration Rock I gazed at the place where Bligh landed on his intrepid boat journey after the mutiny. At Lizard Island I climbed the mountain that Captain Cook must have climbed to view the passage through the outer reef that he had successfully navigated. Pounding waves on either side of a narrow gap bore witness to their lucky escape from the reef's clutches.

Catching Fish

Most of my diving on the Great Barrier Reef took place from a small fast powerboat, *Hustler*, skippered by Iain Croll, managing director of Magnetic Island's Marine Gardens. I used to tag along on his trips as crewman and diving accomplice. On one of these trips we were returning home from a day's diving with a valuable cargo on board. The wind was strengthening, and you could have cut the atmosphere with a knife.

We braced our knees to cushion the shuddering impact as *Hustler*'s bow pounded into another foam-flecked wave. She thudded into a deep trough, and Iain's cheek muscles tightened as our downward movement came to a sudden shattering halt. Twin inboard–outboard engines roared steadily as we cut into the next wave. Astern lay Great Palm Islands and ahead the wooded peaks and boulder-strewn coast of Magnetic Island, off Townsville. From the Palms we had steered a wide inshore arc, taking advantage of the shelter created by Brisk, Esk, Herald, and Rattlesnake Islands. The concern so obvious in our expressions was not for *Hustler*, who had braved much more menacing seas, but for the coffin-shaped box that lay between Iain and me. Its lid was bolted down with braces, and from its side came two tell-tale plastic tubes through which flowed a steady trickle of air bubbles. Inside, suffering we knew not what, swam thirty-three coral reef fish. It was for them we worried. How were they reacting to the relentless battering of a fast hull in rough seas? If they died, our efforts over the last two days would have been wasted.

As the shelter of Magnetic Island approached, I recalled the excitement and fascination with what for me had been an entirely new experience. Magnetic Island Marine Gardens was at that time a unique display of coral fish and invertebrates in their natural habitats. My immediate delight at seeing such a fantastic marine aquarium led to me asking Iain persistently about how he managed to catch so many healthy

specimens for display in his tanks. Once the trade winds of winter abated
and whispering nor'easters left Barrier Reef waters transparent and tranquil, we headed out to one of the reefs for what was to be the first of
many fish-catching expeditions. It was a steep learning curve for me, but
I soon realised that this was one of the best possible ways to study fish
behaviour and ecology.

This was also the season of mackerel fishing, and the first sign of
Bramble Reef was the mackerel fleet spread over its sheltered waters,
resting after a hard night of fishing. We too worked our way over the
top of the reef and anchored about a hundred yards in from its seaward
edge. While Iain radioed our position to Townsville, I hopped over the
side and picked up a small clam that we needed as bait. Then, with rods
and reels in hand, we both took to the water in a display of eccentricity that the commercial fishermen must have found very amusing.
Snorkelling along the surface, we dangled our baited hooks in front of
many attractively coloured fish. Our eagle-eye view of the action below
showed what must go on around a sport fisherman's line deployed in
the normal fashion. Tiny, drably coloured fish were first to approach the
hook. They hovered close, all the time attracting more fish to join the
gang. Eventually a more dominant 'leader fish' peeled off from the throng
and took a nibble of the bait. This was a signal for a mass attack by all
the other fish, who knocked the bait back and forth, sending vibrating
signals up the line.

Now that the bait had proved to be a centre of interest for perhaps
twenty fish, others approached and hovered in the background, awaiting
their own chance for a tasty bit of clam meat. These included more
brightly coloured parrotfish and distinctively patterned wrasse. The
parrotfish had an annoying habit of lunging at the lead weight rather
than the hook. After a while an impossibly garish harlequin tusk fish
appeared on the scene, proudly displaying its vivid red, yellow, and blue
stripes. It took one look at the bait and without hesitation pushed its
rivals aside before swallowing it whole. I gently reeled in my catch and
swam back towards the plastic drum that Iain had tied to the boat as
a temporary keep for live fish before transferring them to the onboard
tank. Wire cutters hung from the drum, and I carefully cut the hook in

two so that the fish would be able to spit it out without injury. My first harlequin fish dropped into the floating bucket, joining those that Iain had already captured. I too was hooked on this bizarre game. Time for round two. I replaced my hook and bait and swam off after more future stars of the Magnetic Island Marine Gardens.

There were many fish that we could never catch by hook and line because they either played with the weight, like parrotfish, or because they showed little interest in the bait, like butterfly fish, moorish idols, and surgeonfish. I knew I would not be satisfied until we had trapped some of these too. Iain pointed excitedly at the unbelievable, delicate form of a moorish idol trailing its long, filamentous dorsal fin in and out of coral crevices in the reef shallows. He tossed his rod and line into the dinghy and pulled out a monofilament net. This was about 10 metres long by 2 metres high, weighted along the bottom with a thin chain and held upright by a line of floats along the top. Dumping the net in front of a large crevice, we quietly snorkelled down to spread the chain along the sand at the opening of the crevice.

I swam in a wide arc so as not to frighten the moorish idol, gradually ushering it towards the net. Monofilament nets are now banned, since they are so efficient and virtually invisible when deployed in this way. I had great difficulty in identifying the net, but the fish sensed its presence, swam along its face and started to veer away as it approached one end. Remembering my fishing rod still in hand, I threw it like a spear in front of the moorish idol, which panicked, turned away from the rod, and swam directly into the net. Iain dived immediately and gently scooped it away from the net in a small hand net. Triumphantly he broke surface, spat out his snorkel, and announced that this was the first moorish idol he had ever seen on this reef, and only the second that he had succeeded in catching. It was indeed a beautiful specimen, and I shared his sense of achievement.

After several more hours of collecting fish for the aquarium, we climbed back aboard *Hustler* and filled the wooden 'coffin' with seawater. Air pumps forced bubbles through diffusers, and the captured fish looked in prime condition, displaying their resplendent colours against the white walls of the tank. We filled it to the very top and jammed on the lid with its rubber seal before battening down the braces. A southeaster had been brewing while we were engrossed in our work, and the trip homewards was rougher than we expected. As *Hustler* continued to furrow the waves, I recalled the excitement of our unique hunt.

Back at the Marine Gardens, we filled another tank with seawater, and as we watched the moorish idol explore its new home, I asked Iain how long he expected it to live. I knew the answer already. There was no chance of it starving or being eaten or suffering oil pollution, or being poisoned by red tide, or being crashed against the reef by a pounding cyclone, or being snatched by birds. Here it would probably live longer than in its wild habitat. A group of American tourists passed by the tank and remarked how 'cute' the parrotfish were. If only they knew the efforts that had been made to catch them, or the excitement and satisfaction we experienced in doing so.

I should re-emphasise here that many of our activities on the Great Barrier Reef at that time – the late 1960s – would not be allowed today. Nevertheless we were considered pioneers of marine conservation, pre-ferring to leave the fish and invertebrates untouched unless we could argue that the end justified the means. Public-display aquaria such as the Marine Gardens were an essential part of building public awareness and support for reef conservation.

Occasionally we would be overcome by the excitement of a new find on the reef. There was one fish that Iain would describe to me as if it was a figment of his dreams. It was so exquisitely beautiful – so impossibly coloured, with such a neat design, and so rare. On homeward journeys, after a day on the reef, he often murmured: 'I'd really like to find some blue tang.'

Tuesday 11 December, 5 a.m., Iain kicked me awake, suggested steak and eggs for breakfast, gave me a raw egg in milk, and together we tiptoed out of his house and into the cool early morning. *Hustler* still lay on her trailer at the top of the beach in Nelly Bay. We sweated with iron plates to prevent the heavy load sinking into the soft sand, and finally had the craft afloat. The plan for the day was much like our other fish-trapping expeditions. We headed for a new reef, Grub, 80 kilometres south-east of Magnetic Island. The light breeze that usually accompanied us on these early morning excursions had not sprung up yet, and it was glassy calm. By 9 a.m. we were anchored and searching for fish.

We fished all day, and when we finally prepared to leave, the tide was low and many coral heads protruded above the surface behind us, while breakers crashed heavily on the reef edge in front. We were almost trapped there until the tide rose again, by which time folk ashore would be worrying about us. I heaved up the anchor and we drifted slowly across the reef. Concerned about hitting one of the submerged heads, I jumped in to keep an eye on the depth while Iain held the anchor in his hand, ready to chuck it over if I yelled at him. I enjoyed drifting across the reef like this. It was late afternoon and the fish were becoming more active. They had left their hideouts and were feeding on corals, algae, and various small invertebrates. In their eyes I was an inanimate shadow drifting overhead, unmenacingly. They seemed unconcerned by my presence or that of the boat. I ducked under again to check the depth ahead. *We should just miss that coral head*, I thought, and came back up.

After 15 minutes of this we did not seem to be making much progress towards deeper water. Iain had suggested we start the engine and make our way slowly along the reef to where we thought there may be a channel, and then suddenly I saw them. Iridescent blue with a black pattern, more reminiscent of a Swedish contemporary design than anything one would expect to see on a fish. Not just one of them either . . . two, three, five. 'Christ,' I muttered into my snorkel, 'there must be a dozen of them.' I surfaced, spat out my snorkel, and shouted to Iain. 'Blue tang, blue tang. Stacks of them.' He froze, staring in disbelief, then galvanised into action. Flinging the anchor overboard, he fell in with it, clutching his mask and fins. We chuckled to each other underwater as we set the monofilament net and caught four of them. But it was getting late, and we knew we had to make our way home. 'We'll come back soon and pick some more,' Iain told me. We steamed into the sunset, and there was no need to speak. We were both overjoyed with the day and fully content with life. But I never did make it back to Grub.

Later, when I eventually arrived back in the UK, there was a letter waiting for me from Iain:

... last Saturday, went out to Grub and caught a dozen of *your* blue tangs. Hope you don't mind. It was a great day – sea like a mirror and only about four feet of water where the tangs were, making catching very easy. Annoyed by a two metre long whaler shark – amazing he was so shallow. Saw dozens of peacock wrasse but concentrated on the tangs. They look very impressive in the tank where the batfish are.

Pegasus and the Whitsundays

Not all my diving was with Iain. Often I took *Pegasus*, the university research boat, and went in search of *Spirorbis* with one or two diving companions. *Pegasus* was a 5-metre open speedboat, underpowered by an 18 h.p. Evinrude engine. She was a reasonable sea boat, and only once did she scare the living daylights out of me.

It was when my girlfriend at that time, Joan, and I decided to take a weekend in the Whitsundays, exploring for ourselves and doing some diving. We set off from Townsville on Friday evening and by 11 p.m. were wending our way among the rolling hills east of Proserpine. A full watery moon picked out the skyline, and the fragrant night air told us the land was rich. Shute Harbour lay where the land met the sea, forming a well-protected bay. We parked near the slipway and set about finding a suitable campsite. It was silent except for the lapping tide and gentle frapping of boat rigging as yachts rocked on peaceful moorings. Moonlight was so bright that it cast distinct shadows. As our eyes became accustomed to the low light, we could clearly recognise the harbour entrance. 'Let's go now,' I suggested.

We launched *Pegasus*, made our way out of the harbour, through the channel, and headed for the dark shadow of South Molle island. The night was so warm and clear – only the engine destroyed the peace. After landing on a deserted beach and mooring the boat, we lay our blankets on the sand, surrounded ourselves with mosquito coils, and gazed at the southern sky before falling asleep. Next morning we set off across the notorious passage that separates the Whitsunday Islands from those nearer the coast. A strong tide kicks up steep seas when it turns against the wind, but on this breathless morning we had no problems.

We dumped our heavy gear on deserted Henning Island, covering it with palm fronds to conceal it from visiting fishermen, and took *Pegasus* on a tour of the nearby islands.

By midday, storm clouds were forming and a fresh wind was whipping up a short choppy sea amongst the semi-protected passages. We headed back to Henning and made it just in time against a 4-knot current. As we approached the shallow water around the sandspit, our engine cut out of fuel. If that had happened ten minutes earlier, we would have been faced with more serious challenges. But we had no time to wonder about such possibilities, since a sudden intense rain squall left us with the task of safely mooring the boat and building a shelter. Out in the Whitsunday Passage the squall was driving huge waves, and I could see that we were stuck, for the time being, on this lonely, remote, and uninhabited island.

It was fast approaching sunset, so we had little time to build ourselves a house. Joan had spotted the wreckage of a trimaran yacht among huge boulders around the headland close by, so we took *Pegasus* in search of useful flotsam. Lodged among the rocky crevices we discovered the remains of the deck, a spar, and part of a rudder. We lugged them to the water's edge, and our outboard coughed and spluttered as we towed them back to our chosen campsite. After leaning the deck, spar, and half a rudder against a stocky tree, we tied the spar into a supporting position, split some large plastic bags to use as roofing, and then began to build up surrounding walls, using stones carted from the rear of the beach. By this time the wind was howling at gale force while rain, travelling horizontally, mixed with salt spray from the fuming sea – such a contrast to the morning's calm conditions.

This was cyclone season, so we could not afford to treat the weather lightly. Our makeshift shelter creaked and strained as the lashing wind and rain threatened to destroy it. It was a long night, but somehow we managed to catch snatches of sleep, and by dawn I had decided what we must do. If we left early in the morning, wind and tide would be with each other, producing, I hoped, calmer seas. We carefully stowed the gear on board and headed out to the white caps in the passage. Once out there, there was no turning back, since it was safer to head into the waves than to take them side on. There was 8 kilometres of open ocean ahead before we could hope for the protection of Long Island. For once, *Pegasus* was under a real test. I told Joan, who was a novice sailor, that there was absolutely no need to worry, but issuing her a second lifejacket conveyed a conflicting unspoken message that revealed my true concern. The middle of the passage had 3-metre-high waves racing through like express trains. Each one picked up the tiny boat, and we rocked precariously on a wave crest before sliding back into the trough. Then I revved the engine and forced her up the next wave, fighting to keep control.

Nearer Long Island the waves became so massive that I was afraid to let *Pegasus* surf down them, so I had to keep the engine driving us forward, punching the water as we fell into the troughs, as well as when we rose out of them. A headland slightly to leeward marked certain shelter, but we could not make for it. Instead I had to keep the little boat pointing at the wave-battered cliffs. If we approached that maelstrom too closely, we would be finished, and yet there seemed to be no choice. I closed my eyes as a large wave approached, threatening to roll us over as we climbed its steep curling wall of water. As her engine revved, *Pegasus* took off like the legendary flying horse that had inspired her name. Now there was no controlling her. The bow lifted, spray shot out, and we flew in front of the threatening wave. Instinctively Joan shifted her weight forward, holding the boat on a plane like a surf boarder. We had managed to avoid a capsize, and within seconds we were alongside the headland. Just as the wave broke, we emerged into calmer water on the sheltered side of the peninsula. We had made it. *Pegasus* had earned her wings.

Before ending my account of diving in Australian waters, I must tell you about some fascinating wreck diving that I was lucky enough to do on the remains of the SS *Gothenburg* that went aground on 24 February 1875. She had been running south under a brisk wind, inside the protection of the Great Barrier Reef, when she struck Old Reef, northwest of Holbourne Island. She was carrying passengers and cargo, which included over 90 kilograms of gold. The wreck had only recently been discovered by divers, and there had been some general confusion about its precise position. Fortunately, our captain had the location marked on his chart, and our salvage vessel spent two days moored there. I dived with Ian Carver, Graham Costain, and Peter Rubioli. I was surprised by the condition of the wreck after spending a hundred years on the seabed. She lay on a slope with her bow on its port side in about 10 metres. Her midsection still stood upright further down the slope, whilst her stern section was lying on its starboard side at around 25 metres.

We lowered a bag of tools down onto the ship's deck and plunged in after it, planning to salvage whatever was removable. Working together, Graham and I concentrated on an area where the crew's quarters had been, identified by toilet bowls and shower recesses. Scratching at a coral-encrusted bowl, we discovered it was solid lead, coated with porcelain. Amazingly, our shifting spanner loosened the holding bolts, and we removed toilet and piping. Lifting it to the surface posed its own problems. We attached an air bag, filled it with air from our scuba mouthpieces, and watched as it accelerated to the surface. As the historic toilet reached the excited hands waiting to heave it aboard, I wondered about the story it could have related about the wrecking. If only toilets could talk.

Departure from Australia

Australia was an exciting country to visit, and I shall always be grateful to the people I met there. My research had gone well, both with sorting collections made in New Zealand and with an extensive new collection from the Great Barrier Reef, coastal habitats, and islands. I became involved in the heated debates around crown-of-thorns starfish and conservation of the Great Barrier Reef. There were widely divergent views regarding the cause of crown-of-thorns starfish aggregations that were killing large areas of coral. One camp was convinced they resulted from human intervention, whilst the opposite camp maintained that the aggregations were a normal event on coral reefs. I was a proponent of the Natural Causes theory. With the wisdom of hindsight, I now think there was truth on both sides.

When I sent a write-up of work that I had undertaken to my mentor Prof. Knight-Jones, he urged me to return to Swansea to complete a Ph.D., abandoning plans to submit for a master's degree.

This proposal was met by fierce resistance from the head of the department in Townsville, Prof. Burdon-Jones, who seemed entirely focused on the academic kudos that would result from the research being published solely under the name of his university. Disappointed by this unwillingness to compromise by having joint research institutes listed in publications under my name, and highly attracted by the prospect of fast-tracking a Ph.D., I made plans to return to Swansea to complete writing up my spirorbid research under the supervision of Prof. K-J and his wife, Phyllis.

My research and travel had been sponsored by Rotary International, and by the time I left Australia I had spoken to fourteen Rotary Clubs in Queensland and to their District Conference. To enable me to make the most of the journey home, Rotary International granted me a 'Return Route Speakers Programme Award', enabling me to visit many more Rotary Clubs en route to the UK. I was especially touched by the fact that both my Rotary councillor, John Saint-Smith, and past district governor Dick Ayrton were at Townsville airport for my 6 a.m. take-off for the final phase of my Rotary Scholarship year.

10 Pacific Journey

New Guinea

Take-off from Townsville airport involved me sitting in the vacant co-pilot's seat on a bush pilot's Cessna. At my feet were the controls – one false move, and we would be in trouble. It was 90 per cent cloud cover, but as we flew north, along the coast, I was able to pick out the island of Bedarra. The sight of it took me back to Noel Wood, the artist who for many years had lived a hermit's existence there, and to Joan's friend Eric, who had set off with Noel for the remotest regions of Cape York peninsula.

We landed at Cairns, where there was just time to complete the formalities for leaving Australia, and I staggered around dazed, sick, and overtired, with a massive hangover from the previous night's celebrations. I sank into my seat on the jet plane that dwarfed our friendly Cessna, leaving me a bit sorry for it. I nursed my innards all the way to Port Moresby. At one stage of the flight our hostess leaned over to wake me. 'Take a look, it's rather beautiful,' she whispered. I gazed below us where ribbon reefs at the northern end of the Great Barrier Reef are strung out. In places the blue-brown interface of the reef was broken by curling white breakers looking, from this height, like dabs of paint on an unfinished canvas. The scene was the same for hundreds of kilometres – long coral reefs plunging straight into the deep blue ocean on the outside, and turquoise shallows with sandy patches on the sheltered side. Before landing, I caught a brief glimpse of fishermen in dugout canoes, and reefs that closely fringed the verdant coastline.

I made my way slowly through Immigration and Customs, hearing my name called five times on the public address system, asking me to report to Ansett's information counter. Customs, however, were taking their time, and we hit a temporary wall due to the specimen of crown-of-thorns starfish that I was carrying. Eventually we agreed it was a 'biological specimen' and all was well. At the Ansett desk, I discovered Rotary's representative had given up waiting for me. This was fine, since I was not up to much small talk. I jumped into a taxi to Motel Erma and slept until 7 a.m.

Later that morning, I flew from Port Moresby towards the highlands and Goroko. The plane made two attempts to penetrate the low cloud cover that was locking in the rugged peaks, and eventually we turned and landed at Bulolo, a smaller settlement below the clouds. Deciding that the village did not have enough accommodation for its unexpected guests, we took off again and flew down to Lae, on the coast, where we stayed at the airline's expense. I was placed in Klinkii Lodge, sharing a room with the local manager of cargo and transportation for a local shipping company. He insisted I also share his rum and coke. Finally he collapsed onto his bed, and the next I heard from him was at 3 a.m., when he sang a haunting eastern melody, still fast asleep.

The following day we tried for Goroko again. The pilot navigated us through a small hole in the cloud and then, with more hope than conviction, dived the plane at the just-visible airstrip. Minutes after our landing, the clouds had closed in on us, and we had no idea how long it would be before we could take off again. Goroko is set in a long valley among the highlands of New Guinea. It is surrounded by rugged mountains covered in deceptively inviting grassy slopes; the skyline is an uneven line of pines. My lunch at Bird of Paradise Hotel was especially memorable. I was served by tattooed local people dressed quite untraditionally, with black cummerbunds and smart bow ties. Outside the window, just a few metres from where I devoured my prawn cocktail and Steak Diablo, walked traditionally clad tribesmen from the hills. Men wore a variety of dress, often with a bare bottom, their penis partially covered in a sheaf. Women mostly had bare breasts, and the young girls looked dignified in colourful arrays of grass and cloth scantily covering their genitals. Matted hair lent an extra flavour of mystique.

After lunch I escaped the hotel, walking in the direction that the locals appeared to be taking. Beyond the town there were no other white people, except a few in cars that whipped past us without slowing down. I was as much of a spectacle to the tribesmen as they were to me. Dressed in sandals, white checked shorts, and blue Tahitian flower shirt, with spectacles and bushy sideburns, I was a strange sight, even acknowledging that my skin was a different colour. But there was a mutual respect between us. When our eyes did meet, there were smiles of friendship and greeting. After passing the airfield and golf course, where formally clad sportsmen pitted their wits at potting their balls, I discovered the reason for this mass movement of traditionally clad locals through the town. They had come to market their vegetables and handicrafts. Mostly, yams were for sale. Small groups were scattered around the perimeter of the field, and there was a sheltered area of stalls in the centre.

Tribesmen moved, apparently aimlessly, between the different groups, and I moved with them attempting the impossible task of becoming inconspicuous. It was easy to take photographs, since they had no notion of camera shyness. In late afternoon, I returned to the airport and to a more chaotic and emotional atmosphere than had prevailed earlier in the day. Along the barrier fencing, and spilling out over the airstrip, were two or three hundred New Guinea highlanders dressed in their traditional and colourful ways. They were wailing mournfully at the imminent departure of young members of their families who were about to be despatched to a Catholic school in Madang. It was difficult to imagine the heartbreak that the elders must have felt. I watched, sharing their sorrows, as an elderly woman, naked to the waist and with beads around her neck, wept pitifully as her son walked away from her. He was dressed in Western clothes, and ahead of him lay the promised benefits of 'civilised' education. Here in these remote outposts of the New Guinea highlands, we were witnessing a critical transition from an existence that had scarcely changed in centuries to technological living, compressed into a single generation. During the five decades since this encounter, we have indeed witnessed a damaging decline in culture and respect for tribal customs, which seems to be the inevitable impact of globalisation.

The day left other impressions worth noting. I realised that, unlike in many other tropical locations I had visited, I did not encounter a drunk man on the streets – except for a European one. Nobody attempted to beg money from me. I had not been accosted with offers of a cheap 'sister' or stolen watch. I did not have the feeling that thieves were waiting for my back to be turned. I felt at ease in Papua New Guinea (PNG). The natives, if one must call them that, were friendly and polite.

It is a different story today. The crime rate in PNG has climbed steadily since 1970. The current report from Human Rights Watch lists it as among the most unsafe and corrupt places on our planet, despite being a resource-rich country:

Almost 40 per cent of the population lives in poverty. Former United Nations High Commissioner for Human Rights Zeid Ra'ad Al Hussein visited PNG in February 2018 and called on the government to tackle a long list of abuses, including corruption, land rights abuses, gender-based violence, and attacks on activists and journalists. In June, authorities confirmed that the country was facing its first polio outbreak in 18 years, prompting an emergency vaccination campaign.

Chronic problems continued to plague the criminal justice system in PNG, including abuses by police. Overcrowding and dire prison conditions have led to prison breakouts. PNG continues to see high levels of violence and political unrest since the 2017 election, which was marred by widespread electoral irregularities and violence. In June 2019, in the Southern Highlands, a mob set alight a passenger plane in an election-related protest. And so it goes on.

So what happened to the complex, balanced society that beguiled me in 1970? I am sorry to state the obvious: we did. The arrogance of colonialism has not died, whilst the rampant explosion of commercial exploitation, regardless of social or environmental consequences, is a fact borne out by evidence wherever one looks. It is a sad picture of how destructive humankind is towards the very resources that nurture and sustain societies.

Madang

Our plane took off that evening. We skirted the mountains, green hills, and winding river plains towards the coastal village of Madang. From the air it is a tapestry of reefs, tiny islands, and muddy creeks. The airport bus carried the pilot, myself, and one other passenger to the village.

On my first evening in Madang, I walked along the shoreline to the narrow bridge that runs over the creek near Hotel Madang. On the seaward side of the bridge were two palm-fringed shores, widening out to the open sea. On the north side is another creek, and from this there emerged, in slow line-ahead–line-astern formation, nine dugout canoes, each crewed by one or two fishermen. The silent flotilla crept out to sea towards a thundering line of breakers on the reef. For a moment I thought that I had never seen a more magnificent scene, nor that humankind could be more in harmony with their natural environment than here at Madang. But these were the thoughts of a romantic. How much easier would it be with outboard engines and conventional hulls? And yet the point seemed to be that it is the search for 'unnecessary efficiency' that has led civilisation to the brink of self-destruction. Perhaps the dugout canoe and paddle are, after all, at the optimum level of necessary efficiency – or else why has humankind survived so long, apparently satisfied with it, and been so successful in carving out a living in such wild and wonderful places? It seems to me that mechanisation leads to more mechanisation, until our ability to coexist with nature is gone.

Rotarian Ken McClean met me the following morning and we chatted about Madang and the local way of life. As he put it, 'We work all of our lives in order that we can spend some of our days in such idyllic places as these coral islands and live the carefree existence of these indigenes. What do we do? We interrupt the smooth course of their existence, make them wear shoes, and encourage them to join the race of materialistic civilisation.' Ken knew what he was talking about. He was not suggesting that progress in fields such as education and health should be held up, but, as he said, 'It does make you think, doesn't it?'

I had organised to go diving while in Madang, and local resident (and character) George Farrow took me out to the reef in his houseboat. Local diver Rod Jeffrey and I dived on the sheltered southerly side of Pig Island, which is right on the barrier reef. We went straight down to 30 metres and started to collect some pearl oysters that were attached to coral fans. There were a few large fish around, and I was keeping an eye out for sharks. Suddenly I felt a firm grip on my elbow. I nearly jumped out of my skin as I turned to meet a 2-metre silvertip shark. It was quite agitated as it patrolled the reef, swinging its streamlined body through rapid turns, each one bringing it closer to us.

We settled into a depression in the steep coral cliff and admired the shark's grace and power. But this individual seemed bent on more aggress-ive thoughts than a walk in the park. It came closer and closer until I could make out every feature of its body, despite my short-sightedness.

Rod was also noticing the danger signs, and he calmly unscrewed his five-prong spearhead to replace it with a cartridge head or 'smokie'. I watched as he trained it on the shark and was surprised when I saw him squeeze the trigger. 'Too soon. Too soon,' I mouthed to myself. The shark lashed its body into another sharp turn and the spear glanced off its back, failing to explode.

Normally, this would have been ample surprise to scare away a shark, but this was a more determined individual. Instead of disappearing into the murky haze, it doubled back and came even closer than before. Now we were defenceless. I actually remember smiling to myself as Rod and I leant over the ridge in front of us and rather sheepishly pulled in the line to retrieve the spear. There was hardly any point in reloading the gun, since our only safe defence now was to hold the spear by hand and prang the shark if it attacked. Our decompression meters were warning us to begin an ascent, so I signalled to Rod that we could not wait for the shark to get bored. We needed to face it head on as we surfaced, with our backs to the reef. Thankfully it stayed down in deep water where big fish swam and where sharks generally hunt. The boat was waiting for us, and we climbed its ladder with a real sense of relief.

There have since been mortalities from shark attacks in Madang. There is a video clip online, with over a million views, showing a silver-tip shark, attracted to vibrations of a shaken plastic bottle, attacking a diver at 57 metres. Madang has been noted as having some of the most shark-infested beaches in the world, with at least six attacks since 2006. On the following morning, after another, less risky dive with Rod, I flew along the north coast of PNG, westwards, to Wewak. From the plane I had impressive views of the meandering Sepik river.

Wewak

At Wewak I was met by Rotarian David Holman, who hosted me during my stay. His whole family made me very much at home, and I was amused to find that their youngest daughter spoke pidgin English. 'They usually pick that up first,' Mrs Holman told me. 'It's quite easy for them to switch later on.'

At a dinner where I addressed the local Rotary Club, I met Max, the local club president, who was also a missionary pilot, making many hazardous flights to treat and evacuate sick or injured indigenous people from some of the most inaccessible regions of New Guinea. He had just returned from one such flight and told me about it. A young boy had been bitten by a highly venomous snake and had been lying in agony in his village, which lay on the banks of the Sepik river. If he did not receive antiserum within 12 hours, he would die.

Max took off in late afternoon, and the only place to land was on the river itself. The rest was thick jungle. A 7-knot current was carrying logs and branches in a turmoil of muddy water. The villagers had done their best to clear a short section for the float plane to land. Trees hanging over the river banks left literally a few inches each side of the wing tips. After touching down on the water, Max had to taxi along the winding river to the village itself, avoiding drifting tree trunks on his way. One hit from these on his floats, and the plane would be finished. Max also mentioned that these waters were heavily infested with large crocodiles.

He made it to the boy, administered the antiserum, and then attempted to take off with the boy on board. Villagers lined the route in front of him, holding burning flares to guide his way. This time, Max was unable to see the branches either side of his wing tips as he emerged through the forest canopy and set course for Wewak. He returned to finishing his dinner and told me he had only landed an hour ago. Each day his skills as a pilot and doctor were put to the test, not to mention his faith in God. To look at, Max was a small man. To me he was a giant.

Rabaul

I was travelling in one of the more remote areas of the world, where communications sometimes took bizarre twists. Having flown from Wewak to Lae, with a view to backtracking it to Port Moresby, my plans changed and I decided to explore a much less trodden route of island-hopping, via New Britain and Buka, to the exotic Solomon Islands. After rewriting my concertina-stapled ticket, adding to the symphony of sun, sand, and sea that I was so eagerly lapping up, Trans-American Airline (TAA) flew me to Rabaul in New Britain at no extra charge. Since the arrangements had been revised at the last minute, I needed to send a message to my next stopover in the tiny, rarely visited settlement of Buka.

The telegram operator at the post office informed me: 'Earliest we can get a telegram to Buka would be Monday.' That would be two days later.

'But surely you can radio or telephone,' I said.

'No luck, I'm afraid. Radio's not working. Now if you want to telegram London or New York, we could help you, but I'm afraid Buka is another story.'

I confirmed my flight at TAA and made further enquiries.

'Can you radio Buka?' I asked.

'Sorry, radio went bust a few weeks back.'

'Tell me, what is there in Buka?'

'Nothing – why on earth do you want to go there?'

'I'm hoping to dive in Buka Passage.'

'Five- to eight-knot current and lots of sharks there,' he told me.

'I'll be careful. Any hotels there?'

'Well, I suppose you could call it that' came the reassuring response.

I felt that Buka was going to be an interesting visit and was glad I had made the decision to go there. But I was still in Rabaul, where I had hooked up with local dive guide Kevin Read. Kevin taught diving to local residents and visitors and told me that the greatest danger he observed was overconfidence of divers who were experiencing the pleasure of warm, clear, comfortable waters that make you feel you could stay down for ever. He recounted the story of one such diver, who went to 92 metres (c. 300 feet), ran out of air, took seven minutes to swap tanks in the dinghy, and then went to only 3 metres to decompress. He died.

'We're going to the wreck,' Kevin informed me.

'Which one?' I asked, knowing these waters abounded with reminders of WWII battles.

'Bill's.'

'Where's that?'

'Along the coast – stern at just over fifty metres. Bow's only fourteen metres.'

I sat back in the VW, surrounded by diving gear, as Kevin charged the coral roads, treating corrugations and bends with disregard. Out of town, through small settlements, past local women carrying their purchases home from town in net bags suspended from their foreheads; along a coastal path with occasional glimpses of a topaz sea and fresh white breakers on the reef edge, which was about 150 metres from the beach; and finally to a screeching halt that sent chickens scurrying to the shelter of tiny huts in the jungle clearing.

We launched the dinghy and headed out along the seaward side of the reef. When Kevin had fixed our position by transects firmly ingrained in his mind, he jumped overboard, clutching our thin warp. He snorkelled down to 14 metres, tied the mooring line to the wreck, and resurfaced. Gear on, over the side, a quick buddy check, and together we set off to explore. We hit the seabed at 54 metres and, despite mild narcosis, I began to collect spirorbid tube worms. When Kevin signalled that we should decrease our depth, I floated up a few metres so I could get a good view of the ship. There she lies on the sloping reef, I reflected. That's the funnel with the crow's nest on it. The whole ship is intact. It must have been an American cargo vessel.

On my way forward and into shallower water, I paused at the crow's nest, climbed into it, and took another fisheye view of the scene that was laid out before me. Kevin had already moved on and was hovering over the forward hold. *That should be really interesting*, I thought. I finned over to him and we entered the dark cavern of the ship. Our torches illuminated inside walls, and we were careful not to raise the thick layer of fine sediment which had settled on the floor. A door hung half open, and we could see the companionway leading aft. A ladder went down into the even blacker guts of the ship. In the fore section of the hold, my torch beam picked out a massive coil of orange rope. As soon as I touched it, it disintegrated. Reaching deep into the silt, all I could find was old leather shoes and an empty wine bottle. It was an eerie feeling to be the first to see this since it was blown up around thirty years before our dive.

My decompression meter was approaching the red zone, so I left the hold and made my way to the bow, still clutching my hoard of debris, all encrusted with tube worms. On the way back, I took a good look at the coastline and could clearly identify the volcano that defines Rabaul's skyline. There have been major eruptions in recent years, most recently at Manam in January 2019. A mountainous island, Manam has steep, densely forested slopes that were covered by a profusion of plant life. Coconut palms were randomly scattered among the other trees, adding a tropical elegance.

Before I left Rabaul, Ken Surrage had promised to take me for a dive on a sunken bomber. On Sunday afternoon, following a wreck dive in the morning, he arrived straight after lunch to take me for another dive. Fighting after-lunch lethargy, I joined Ken for what was to be one of the most extraordinary dives of my entire life. It came to be about much more than seeing a bomber plane underwater. Indeed, when we arrived at the clearing close to where the plane lay, the wind had whipped up the surface and created virtually zero visibility. But I was not off the hook. Ken knew another wreck where visibility would be much better. Back in his car, we drove through the outlying villages, where local children confused by our antics still flashed smiles and ran alongside us, squealing merrily as we negotiated the bumpy road.

We headed back through the town and across to the other side of the massive harbour. As we kitted up at the new site, rain chilled us but only served to accelerate our dive into the lukewarm brine. Visibility was about 10 metres, and the wreck was a tangled mass of metal. Salvage people had long ago blown it up to extract the condensers and propeller. Barnacles, algae, limpets, corals, and two beautiful giant murex shells, all harbouring tube worms, were collected for later examination. Finally, our air exhausted, we surfaced, packed up our gear, and headed home. It was then that the surprise hit us. Along the six-kilometre route back into town, almost every tree that had been bordering the road now lay across it. Villagers were out with their saws and axes, harvesting the wood and clearing the route. Blissfully unaware of the world above water, we had just lived through a direct tornado hit.

It was a chaotic scene in town too. When we eventually reached Ken's house, we found that one tree had crashed through the roof of a car in his yard, and another had closely missed his friend's car. Later I spoke to Kevin Read, who instead of diving with us had gone for a sail in the harbour. Needless to say, he capsized.

Buka

Next day I flew to Buka. After seeing from the air the incredible maze of islands and the famous Buka passage, I silently congratulated myself on coming here. I approached a local guy. 'Excuse me, where can I find a hotel?' I asked.

'No hotels here, mate.'

Then another man stepped in. 'Go and see Ah Foo. He'll fix you up.'

I met Ah Foo in the local store and was finally dumped on a wharf and told to wait for a speedboat, which would be over from the island of Sohano before long. In addition to my baggage, I had somehow picked up a bag of bread that I was to deliver to the island. I sat with my feet dangling over the edge of the jetty and watched an 8-knot tide rip through the passage. Eventually a Boston whaler approached, in semi-crabwise fashion, from the direction of Sohano.

'Hi there. Welcome to Sohano. My name's Jim.'

A young American man with lean features, deep brown tan, and sun-bleached long hair offered me his hand. As we headed back to the island, Jim explained that his father was developing a hotel site on Bouganville, across the passage. Pending its completion, they were putting up guests in their own home.

I was only there for a day, so that afternoon I donned facemask, flippers, and snorkel and made some collections in the channel. The high-energy pass was a nursery ground for many kinds of reef fish. Juvenile triggerfish, butterflyfish, and many wrasse darted to and fro among the coral. As they grew larger they would no doubt be carried on the tide to more extensive reefs.

Next day, I flew from Buka to Honiara on an island-hopping small plane. As I did so I reflected that my short time in what has become known as the Coral Triangle had revealed the most exotic and exciting terrain and undersea environments I had ever encountered. Coral cays, reefs, volcanic islands, and even a recently erupted undersea volcano all added up to one of the richest assemblages of life on our entire planet.

Old Friends

Honiara brought a change of pace and tone to my travels. It was a small town stretched along the coral coast of the largest of the Solomon Islands group, and provided the administrative centre for what was then known as BSIP (British Solomon Island Protectorate). I was in for a few surprises. On my first walkabout, I entered a store called Breckwoldt's to investigate purchase of travel insurance. Behind the counter, a smiling face greeted me. 'Hello, I think I know you,' she said. I was looking at a lightly tanned girl, about twenty years old, with long, straight black hair, slim build, and sparkling brown eyes. I was 30,000 kilometres from home. This could not be happening. I studied the face carefully – that disarming smile – yes, I did recognise her. She was Nasaleta, a member of my form at Elaine Bernacchi School, whom I had taught on my VSO stay in the Gilbert and Ellice Islands.

I had not seen her or any of my Gilbertese friends in nearly five years. It was an emotional reunion, and that evening I took Nasaleta to dinner. We had both changed. She was now an accomplished, sophisticated woman with eye-swivelling beauty and a poise and maturity that made me proud of her. I had changed too, no longer an overgrown schoolboy pretending to be a teacher, but a much-travelled university graduate on his way to a doctorate. Nasaleta brought me to a small restaurant in Chinatown, and we chatted about old times and old friends in the Gilberts. The whole vibrant, exciting atmosphere of Tarawa enveloped us as we renewed our friendship.

Malaita

But that was not the only coincidence to confront me in Honiara. I had been asked to do a radio interview about my life and travels, and arriving early had gone to the Guadalcanal Club, next door to the studio, for a quick beer. Standing at the bar was a face I recognised but had not seen in four years. It was Eddie Brooks, a district administrative officer for the Gilbert and Ellice islands and now a district officer at Auki on Malaita. 'Why don't you come over and visit us?' he asked. 'You can stay with us, and I'll arrange a boat so you can collect those tube worms that you're studying.' I accepted without hesitation and pulled out an atlas at the first opportunity, since I knew nothing about Malaita.

I flew from Honiara to Malaita the following afternoon. It is about the largest of the islands in the Solomon group and lies 80 kilometres east of Honiara. True to his word, Eddie produced a dinghy and local guide for my exploration along the coast. 'They've made villages on manmade islands in the lagoon,' Eddie told me. This was something I really wanted to see for myself.

Every few hundred metres, we passed one of the artificial islands. They were of varying shapes and sizes, but all stood out from the mangrove shoreline and within the shelter of the fringing reef. Each was constructed from coral boulders that must have been hewn from the reef itself and carted on rafts to the building sites. Sometimes there was just one house on an island, and often there were bridges joining nearby islands. Dugout canoes were paddled back and forth, in and out of these watery homes. A group of three women in a long canoe waved as they passed us, on their way out to the reef to catch their next meal.

'Why did they build them here?' I asked the boatman.

'Too many mosquitoes in mangrove, and sometimes the pagans come down from the mountains,' he told me. I looked up at the mountains. 'Pagans' lived here. Later Eddie told me there were people living up in the hills who had not even met the normally intrepid missionaries. Administrative officers on census patrols did not dare to enter some regions.

Towards midday, a mist shrouded the mountains and limited our vision along the coast. We cut the engine and drifted for a while. A canoe paddled by two girls passed, and I strained my ears to listen to their lilting rhythmic singing in perfect harmony. The air hung heavy and still. From up in the mist came the haunting notes of a trumpet shell horn. Someone was calling the family home. I shared my packed lunch with the boatman, and we headed back to Auki. Late that evening, I flew back to Honiara and dumped my baggage in the room of one of the local bank boys, where I had been offered a bed for the night.

Risky Scuba

Scuba diving in the early 1970s could be quite haphazard in terms of skills, knowledge, and safety. I have already referred to regular dives to 60 metres or more, casual decompression discipline, and unaccompanied dives, together with use of explosive shells instead of prongs on spearheads. The Solomons provided a wake-up call that my diving buddies in New Zealand would have simply not tolerated.

I joined a Sunday gathering of the newly formed Solomon Islands Skindiving Association. About thirty folk gathered at the Bonegi One wreck site. For most of the afternoon they chased fish in a relatively small area, loaded spearguns pointing at each other almost as often as at a fish. There had recently been a snag with the type of gun they were using, which had been firing automatically without pulling the trigger. I saw several loaded guns leave the water – a cardinal sin. Most spearfishing was done with scuba tanks on their backs.

The divers had kindly arranged for me to have a scuba dive, and I waited until the shark-feeding hour, just before sunset, to know who would be my buddy. Then I learned that I would be alone on the dive. Reluctantly I set off along the surface with Ray, who was snorkelling. About 200 metres out from the shore, he stopped. 'OK, Pete, if you head straight down from here, you'll hit the stern of the wreck on the bottom. Shouldn't be any problem.' And I dived.

I knew this was wrong but felt that a quick dive by myself, to 20 metres or so, would be safe enough. I kept swimming straight down. Surely I should be near the bottom by now? I must be nearly 30 metres deep. I already felt a mild narcosis. It was dark, too, since the last rays of sunlight were glancing off the sea's surface. I could see the wreck now, but Jesus, it was at least 40 metres deep. I checked my depth gauge: 39 metres, and the wreck still below me. The intensifying narcosis accentuated my anxiety. *I must be careful*, I thought. My lips were numb, and I could not feel the mouthpiece that was delivering my air.

I hit the wreck. Alone and lonely. A giant grouper lurked in a massive hole, created by salvage divers, at the stern of the ship. Pearl oysters clung to the tangled metal. I tugged at these to fill my sample sack and felt narcotic fuzziness cloud my mind. *That's enough*, I thought as I pushed off and made for the top.

Back ashore, I tackled my friend. 'How deep is the stern of the wreck, Ray?'

'Oh, about 50 metres, Pete. Why do you ask?' There was little to be gained by an argument.

New Caledonia

Continuing on my slow journey across the Pacific, I sat in an ancient plane that rattled its way from Vila in New Hebrides to Noumea in New Caledonia. I had left Honiara earlier that day and was faced with the choice of spending three weeks in Vila or getting straight back onto a plane and flying onwards to Noumea. The flies that plagued me in the dusty town of Vila clinched my decision: I would keep moving. The jalopy in which I flew was jam-packed with French passengers who brought with them a strong aroma of garlic. They protested musically at each shudder of the plane fighting turbulence. They shouted, nudged, shuffled, and ate nearly all the way. Finally, our crumbling machine landed roughly at New Caledonia. We bounced twice. The wings narrowly missed being shorn off as we heeled to port and starboard. I was glad to arrive.

Noumea itself seemed to be a complex of industry and tourism. There were more bright lights than I had seen since Townsville. Despite my prejudices, I decided I could grow to like it – at least a little. But my hopes were never really met, despite some excellent diving over rich healthy reefs. For once I felt trapped by an inflated economy in a tourist resort. I was glad to fly back to the summer warmth and sincerity of New Zealand, which I had left exactly a year previously.

Back in New Zealand

I returned to the Marine Research Laboratory at Goat Island Bay and settled in for a few weeks. My old friends Roger Grace, Tony Ayling, Mike Barker, and Barry Russel were all still there, and we picked up where we had left off. It was very useful to be able to study some of the live species that I had identified in the collections from NZ, made during my previous visit, whose preserved specimens I had worked on while at Townsville. I did a return trip to the Poor Knights, this time with Wade Doak, editor of *NZ Dive* magazine, with whom I had been conducting a vigorous exchange of correspondence. During this second visit, I worked with a transect line, recording tube worms at different depths.

Much as I loved the scene at Goat Island and its surroundings, my friends insisted that I could not leave NZ without visiting the south, including Wellington and Christchurch. Readers may be excused for skipping some of the detail of my academic research, summarised below, but will be happy to know that it was a highly productive year, culminating in a monograph on New Zealand Spirorbinae, together with an extensive collection from Australia.

New Species and Genera

The scientific publication, which ran to sixty-eight pages, recorded twenty-four species in eight genera, nine of which had never been described or named before and were what we call 'new species'. I was thus responsible for naming a *Protolaeospira* as *gracei* (after Roger Grace) and a *Metalaeopsira* as *clansmani* (after the trimaran in which Gerry had taken us out to the Poor Knights).

I am aware that readers of this book may not be scientists and may never have discovered or exhibited a fascination with tube worms and their anatomy, ecology, behaviour, and distribution. I am the first to admit that the thought of becoming one such person was very far from my mind when I set out to emulate Jacques Cousteau, Hans Hass, or, if my luck held out, James Bond. After all, worms are not the sexiest of organisms to grace our planet, and the world was not exactly holding its breath to come face to face with the latest revelations from the world of Spirorbinae. So what exactly was the attraction, given all the highly attractive alternatives, that led me down this esoteric pathway? To give you the answer, I need to be brutally honest in ways that do not necessarily reflect well on my character. It occurs to me that the truth in this regard may in fact provide valuable lessons on steering a course through the jumble of coincidences and consequences that make up the matrix of experience that is sometimes referred to as one's career.

Plan A: Shortcut to fame and glory

As a child, I had crystallised my goal in life, which could be loosely summed up as following in the footsteps of David Attenborough: bringing marine science to the general public in dramatic encounters with underwater creatures, just as he was doing through his *Zoo Quest* books that chronicled his adventures in jungles, deserts, mountains, and other wild places. An alternative option was to seek a life of adventure in the sun, surrounded by enthusiastic, attractive, like-minded members of the opposite sex. An addendum to these worthy ambitions was that there would be copious amounts of sailing in sparkling blue waters inhabited by friendly dolphins, giant whales, and scary sharks that promised not to bite.

The only thing that could have diverted me from these noble ambitions was an offer from Elvis Presley to pick up the slack as he tired of being the king of rock and roll. But I realised early on that not having a note in my head effectively ruled me out of such a job, even if it had become vacant. So it would have to be plan B.

Plan B: Spirorbinae – the key to achieving ambitions

My professor started it all, and perhaps it is not surprising that he found fascination, satisfaction, and, I think, solace in identifying, describing, and in many cases naming the tiny tube worms that occurred in almost every intertidal or shallow marine habitat. It was certainly a far cry from the role of gunnery officer that shook his gentle nature to the core in WWII. It was Prof. K-J who, in 1968, encouraged me to join his small team of taxonomists and marine ecologists dedicated to unravelling the detail, diversity, and distribution of Spirorbinae, and I have never regretted the decision. The light bulb moment came when I realised that this could provide the key to open many doorways that I would later walk through to satisfy my basic instincts. Academic credibility and status, in the form of higher degrees, were ladders to success. In short, I needed a Ph.D. to further other goals. Without it there would be no exotic travel and adrenaline-filled adventures.

Before that realisation illuminated my future, I was considering all sorts of options to gain a doctorate in marine science. Ambitious ideas such as breeding marine tropical fish, finding ways to propagate coral reefs, and decoding whale song all seemed to fit the bill for some high-profile rewarding research. The words of a respected senior scholar brought me down to earth. 'There is no particular merit in choosing the most difficult subject to form your doctoral dissertation,' he told me. 'Some people might regard that as poor judgement if the same result can be achieved in half the time.' So when Prof. K-J invited me to join his team – 'Why not give me a hand with sorting out the Spirorbinae, old chap?' – I jumped at the opportunity. Eighteen months later, I had my doctorate degree and doors were opening. They still are.

That is not to say that researching spirorbids was not rewarding and exciting in itself. I even achieved recognition in having a whole genus named after me: *Vinearia*, presently containing the species *Vinearia koehleri* and *Vinearia endoumensis*. I am the first to admit that not everyone would welcome such personalised inventions of nomenclature, created by fellow taxonomists, in recognition of one's contribution to science. Neither is it all plain sailing for the recipient of such accolades. There is always the danger that an awkward scientist will shoot down the logic that led to the creation of such an epithet, arguing that prior names are still valid and that one's own treasured hold on fame and glory should be cast into oblivion. Unfortunately it's not just new species names that are at risk. The whole field of taxonomy, and those who dedicate their careers to the field, are at risk of extinction at the human level.

In an article published in *Bioscience* in 2011, Lisa Drew discussed the threatened 'extinction of taxonomists'. The figures are astounding, and daunting. Almost two million species – 1,922,710 – have been identified. In 2008 alone, researchers newly described and named 18,225 living species.[2] The decade-long *Census of Marine Life*, which ended in 2010, estimates that the ocean holds more than one million marine species, excluding microbes. The task of recognising, describing and preserving the holotypes and paratypes, depositing them in museums and publishing this work, is overwhelming. It is also, on a broad scale, inadequately valued or funded. As a result of climate change and our impact on nature, threatened ecosystems may be destroyed before their unique species are even recognised. The question is, does this really matter? It is a debate that needs to take place among scientific organisations before it is too late to turn back the clock.

Homeward Bound

My route back to Europe involved two weeks in Fiji, a week in Pago Pago in American Samoa, a few days in Honolulu, and then on to Los Angeles, where I met up with family friend Judy Ehrmann. From there I flew to Toronto to meet my brother, Andy. Karen, an ex-girlfriend of his, invited me to join her on a 3,000-kilometre hitchhike right across Canada, by the northern highway, to Vancouver. By the time we reached that city, we had had enough of each other, and I was ready to fly back east. Loan of a student card enabled me to buy a cheap flight to Toronto, and from there it was just one more plane journey to London. It had been a busy year, and it was also time for me to get my head down and write up the main body of my research on tube worms.

Shortly after settling back into sorting my collections in Swansea University, I asked Prof. K-J if it would be OK to attend a seminar on coral reefs at the Royal Society in London. I had not expected that this would further delay my laboratory work and divert me to a whole new sea of adventures. The Red Sea had lived in my imagination for years, and now I was given the opportunity to turn my dreams into reality.

11   Red Sea

First Red Sea Dive

I was standing at the eastern extremity of the Nubian desert, gazing towards Mecca. Port Sudan lay eight kilometres to the north, but out here in the searing mid-morning heat there was little indication that a bustling Arab city existed beyond the haze. My closest companions were skinny camels whose projecting rib cages bore witness to a continuing drought. The white-painted Land Rover in which I had bounced across a trackless desert glistened so brightly that it was painful to look at, but I was grateful for the narrow strip of shade that it afforded. I had parked as close to the Red Sea as I dared, but there were still several metres to cover before I reached the relative comfort of the tepid shallows.

I marched out of the shade barefoot, clad only in a pair of football shorts, carrying mask, snorkel, flippers, and my underwater camera. Burning sand brought to mind Fijian fire-walkers. Was the sand actually white, or was the heat making it look that way? Not stopping to find out, teeth clenched, I made a dash for the water, in the process disturbing just about everything that could run, fly, or swim. Egyptian vultures were already circling on thermal currents high above me, and now two startled reef herons took off. A solitary gazelle must have been resting at the water's edge, for it too leapt into the air, half running, half gliding towards the Red Sea hills. Even the camels shifted their posture. Reaching the water, I splashed my way to the deep channel which I had selected as a good place to experience, for the first time, Sudan's fringing coral reefs.

Much has been written about diving in the Sudanese Red Sea, but most attention has been focused on the offshore reefs such as Wingate, Towartit, Sanganeb, and Shaab Rumi. I had decided that fringing reefs close to Port Sudan were as rich in marine life as some of the offshore reefs. They abound in fish life and, in places where coral growths are prolific, such as outside the pass through which I was snorkelling, they could provide a marine biologist or underwater photographer with a lifetime's work.

I had crossed the lagoon zone and was approaching the reef edge. Immediately inshore from the reef crest was an area where most corals were dead and cemented together to form a fairly flat reef top whose regularity was disrupted by crevices and isolated coral colonies. This might be described as the vermetid zone, for coralline rocks and live corals were bored into by large numbers of worm molluscs, or Vermetidae. The neatly cut round holes were easily distinguished by brown opercula, closing off their entrances. Holes vacated by the vermetids were often occupied by another rock borer, the cosmopolitan sea urchin *Echinometra matthei*.

Fewer corals lived here than on the reef crest or outer slope, but several species formed isolated colonies. Bushy clumps of pink *Pocillopora* projected above the reef flat. These were often speckled by white scars where polyps had been scraped off by parrot fish, wrasse, or puffers. *Tridacna* clams also projected above the reef surface, their valves encrusted with pink calcareous algae and brilliant, incandescent-blue bulging mantles, rendering them conspicuous. Other corals, such as *Favia* or the octocoral *Tubipora musica* (organpipe coral), occupied crevices. The latter were covered by green living polyps and exposed their bright red skeletons only when broken off from the reef and washed ashore.

Fish and corals became more abundant near the reef crest, but I found several species that were well adapted for life in this challenging zone. A sinuous pipefish, *Sygnathus*, wriggled its way through grazed algal turf that matted the cemented dead coral rocks. Its fawn colour-ation and disruptive camouflage of black spots made it almost invisible at times. Moon wrasse, *Thalassoma lunare*, were also common in this area. Their pugnacious manners helped to ensure that they caught whatever detrital food was on offer.

Closer to the reef crest there was a zone colonised by fire fan coral (*Millepora dichotoma*) and the plate-like form *Millepora platyphylla*, which tolerates the highest-energy environment of virtually all corals. In deeper pools, large, rounded heads of brain coral, *Platygyra lamellina*, occurred rather sparsely. The soft coral *Sinularia* was abundant in this habitat and is often associated with the millepores. Small umbrellas of *Acropora* extended towards the reef crest, forming shaded crevices where many small fish sheltered. I broke open a clam shell and left it there to see what fish were hiding. Predictably, moon wrasse were first on the scene. A juvenile grouper also emerged from a nearby crevice to observe happenings from a safe distance. Its revolving eyes seemed to focus in every direction as it assessed the danger that I posed versus the obvious desirability of a piece of clam meat served in an open shell. After a few minutes it decided the risk was worthwhile and grabbed a bite of the meat. The brightly striped regal angelfish's appearance at this dining table was the cue to focus my camera. The fish was rather shy, withdrawing to its darkened crevice after each bite.

Not all the fish were interested in the clam meat; small banded damselfish (*Dascyllus aruanus*) hovered above thickets of *Acropora*, retreating among the coral's branches whenever I approached. Surgeon fish dashed back and forth, grabbing bites of algal turf whilst avoiding defensive attacks from aggressive damselfish such as *Stegastes nigricans*. The small cleaner fish *Labroides dimidiatus* danced at its station near the reef edge, and I saw many more cleaners deeper down, off the reef slope.

On the crest of the reef I found a blowfish, *Arothron diadematis*, completely engrossed with chewing *Pocillopora* polyps. It was also enjoying the attentions of a cleaner wrasse. A row of fire coral fans marked the reef edge. Each fan was broadside on to the long reef current. Uppermost colonies formed an overhanging lip under which the shaded reef wall was covered by crustose coralline algae, with various *Acropora* corals forming umbrellas, tables, plates, or thickets occupying this shallow habitat. Somewhat deeper, at about 3 metres or more, large, smooth, rounded colonies of *Echinopora* dominated. This section of the reef had a high percentage cover by live corals, and I was not surprised to see signs of the crown-of-thorns starfish, *Acanthaster planci*. Four small white patches on an *Acropora* table indicated recent feeding activity, and a search of nearby crevices quickly led me to the culprit: spiny starfish. I was reminded of how patchily distributed they can be on healthy reefs, and how well they camouflage their presence when not forming aggregations.

Close to where I found the starfish on the almost vertical reef wall, I noticed an orange sponge with long narrow tubes extended out towards open water. At about 10 metres the reef wall levelled out to form a terrace of coral rubble and sand. Large rounded heads of *Porites lutea* formed isolated patch reefs rising towards the surface. Giant anemones were attached to coral rocks near the reef edge, and clown fish hovered above their tentacles, enticingly attractive with orange heads and sky-blue vertical stripes across their bodies. The reef was cut by several deep ravines, and shoals of sweetlips and jacks occupied the ravines, seemingly attracted by increased current flow. They were accompanied by unicorn fish, sailfin surgeons, snappers, and several large Napoleon fish that swam sluggishly along the reef face, investigating crevices or pausing to accept visits from cleaner fish. They were quite shy, and I had difficulty approaching them.

This was one of my first Red Sea dives. I was not anxious to encounter sharks but was excited by the visit of a large guitarfish. Half ray, half shark, it would have made a great picture, but my camera was by then set to take close-ups, so I determined instead to fix the extraordinary image in my memory, with or without the camera. I can still picture the guitarfish, over fifty years later. By this time I had spent more than three hours in the sea, and sunburnt shoulders warned that it was time to head for shore. There were already too many details to recall, and I knew that I would return on many occasions to dive on Port Sudan's fringing reefs. Forty minutes later I was driving through the bustling city, almost home.

Red Sea Retrospective

In 2018, while I was going through treatment for an enlarged prostate and not feeling like doing much, I was approached by my old friend and scientific colleague Dr Dirar Nasr, with whom I had spent many wonderful days in Sudan in the 1970s. Dirar is an inspirational scientist who never lost his sense of humour. Guided by an unshakeable faith in Allah, he epitomises what true Islam is all about. We dived together in Suakin harbour and off Port Sudan, on the wreck of the *Umbria*.

Dirar introduced me, via the Internet, to Dr Najeeb Rasul, who was co-editing the Springer Oceanography volume in which our chapter on dugongs would eventually appear (*Oceanographic and Biological Aspects of the Red Sea*, 2019). Dr Rasul asked me to write a chapter that would describe the key elements of my own research in the Red Sea. At first I demurred, and then I decided to take up the challenge, if only to take my mind off my health issues. If any readers are interested in the scope of my Red Sea research, I would refer them to this volume, listed in the Appendix, and parts of which are summarised below.

Crown-of-Thorns Starfish

You don't hear so much about the crown-of-thorns starfish today, but back in the late 1960s and early 1970s it was centre stage in world news. Plagues of the spiny sea-stars were consuming vast swathes of the Indo-Pacific's coral reefs, leaving their parched white skeletons exposed to decay and fouling by sea weeds. They devastated healthy reefs and scared the living daylights out of all who saw them in action. I dived head first into the raging controversy over what was going on. Were these massively damaging swarms caused by human activity, or were they natural events, part of the ebb and flow of reef development? The Cambridge Coral Starfish Research Group (CCSRG) was established to study the biology of crown-of-thorns starfish and related coral reef ecology. Its director was Dr Christopher Roads, a keen spearfisherman, champion marksman, and deputy director of the Imperial War Museum in London.

I was in the group's advance party to Port Sudan, and our small team was later joined by Rupert Ormond, Dr Andrew Campbell, and Dr Roads, complete with hovercraft and other gadgets. We took possession of the reef platform that had been erected a year previously and which became a home from home, right on top of Harvey Reef, named after fellow expeditioner Andrew Harvey. A picture is worth a thousand words, and images of the scaffolding structure on Towartit reef complex convey a vivid impression of what it was like to live on this tiny coral reef. Lying on our backs on the upper deck, we counted shooting stars, played ancient planetary gazers, and listened to the waves rippling at the reef edge just a few metres away. There was no electricity, no telephone, and no supermarket around the corner. Instead there was a reef full of fish – where we tended not to fish – and two outboard powered dories (ex-army bridge boats) that brought supplies out to us and took ashore any rubbish that we accumulated. Our most valuable asset was a diving compressor that enabled us to spend hours and hours underwater, mostly in the top 10 metres or so.

We got to know individual fish by name, and I realised that, despite its relative lack of experience, our team was in a position to conduct some valuable marine research on the reef's complex ecology. My own interests at that time embraced larval cultivation of crown-of-thorns in the laboratory, investigating ecological impacts of fish behaviour in reef environments, and monitoring the seasonal ebb and flow at the interface between corals and sponges, which were in constant competition for space on the reef. When it came to the macroecology of crown-of-thorns and the causes of their 'plagues', I held the unpopular opinion that this was primarily due to natural causes. My 1970 paper in the journal *Nature* set out this argument,[3] and I developed it further in 1973.[4] My early interest in photography had by now found expression in underwater photography, supported by a variety of cameras and housings. I was particularly proud that my picture of a pufferfish eating a crown-of-thorns starfish graced the cover of such a prestigious magazine as *Nature*.[5]

In addition to participating in this summer expedition, my research in the Sudanese Red Sea was enabled by stints as deputy director of CCSRG; as project researcher, funded by the Overseas Development Authority; as director of Suakin Marine Laboratory; and as a lecturer at Khartoum University, a position I held until I departed Sudan to join the Saudi–British Fisheries Development Programme as its senior scientist. Looking back on those heady days, I clearly recall the stimulating atmosphere of enquiry, discovery, and excitement that ruled our lives.

Far from camping in the searing desert or making do in shaky government housing, we were based in what had until recently been the somewhat palatial headquarters of the Eastern Telegraph Company (ETC), later to be merged into Cable and Wireless Company. With our own bedrooms, ceiling fans, and even the odd air-conditioning machine, together with a group kitchen, food store, and open veranda next to a disused tennis court inhabited by African black kites, we were embarrassingly comfortable, and we knew it.

The kites that loved to perch on nearby trees or overhead wires seemed to recognise us as individuals. Any signs of aggression towards them were greeted by purposely directed dive-bombing that narrowly missed clawing at the human intruder's sunburnt scalp. The mistaken enmity was not quickly forgotten, and even the most innocent and passive ambulations in the vicinity of their nesting trees were likely to be met with warning dives at any previous culprits, whom the kites clearly recognised. The few remaining staff at the ETC knew the rules of this frightening cat-and-mouse game. It took some members of our own team a little longer to become accepted as benign passers-by.

Following one particularly noisy altercation, a recently hatched, more-or-less featherless kite fell to the ground from one of the nests in the garden and was in immediate danger of being caught by one of our resident cats. I rescued the young bird and took it into the laboratory at one end of the ground-floor corridor. I fed it three or four times a day, and it soon thought of me as a caring parent. Welcome and fascinating as this was, the bird quickly started to outgrow the vulnerable surroundings of the larval rearing laboratory. Within weeks it needed to learn to fly and be set free. We established flying lessons as soon as its wings were fully feathered, and it soon became mobile, half gliding and half jumping from one laboratory installation to another.

After about ten days of this in-house practice, it fled the nest, disappearing over the roofs of the city. We assumed that would be the last we would see of it, but we were mistaken. That evening I had some British guests at the Eastern Telegraph building and decided to take them to see my recently acquired apartment, about half a mile away, across the town. On opening the door of the apartment, I caught a glimpse of a bird skidding around a corner of the outer verandah. Sure enough, it was my kite. It had never seen my apartment before, and yet, of all the balconies and all the buildings in the urban hotchpotch of Port Sudan, it chose mine. We never did figure out why, but we were happy to take the bird back to Eastern Telegraph to complete its flying lessons and give it a well-earned meal.

During my year in Australia, at James Cook University, I had come in contact with Dr Robert Endean at Heron Island. Dr Endean had recently led a study on *Acanthaster planci* in which he had pointed to the likelihood that the larval life of the starfish lasted 'a matter of a few days'.[6] He was apparently unaware of the larval rearing experiments undertaken by Mortenson, published in 1931, which had already demonstrated a relatively long planktonic larval life for this species, lasting two or three weeks, depending on local conditions (temperature, salinity, organic concentrations, seabed characteristics). Meanwhile, studies by Henderson and Lucas (1971) demonstrated a planktonic larval life of four to five weeks. The issue was important and fundamental to studies of what caused the starfish aggregations.

Back in Port Sudan, I became engaged in raising the larvae of *A. planci* and in the international debate on whether or not the phenomenon of starfish aggregations was caused by humans' disturbance of the natural environment. Endean thought it was. I begged to differ. In my retrospective chapter for Springer, I lay out the arguments on both sides and suggest that there is no absolute affirmation to either side of the debate.

Fish Behaviour and Reef Structure

My paper describing the ecological importance on coral reef development of aggressive behaviour by damsel fish, published in 1974 in the journal *Marine Biology*, struck a chord with several research teams. I had initially noticed that the habitat of damselfish in shallow reef habitats often comprised loose rubble rather than firmly cemented coral fragments. On coral reefs, where calcium carbonate binds just about everything together, this was unusual. Absent-mindedly reflecting on the observation, I suddenly turned the facts on their head. What if the rocks were loose *because* of the fish's behaviour, rather than the fish selecting loose rubble as a suitable habitat? The remarkable feature of the fish was their aggressive behaviour. I developed the hypothesis that it was their aggressive behaviour that dictated the ecological structure of the reef. It sounds simple today, but at that time, it was considered to be a significant perspective of the linkages between fish behaviour and reef ecology.

Khartoum University and Suakin Marine Laboratory

Dear Mum and Dad,

Have accepted post as lecturer in marine biology and director of Suakin Marine Research Station – involves total salary of about £2000 to start – 3 months' paid leave in UK – 3 months lecturing in Khartoum – 6 months in Port Sudan and Suakin. I start full-time in October this year and then do 2 months Jan/Feb back with Cambridge Group – then carry on in Port Sudan and Suakin as marine lab director.

Even today, forty-seven years later, I look at this letter laying out my life's dream job and can hardly believe I was so lucky. The letter is dated 15 May 1973 – seven months before Paula and I were married (29 December 1973), and Paula was as excited as I was to be set free among some of the most dramatic coral reefs in the world.

I had other reasons to celebrate that summer. 'I have just raised my first load of *Acanthaster* – from egg to starfish – so have fulfilled that part of my contract,' I wrote. And my financial situation was improving, allowing me to pay back family loans. 'I hope you got my cheque for £250,' I wrote. 'My account is in credit but I have paid back lots of money in the last six months so it's not that healthy yet.'

Romance, Marriage, Baby

And how did I meet Paula? That's a long story. After completing my Ph.D. at Swansea in 1971, the world was my oyster. In those days a university lectureship virtually guaranteed a job for life. What direction should I follow? The die was cast by my professor and trusted mentor Professor Knight-Jones, who encouraged my pursuit of some exciting diving off the west coast of Ireland. With my academic grant about to expire, I needed something to keep me going, and Prof. K-J knew just the person who could help.

'Do you remember Peter Vine, Paddy?'

'Yes, Wyn, he sang "Galway Bay" on your last night, when we all ate oysters down in Salthill.'

Pádraig Ó Céidigh, head of the department of zoology at the National University of Ireland, Galway, was referring to a somewhat raucous field-course farewell drinking session that he had hosted in 1969. I think this was news to Prof. K-J, who was hoping for a more elevating name recall, but he went with the flow.

'Well, he's just finished his Ph.D. – damn good piece of work too. He's interested to do some deep diving off Galway and look at spirorbinae over there.'

'Well, he's very welcome.'

'Do you think you could do anything about funding?' my professor asked Paddy.

'Leave it with me' came the enigmatic response.

About three weeks later, I received a letter from the Irish Department of Higher Education, appointing me as a research fellow with a postdoctoral fellowship. I had not, to my knowledge, applied for the fellowship and had no idea how this miracle was achieved. I had only one other wish – that I would find a romantic thatched cottage to live in for my two years in Galway. It was June 1971, and I was about to take off for the Seychelles as leader of a small expedition there. With a two-year fellowship in the can, I was free to pursue some more social activities. Joan, my girlfriend from Australia, arrived over in London and I met her off the plane before bringing her to Swansea. I had proposed to her as soon as my Ph.D. had been announced, and Joan had managed to gain acceptance as a radiographer at a hospital near Swansea, just before I revealed that we would be moving to Ireland and I would be away in the Seychelles for the next six weeks. By the time I returned, and we moved to Galway in late 1971, the relationship was becoming strained, and we eventually broke it off. Meanwhile, I had rented the finest thatched cottage in Galway. I was living there on 30 January 1972, a date seared in memory by the events of Bloody Sunday. On the advice of friends, I hid my UK-registered minivan from public view. The atmosphere in town was edgy and tense.

Galway was a relatively depressed city in 1972, with Merchants Road mostly derelict and the local economy heavily dependent on the drinking habits of its student population. Poverty and unemployment were widespread, but if you went to one of its iconic pubs, like the Cellar, any time after midday, you would think the place was booming. Music, dance, women: in short, the craic was mighty. And to cap it all, the miniskirt was reaching its peak, keeping us students on our toes or knees, depending on our alcohol intake. I fell in love with the city and was just beginning to reach out to the surrounding islands and villages when I fell head over heels in love with a Galway girl.

Paula and I still feel something special when we pass the corner of the university, diagonally opposite the hospital, although it has changed considerably since the day in autumn 1971 that I pulled up my Mini to invite her to come for a drive.

'Have you seen Connemara?' Paula replied. 'I'm on my way home. Do you want to come?'

I was single, and the long and winding road through Connemara was just what I needed to clear my head. Paula's uncomplicated enthusiasm was like a tonic, and I was in love before she even got into the car. My heart soared as we flew over the bumpy road to Clifden and the mountains rose up to greet us, demanding attention and admiration.

I should explain that Paula and I already knew each other, for she was a member of a small Zoology class to whom I had recently delivered a slide show on coral reefs. She recounts that with my deep tan, long hair, and well-formed physique, I had caught her eye as she sat, well positioned, in the front row. Her infectious smile, lithe build, enthusiasm for life, and appealing independence drew me to her like a magnet. Following a series of chance encounters in the Cellar or one of our other watering holes, our roadside meeting had been just waiting to happen. We were immediately on a roll, in love from that moment to this.

Paula came out to Port Sudan for December 1972/January 1973, and we were married a year later on 29 December 1973. We returned to Sudan almost straight after our wedding in Ireland, and our honeymoon was on our good friend Halim's boat, the *Sara*, named after his daughter. We headed south and into Eritrean waters. Along with the two of us, celebrating our love, there were six or eight other people on board, and zero privacy. Recognising this as an issue for the perfect honeymoon, everybody regularly decamped from the boat to the desert, leaving us to 'get on with it'. It worked well.

To begin with, Paula participated in the coral reef research programme and travelled with me to Suakin, where I was director of the new marine laboratory, or to Khartoum, where I fulfilled duties of my new posting as a university lecturer. As it became hotter, we all slowed down and Paula found herself spending as long as possible underwater, hanging off the lighthouse reef at around 6 metres deep, enjoying the refreshing cool waters, or diving with us off the Cambridge Reef Platform.

Our first baby, Catriona, was born a year after our marriage, in Khartoum on 11 January 1975. I was present at the birth with twelve towelling nappies at the ready. Catriona's christening at the Catholic church in Port Sudan was attended by Catholics, Protestants, Muslims, Hindus, atheists, and agnostics. We had wanted the godfather to be our good friend Captain Abdul Halim, but his Muslim faith made this impossible for both Catholic and Muslim authorities to accept.

Jack Randall, Fish Man (1924–2020)

There was no Internet in 1973. I had never seen a mobile phone, and even landline telephones hardly existed in Port Sudan. When I did want to make a call, I would queue for use of a phone screwed to the outside wall of the post office, across the city garden from our HQ at Eastern Telegraph. The isolation from the western world had its advantages, but when it came to keeping up with scientific research on topics of global interest, it had its challenges. I depended on the library at Khartoum University and InterLibrary Loans to obtain papers on topics of interest. On top of that, there was a strong incentive to write letters and establish cooperative relationships with fellow scientists who may have already solved issues on which one was working, or may know who had done so. I made a carbon copy of each letter that I typed on an old Remington typewriter, and, over time, certain correspondence caused files to bulge, and plans to turn into 'feet on the ground' visits by the best in the field of coral reefs and tropical marine biology. At the pinnacle of this process came Dr J. E. Randall, known to everyone as Jack Randall or just Jack.

Randall's scientific credentials are very impressive, with 902 published papers, 48 on the Red Sea; he has named 799 new species and has written 13 regional fish guides. I did all I could to encourage him to advance our knowledge of the Sudanese Red Sea. Diving with him was an experience that few people could forget. He was tireless, fast, and nimble underwater – fearless when it came to sharks and ruthless in his fish collecting whenever there was so much as a sniff of new species involved. He was also a loner when it came to diving, giving his buddy the slip almost as soon as he entered the water.

His use of rotenone was highly controversial, but he did not see it that way. With coral reef fish adept at hiding deep within the reef crevices, fish poison was the only way to catch them, and Jack pursued his goals with the determination consistent with his record. Basically this involved mixing the poison with seawater in a plastic bag, then scattering it over a section of reef. Fish and invertebrates emerged from the reef in a comatose condition, enabling them to be netted and brought back to the surface for measurements, photographs, and other studies. It was unedifying and insensitive, but it worked.

The other main sampling that Jack engaged in was spearing specimens, and in this he showed grace and style together with technical expertise. A superb swimmer and free diver, Jack would often work without scuba. His aim was always to prong the fish as it turned, meaning that the spear entered and left on the same side, leaving a clean side for the photographs that he would take of the fish with fins all pinned, enabling full taxonomic descriptions to be prepared. Whatever one thought about these killing tactics on magnificent reefs, nobody could accuse Jack of not doing justice to his work. He never wasted time or effort to obtain the best possible results, and he was happy to share his knowledge through publication and generous correspondence.

Hans Hass (1919–2013)
Dr Hans Hass was my childhood hero. Aged seven to twelve, I was glued to our television as he and Lotte brought Red Sea coral reefs into our sitting room. *Under the Red Sea* was published in 1952, initially in German, and then by Jarrolds in English. It was Hass's first account of Red Sea adventures, and he followed up with a regular series of documentaries depicting his undersea exploits, initially on board an Arabian felucca, then a dhow, and later from his 50-metre schooner, *Xarifa*.

By the time I reached his old Red Sea stomping grounds, such as the *Umbria* wreck, Sanganeb reef, Shaab Rumi, and the romantic ghost city of Suakin, Hans had moved on to his anthropological studies, writing books and promoting coral reef conservation. But despite the passage of time, he held a special place in his heart for Sudan and the Sudanese. We exchanged a series of letters in which I told him what we were doing, and he encouraged me to promote the introduction of legal frameworks for saving vulnerable marine habitats and their endangered inhabitants.

In his book *Conquest of the Underwater World*, published by David & Charles in 1975, he wrote:

> Underwater hunters however turn up somewhere to indulge their passion for hunting and then disappear from the area, never to be seen again. . . . they are unconcerned about the effect their actions may have. Whale sharks, mantas, jewfish and other giants are killed just to 'make an impression'. This should be stopped at all costs because these very same creatures are slow to reproduce and may quickly be wiped out altogether.
>
> Some successes have already been chalked up. On the initiative of the English biologist Peter Vine, underwater hunting has been banned in the whole area of Seychelles and significantly restricted in the Sudan. There each boat, each group, is allowed only a single harpoon to catch fish for eating.

I was naturally proud to have played a role in Hans's mission against spearfishing and encouraged to think one could really make a difference. My stated mission was to ensure that my own children and grandchildren would experience the reefs as Hans and I had done. Hans was generous in his praise of my effort, and when he came to London to address a large meeting of the Underwater Federation, his wife, Lotte, established contact with me, through an announcement from the stage: 'Would Peter Vine come and talk to us,' she requested into the microphone as about a thousand delegates scratched their heads, wondering who she was referring to. Later that day we took Hans and Lotte to dinner at Borsht N Tears in Knightsbridge. We were all keen to discuss our experiences in the Red Sea and ways that we might help to protect it.

It is hard to believe how laissez-faire governments were over activities that were damaging coral reefs and other underwater habitats. In some instances there may be a case to be made for spearfishing to obtain food, but the growth of diving tourism should sound alarm bells in terms of overfishing of reef-associated species, and lack of sustainability. Indeed, the tendency of spearfishers to remove top predators and large herbivores leads to fundamental habitat changes that threaten healthy coral reefs. I was focused on bringing a halt to spearfishing in both Seychelles and Sudan but hardly realised that we were leading the way in conservation legislation, with laws passed in both countries following our efforts.

I Nearly Sank the British Navy

The loud *whoosh* as air stored at high pressure gushed out of the inflatable's hull came as a complete shock to everyone, not least myself, who was, by any measure of law, the guilty party. I believe I was also the first to predict its potential consequences. The stakes were higher than I cared to imagine. But my guilty feelings did not seem to communicate themselves through the protective layers of wetsuit, mask, and breathing hoses. It took just a few seconds above water to realise that my culpability was not apparent to observers and, most importantly, the boat's crew. The crew were now in rapid response mode, intent on saving both their inflatable and themselves. Had nobody noticed that the rapid deflation of their now sinking vessel coincided, in faultless synchrony, with my own emergence at the side of the dinghy? Based on a quick look around, I realised that this was indeed the case. My heart sank, however, when I learnt the identity of my unsuspecting and unintended victims. I had just mounted a one-man attack on the British Navy, and it wasn't over yet.

'Number one: emergency kit,' I heard the voice of authority belch out in a clearly identifiable Liverpool accent. I should explain at this point that the events unfolding had the potential to cause an international incident. These were not British waters but the heart of the Sudanese Red Sea. The British Navy had sent a warship on a peace mission to Port Sudan – something that not everyone had welcomed. Was this incident going to be interpreted as a hostile act by local forces?

I slipped back underwater and let go of my grip on the offending weapon. It was a short swim to my own boat, tethered to the same historic wreck that the navy divers had been visiting. As I climbed on board, a spray of air and water was still spurting out from just beneath the waterline: the naval dinghy's form had begun to collapse into something more like a deflated plastic turtle than a fast offshore launch. My mind raced through the irony of this bizarre situation. I had been diving on a ship full of bombs, shells, and other armaments that had been scuttled in 1940 when Italy had joined WWII. On that occasion the British had arrested the *Umbria*, only to be outsmarted by its Italian captain, who scuttled the ship, opening some water intake valves, flooding its holds, and placing its cargo of munitions beyond wartime use. Thirty-five years later, British sailors were once again under attack, but this time by their own side, scoring something akin to an own goal.

Only a few minutes earlier I had been swimming at about 35 metres' depth inside the bridge of the historic ship, making my way along the corridor leading to the first-class accommodation. It was a dive I had undertaken on numerous previous occasions, always with an eye for objects that could form part of a collection for display in a mooted *Umbria* museum that would be set up in Port Sudan. On this occasion my attention had been drawn to a window that was precariously balanced, about to fall from its rotting frame. A large grouper swam back and forth through the window opening.

Imagining how appropriate it might be to construct display cases from the sunken ship's own glass windows, I rescued the panel and pushed off from the ship's side. At around 5 metres' depth I looked up through the clear sparkling waters of Wingate Reef to the glittering surface, recognising – or so I thought – our dive-boat's hull, and stretched up my arm to grab the surrounding rope rail. Pulling myself clear of the surface, a corner of the window made contact with the rubberised float, triggering this calamitous *whoosh* – a near-fatal blow to someone else's boat. Who was going to believe the innocence of this act?

My offer of assistance politely declined, I held my breath as what was left of the beleaguered vessel limped back to the mainland, barely buoyant enough to keep the outboard afloat. By this stage, the crew had roped themselves together and had been allocated a series of tasks that appeared to form part of a well-practised emergency routine. Later that afternoon, our team was invited on board the naval destroyer for a cocktail reception. Nothing was mentioned of the near sinking, and I decided that silence was my best defence.

Umbria and Its Bell

I first read of the *Umbria* shipwreck in books by Jacques Cousteau and
Hans Hass, two of the early underwater explorers of the Red Sea. Hass
dived on her in 1950, just ten years after she had been sunk. He describes
the rich assemblage of marine life that the ship's clean metallic surfaces
had attracted – sponges, corals, many other invertebrates, and, of course,
large numbers of fish. I used to love swimming through the ship's cabins,
cautious to avoid stirring mud and losing my way.

My regular diving partner, when opportunities allowed, was Doug
Allan, who had been recruited by the Cambridge Coral Starfish Research
Group as a biological assistant. We both relished the chance to explore
the Sudanese Red Sea, whether by snorkelling or scuba. Doug was also
a keen wreck diver, always on the lookout for mementos of his time in
Sudan. I recall an evening in Port Sudan around the same time as our
botched attack on the British Navy. 'Has anyone lifted a bell off the
Umbria?' he asked, in a rhetorical tone. 'I bet it's still there.' My response
was that it would make an ideal focal attraction for the museum that I
hoped would one day be built. We did not continue the conversation,
and I forgot about the issue.

About two weeks later, Doug and our friend Steve Head came to
tell me their story. The bell was safely on its way to the UK. That was
when I learned that the ship's actual name was *Bahia Blanca* and not
Umbria. She had been renamed by the Italians, but she was still popularly
known as the *Umbria*. My own disapproval of the unauthorised salvage
was mixed with admiration for Doug and Steve's ingenious efforts, not
just in finding and raising the heavy bell but in whisking it away to the
relative safety of the UK. It had been a mammoth task with which they
had had no outside help, until the very end of the operation.

The easiest part of the plan was to find the bell. Doug identified
the mast leaning over where it is traditionally located, and swam along
it until he realised that the heavily encrusted bulge that stuck out from
the mast was the ship's bell. The task of raising it to the surface was
aided by tying oil drums inflated with air from their scuba tanks. Slowly
they towed the salvaged bell to a nearby anchored ship that was waiting
to clear customs in Port Sudan. A friendly British seaman then agreed

to take it on board and arrange for them to collect it in the UK. Once cleaned and polished, the unique bell took pride of place in Doug's home.

Deep Diving

One of the challenges in writing a memoir is to avoid the temptation to gloss over the bad bits. There are some things I have done that don't make me proud and that reflect very poorly on my judgement. Deep diving is one of these. This story involves my diving partner Doug Allan. In the early 1970s, when we were diving the Red Sea every day, the basic physiology of diving with compressed air was widely known to divers, who used decompression tables to calculate safe dive profiles involving maximum depths, durations, and stops that allowed time for decompression, to avoid the bends.

Also known as decompression sickness or caisson disease, the bends is the common name for a well-known consequence of diving too deep, staying too long, and resurfacing too quickly. The potentially crippling or fatal condition is caused by nitrogen in the blood reverting from a dissolved state to one that forms potentially lethal bubbles of nitrogen gas. It is routinely avoided by surfacing in a series of decompression stops, allowing the nitrogen in the blood to return gradually to normal levels and so avoiding the formation of bubbles. On the dive described here, we far exceeded safe limits and were fortunate not to suffer from the bends.

Diving the warm, clear waters of deep offshore reefs like Sanganeb's lighthouse reef had become second nature to Doug and me. Able to free-dive to just under 30 metres, our single 70-cubic-feet aluminium scuba tanks filled with compressed air took us much deeper. From the surface down to 20 metres brought us to a reef shelf that sloped to around 25 metres, before dropping more suddenly to around 40 metres and then opening out to a second shelf before plunging steeply into the depths. It was here that sharks – hammerheads, grey reef, oceanic whitetips, and others – spent much of the day, swimming in open water a few metres off the reef slope. And it was here that adrenalin began to kick in as we ventured where few other divers had been – 'diving', as Hass had put it, 'to adventure'. We were inextricably drawn to the mysteries of the deep.

If you ask Google today what constitutes safe diving with single scuba tanks, the answer will be something like 40 metres (130 feet). In response to the question 'How long would a single air tank last at 90 metres underwater?', CMAS 3-star instructor Adrian Corfield describes it as hypothetical, since he claims that the diver would be dead:

> He would have died from seizures that occur with oxygen toxicity at those depths. They happen suddenly without much warning and the effect is to drown. Additionally, even if he did not get a seizure, he would have been under so much nitrogen narcosis that he might just have passed out, or just went into a slumber – once again drowning. In diving, every single metre deeper is a big deal. Every 10 metres brings totally different issues.

Corfield is right when he says that '90m on a tank of air is simply a death wish or a bad mistake'. Doug and I made that mistake and lived to tell the tale – just.

It very nearly did not have such a happy ending, and we came within seconds of never seeing the surface again. The numbers have been etched in my brain ever since. At 87 metres, just short of Corfield's description, our bottom time was limited to seconds rather than minutes, and our exaggeratedly conscious heavy breathing was sucking air at almost nine times the rate of consumption at the surface. With no spare air, we needed to work fast. As soon as we hit the seabed, I placed some stones in my dive bag and checked how Doug was doing. Instead of helping to collect specimens for my research on tube worms, he was hanging in the water taking in his surroundings. We were already overdue for our ascent, and I signalled to him that we should make our way back up the slope. I breathed in and started the long climb. Almost immediately I felt Doug grab my arm and signal for a vertical ascent.

Of course. Why had I not thought of that? We did not have enough air to ascend at the reef slope's acute angle. Our only chance was to swim vertically, following our exhaled bubbles. Losing sight of both the seabed and the surface, suspended in what seemed like an enormous goldfish bowl, we ascended through the shark zone, hoping we would reach the first decompression stop with enough air left in our tanks to counter the lethal self-inflicted cocktail of oxygen toxicity, nitrogen narcosis, and the bends. 'If the right one doesn't get you then the left one will' was drumming through my mind as the metres ticked down on my depth gauge. It was a long way up. I remember passing the 60-metres level and realising we were still beyond safe diving range.

Up, up, up, through 45 metres to the more familiar 30-metres level, but we were too far out to see the reef. As we reached 15 metres, we swam towards a welcoming pool of sunlight and the reef wall came closer, welcoming us back to the kaleidoscopic shallows with their mesmerising fish, corals, and other marine life. We made our way to 12 metres on the reef edge and calmed our breathing to extract the maximum time from our bottles. With just a few atmospheres' worth of pressure left in the tanks, we eventually crept up to 9, 6, and 3 metres, sucking the tanks dry before breaking out our snorkels. What a dive! What a life! What a close escape!

Back in the laboratory, at CCSRG's base, I removed tube worms from the few rocks I had collected and preserved them in formalin. 'Sanganeb Reef, 87m' read the label. It was the deepest I had ever dived – or ever would. Not sharing my fears of being quickly overcome by the danger-ous depths, Doug went alone the next day, pushing his personal limits, to reach 92 metres. To this day I often reflect on just how close Doug came to that being his last dive, and what a tragedy it would have been not to have seen him becoming one of our greatest underwater cameramen, with film credits like *The Blue Planet*, *Planet Earth*, and *Ocean Giants* to his name. On a more personal level, Doug introduced us to diving with great white sharks off Mexico, swimming with humpback whales in Tonga, and sharing views of polar bears in the Arctic – all great memorable adventures.

It has become difficult to keep track of diver mortalities, due to their pushing the depth limits. According to an article published in the *Guardian* on 27 August 2017, Tarek Omar, a professional diver based in Sinai, has earned a reluctant reputation as a 'body recovery expert', pulling over twenty bodies out of the notorious Blue Hole at Dahab. One such fatality, which took place in early 2000, involved a Russian diver, Yuri Lipski, who filmed his dive and was last seen trying to inflate his buoyancy vest at around 115 metres. The problem in nearly all such cases is that the symptoms of narcosis affect the brain and one's ability to sense danger or to make responsible decisions, and at depths of 90 metres or more, there is no latitude for error.

Mantas

I was sitting by the decaying swimming pool at Port Sudan's Red Sea Club, a remnant of the colonial era. A collection of well-thumbed literature – old books and magazines – formed the club's library. I was hungry for something to divert my attention from the searing summer heat. *Under the Red Sea* by Hans Hass caught my attention. Translated from the original German by James Cleugh, this racy story had drawn the world's young travellers and explorers to the magical realm of the Red Sea's waters. Before long I was engrossed. Among his encounters with large animals, Hass waxed particularly lyrical on the topic of manta rays:

> We passed a place where numerous pointed wave crests flickered, like flames, over the surface of the sea. On closer observation I perceived that they were not waves, but small pointed fins. No less than forty mantas had assembled there, an enormous shoal of them.
>
> I jumped overboard and saw at a distance two big white bellies confronting each other. But it was already too late. It was far too dark now to photograph and take observations underwater . . .

The following day, Hass and his Sudanese boatmen picked up the trail:

> The whole sea seemed to be on the boil there. The screams of the flocks of birds warned us that we were very far from being welcome. Everywhere small fish were leaping from the surface and being seized and swallowed by the birds. And everywhere below the surface gigantic jaws were sweeping along, swallowing everything in their path.

Hass was quick to dive in and meet them face to face.

> At first I could only see innumerable fish rushing to and fro in excited shoals. They were being chased, not only by the mantas and the birds, but also by mackerel and long fish that had a silvery glitter. Then the wall of fish before me parted and a big manta made straight for me.

A tale of man meets monster followed, with man triumphing despite a vicious blow from an out-of-control manta – not behaviour we associate with these docile creatures in today's more familiar encounters. I was mesmerised and simply had to find this place where giant manta rays swam in such numbers. I hatched a plan.

Although Hass was careful not to name the precise location of the shoaling mantas, he left enough clues to give us a head start. His first encounter had been on his way back from Angarosh reef, a short way into a channel that offered protection from the steep waves they had been experiencing outside the fringing reef. On the second day, they had landed on a sandy islet or sand bank that offered an elevated view of the channel. This could only be Mesharifa island with its adjacent passage. I drew a manta on the chart at this point.

The only way to reach this remote area was by sea, either on a small boat from the tiny village of Mohammed Quol, or on the country's only fishery research vessel, based in Port Sudan. I asked the government fisheries office when they were scheduling their next visit to Donganab – a large protected bay where pearl oysters were cultivated, just beyond Mesharifa. 'Next week. Would you like to join us?' was their friendly response. There was just one piece of the jigsaw left to drop in place, and that was to persuade my diving buddy, Doug Allan, that this would be a fruitful excursion for his underwater camera. It didn't take much to convince him. From the dusty pages of Hass's book, an expedition had been born. We were on our way to rediscover the great underwater explorer's giant mantas.

After several days of preparation in Port Sudan, and some plankton-sampling on the passage north, we approached the entrance of Donganab and could see Mesharifa off our starboard bow. The crew were impatient to visit their families and friends at Mohammed Quol and Donganab, and were not keen to spend time exploring the area. Doug and I jumped into our towed inflatable and promised to liaise with them in two days' time, as they made their way back south. We were off. We were free. We were on our way to meet the mantas. Since it was mid-afternoon, there was still time to take a look at the channel, and we sped across the shallow reef, anxious to get there before the mantas dispersed. I would love to report that the sea was glittering with the wing tips of scores of mantas, but it was not. Instead we caught some fleeting glimpses of them and had to remind ourselves that nature is not predictable. The following day was much the same, with a few dispersed mantas off the outer reef face but not in the numbers that Hass had described.

That evening the Sudanese research vessel re-entered the Mesharifa channel, picked us up, and we watched the sun go down as we regaled our colleagues with tales of sea monsters, mermaids and mantas ... not all as fictional as they sounded. In his own account, Hass had focused on the intelligent eyes of the mantas that seemed to recognise him after a few passes. His mantas were also quite agitated:

> I threw myself aside only just in time as a pair that seemed to have gone absolutely mad tore past me.... Even the brief performance of which I was a witness had so furious a character that the two creatures simply ran down everything that got in their way.

Several years after my less dramatic encounter with Hass's mantas, I had my own adrenaline-pumping meeting whilst involved in filming underwater sequences for the BBC/Discovery three-part series *Arabia: Sand, Sea & Sky*. We had been filming for two weeks, at Sangabeb's lighthouse reef, using a sailing boat that we had brought over to this coast from the Saudi Arabian port of Jeddah. On our return voyage we decided to call in at Mesharifa Channel, where I promised the crew some exciting dives. We were not disappointed. Almost as soon as we entered the channel, we caught sight of squealing terns wheeling and diving over the manta rays' glittering pointed fin tips. Cameraman Peter Scoones wasted no time in getting in amongst them, and I followed at a respectful distance. What followed was extraordinary and, at that stage, had never been filmed before. Nowadays it is not unusual for divers to find themselves within the feeding chains that characterise manta behaviour, but for Hass and for ourselves, the experience was unique.

Imagine a long line of giant manta rays snaking its way through the shallows, so closely packed that each one's head almost touches the forward ray's tail. Thirty or forty mantas swimming in this way, creating an endless chain. I say 'endless' because once the leading ray reached the apparent edge of the plankton cloud on which they were all feeding, it would dive down and connect up with the back of the chain, creating a dynamic loop like a prayer-bead bracelet of gaping mouths every bit as dramatic and coordinated as Hass had described in *Under the Red Sea*. Peter Scoones gently inserted himself into this chain, managing for a while to form part of the feeding loop. I watched, mesmerised, as he filmed the action, trying to imagine the incredible shots that he must be getting.

Hass too had experienced such excitement. After shooting stills, in black and white and colour, he had switched to his movie camera.

> I had been swimming among the mantas for more than two hours and had photographed everything that could be photographed. No wonder I was pleased. The pictures would undoubtedly make a new expedition a certainty. I could see my longed-for research vessel, with swelling sails, bearing down in the offing.

And I could see our own film wowing international television audiences in the UK, USA, and beyond. Reluctantly, we moved into the shallows of Mesharifa reef and made ready for the night. Just before we sat down to dinner, we heard and felt an ominous crunch under the keel. We were grounding. Astounded by the gravity of the situation, there was a crush to escape the saloon and to understand what had happened. With no tide to rescue us, we were in grave danger of being holed and stuck on the reef – for ever. Clive, our skipper, started the engine and one of us called out directions to avoid numerous coral bommies as we crept back towards deeper water. By now, the sun had set and the wind had changed. We motored around to the south side of the island and anchored in Mesharifa channel.

Mermaids and Models

To Sudanese fishermen, dugongs, known as the 'bride of the sea' or *arous al bahar*, are lactating marine mammals endowed with a wide range of human characteristics, especially extreme shyness in the vicinity of their nemesis: humans. They were rarely caught, and dead specimens were the source of heightened interest among the local population. We had the chance to experience this when we accidentally drowned a dugong in a fishing net that we had borrowed from some Yemeni fishermen. The fishermen had been stranded in Port Sudan, living on charity and borrowed money, unable to leave harbour until their debts were cleared. Renting the net to us was a chance for them to solve their problem. I brokered the deal between the fishermen and *Vogue Paris* fashion magazine, which had sent a number of models to create a fashion feature. I was already alarmed by the team's antics when they were reported to have used paint spray guns to brighten up the seabed where the young models were posing. The net was to provide a few sharks for another scene. Killing the dugong was a bonus for them and an utter disaster for me. I made sure to hike the price on any shots of the dugong, so at least the Yemeni fishermen would be able to return to their families. But it was the aftermath of this event that really struck a chord, after the photographer had departed and the fishermen had been paid.

The following morning, I decided to escape the bustle of Port Sudan and take Paula up to Mersa Halot, where much of the recent drama had been played out. It was a quiet, unspoilt inlet and had been particularly peaceful on my previous visit, just before *Vogue* arrived. We parked our Toyoto Land Cruiser at the water's edge, not far from where we had set the net. A reef heron patiently stalked fish in the shallows, and we had disturbed a young gazelle as we approached the inlet or *mersa*. Apart from the tracks of yesterday's entourage converging at the water's edge, there were no other signs of humankind. The sun had risen over an inky blue sea and was just high enough to illuminate the shallow patches of coral, sand, and eel grasses inside the *mersa*. The only sound was from a gentle swell as it broke from time to time on the reef crest.

We were enjoying the sun, peace, and tranquillity of this heavenly desert shoreline when a single loud wailing cry came from quite close by us, just out in the lagoon, about 30 metres away. I jumped up, but all I saw was a small ripple at the surface as if something had just dived underwater. For a moment I could not believe what had happened, but Paula too had been startled by the same chilling wail. There was only one animal that could have made such a sound, and that was a dugong. They were known to let out such plaintive cries when separated from their mates. The creature we had accidentally killed in the net was a female, and here was her bereaved partner. We packed our picnic and returned to the city, finding it hard to discuss what we had experienced.

I had some other personal encounters with live dugongs, in Micronesia and in Sudanese and Saudi Red Sea waters. These are recalled in my book *Red Sea Explorers* (pp. 80–88). In another of my titles on Bahrain, *Pearls in Arabian Waters*, I recount some of the most impressive dugong aggregations: 674 animals off Bahrain and UAE in early 1986, recorded by Saudi Arabia's Meteorological and Environmental Protection Administration. Meanwhile, William Travis's book *Voice of the Turtle* describes massive herds off Somalia that the author was able to usher away from a potentially lethal fishing threat:

> I found huge herds, sometimes as many as 500 strong, swimming freely within and without the reef. They were neither elusive nor shy, being great dumb sea oxen that only responded when you whacked their backs with a paddle, blew conch shell horns or clapped the water with oar blades. During the afternoons the young calves of up to 4 ft long would leave the herd and form a nursery close to the sandy beaches. Here they would play like slow, clumsy puppies. Wading among them, they would dive between my legs, brush against my side and generally use me as a pivot point and scratching post.

Whether such large groups of dugongs will ever be seen again is not certain. According to the International Union for Conservation of Nature, they, like many of their cousins among marine mammals, are vulnerable to extinction. But all is not lost. Whilst researching material for a review chapter on dugongs in an academic publication on the Red Sea,[7] I came across the recent research on Egypt's Red Sea dugongs and the work of a young Egyptian diving biologist, Ahmed Shawky. I was excited to learn how dugongs in the northern Red Sea have become acclimated to swimming with human divers, providing the basis for a unique tourism business and one that depends on the well-being of the dugongs for its very existence. The stark equation does not need spelling out to the fishermen who carry divers to see dugongs, or to the business people who have invested in coastal hotels and diving resorts. Healthy dugongs equals a healthy bank balance. Disappearing dugongs equals a bank overdraft.

Shawky had spent several years surveying the region's elusive dugongs and recording their behaviour. Often this was done without seeing the animals themselves but through measurement and study of the sandy tracks they create as they criss-cross the seagrass beds, ripping up the seagrasses on which they feed almost exclusively. The width of the tracks proved to be proportional to the size of the dugong, and small tracks alongside wider ones signified juveniles still in the care of their mothers. Shawky had also galvanised the support and interest of leisure divers who lacked scientific training but were well capable of finding and watching dugongs underwater. His results were impressive, showing what can be achieved with sustained efforts in the field, and raising hopes for a managed recovery of Red Sea dugongs living in protected marine parks, both in Egypt and other countries bordering the Red Sea. I was pleased to be associated with the timely review in such a prestigious publication. Hopefully it will help to persuade government officials that it is both feasible and justified to protect these shy and charismatic marine mammals.

Diving with Hagen

Hagen Schmid, entrepreneur, photographer, wildlife enthusiast, and a loyal companion, accompanied me on many diving adventures in the

Red Sea. He ran a dive shop near the old Jeddah airport and befriended me in 1975 when I went to live in Saudi Arabia. Amongst our escapades together, we cleansed the Saudi city's seawater intake pipe, part of its main desalination plant. He remembers our times together with much humour:

> Peter's book *Red Sea Safety* contained all kind of practical tips and applications on how to survive in the potentially dangerous waters of the Red Sea, but when our first medical issue arose, much to his embarrassment, the remedy could not be found. It happened during a sail up the Sudanese coast when we anchored for the night in the shelter of a small patch reef. At around midnight the wind direction changed and our boat drifted aground, with the keel sticking fast on a coral head infested by hundreds of black *Diadema* sea-urchins. Aware of the imminent danger and need for action – there being no daily tide at this location – Pete stripped naked and jumped overboard, wedging himself between yacht and coral knoll. Ignoring the sharp poisonous urchin spines, he managed to heave us off the reef and the captain manoeuvred the yacht into safer waters.
>
> Once Pete was back on board we noticed that his leg and foot, speared by hundreds of broken-off sea urchin spines, were rapidly swelling. In an urgent search on how to relieve the good doctor's agony, we turned to *Red Sea Safety* but, whilst he described the effects of sea urchin injuries, there was no cure mentioned. Our fallback position in such circumstances was to use heat (over 50°C) to denature the protein of the venom. A burning candle was employed to deliver hot wax onto his injuries – a rather painful treatment, but we insisted he should offer himself as a trial before his book was reprinted. In the event, the heat treatment was highly effective, 'like turning off a lightbulb,' Pete told us. We forgave him his omission since his quick reaction to jump, without hesitation, into shark-infested waters of the Red Sea, saved our yacht and its crew.

Hagen also remembered the fun we had in Saudi Arabia:

> In 1989 I spent many weeks with Pete when we did the *Arabia: Sand, Sea & Sky* film project. It seemed that he always wanted to be in close contact with his home base. In those days we lacked mobile phones and the only possibility to make a phone call from that location was at the hotel in Gizan, where a single phoneline was available. This was very much in demand by hotel guests and other visitors. At the best of times, attempting to call Clifden 250 (Paula's home number) via its manual exchange depended on gaining the attention of the exchange's operator, Marty. Back in Saudi Arabia, under the impatient scrutiny of other hopeful users, Pete patiently waited for the call to be shunted, via the Cairo exchange, through Dublin's international operator, to Marty and, finally, Paula, whose voice brought a broad smile on his suntanned face.
>
> With voice communication miraculously in place, Pete jumped into action: 'How's the weather?' he inquired with a real sense of urgency that seemed to convince a growing audience that something important was taking place. Throughout the extensive and inconsequential conversation that followed, locals, dressed in their immaculate white thobes, paced the lobby, eagerly waiting for Pete to finish. He was delightfully oblivious of the disturbance his call created – lost in his pleasure at reaching his family in Ireland.

Thanks, Hagen. Happy memories.

Red Sea Arrest – Saga of the Missing Anchor

This story begins in 1989 with meeting the famous underwater filming couple Ron and Valerie Taylor at a scuba symposium in Limerick, where they were delivering one of their dramatic shark presentations. During the interval, I introduced myself as a Red Sea–based scientist, and we immediately jelled. They had recently completed filming *Treasures of the*

Gulf with Australian-born artist Michael McKinnon and were in discussions with him about a similar film series based in the Red Sea. Ron and Valerie had not done much exploration in the Sudanese section of the Red Sea, and they suggested that Michael should bring me on board. Michael rang me while I was in Ireland, and this was how I became involved in the three-part series *Arabia: Sand, Sea & Sky*. Thus began a rewarding association with some very fine underwater cameramen, such as Peter Scoones, and with Michael himself, who brought an artistic flair to all his work.

The Arabia series did well on television, being shown by BBC in the UK and by Discovery Channel in America, and in many countries around the world. I ghost-authored the book *Arabia: Sand, Sea & Sky* on behalf of Michael, and our association strengthened during the making of *Tides of War*, the story of oil slicks and fires connected with Iraq's invasion of Kuwait. A book based on the film was co-authored by myself and Michael and won a gold medal at the Frankfurt Book Fair.

When IMAX films changed the whole visual experience of big-screen movies, Michael seized the opportunity to revisit the Red Sea with an IMAX team. In discussions around the project, we both agreed it was a huge logistical challenge and we needed stunning sequences to justify the expense. I asked him to consider including some sequences from the rich marine life of the southern Red Sea, and shortly thereafter I found myself on board the 30-metre-long motor vessel *Lady Jenny V*, owned by Tony Turner, accompanied by Michael, Peter Scoones, Peter Rowlands, and several diving tourists, in Djibouti, next to Somalia, close to the Bab al Mandeb straits.

In his recently published book *The Summer Isles*, Philip Marsden writes that I 'once spent ten days in a Sudanese jail'. In the interest of accuracy, here is the full story.

Lady Jenny V, which we boarded in Djibouti harbour in April 1995, was skippered by Alex Double, supported by his wife, Tamara, and their friendly parrot. He operated the boat with around ten crew members, all tanned, fit, and apparently well trained. Our mission was not to film, but to assess the reefs of the southern Red Sea for future filming by an IMAX team. One of the crew was late to arrive, so, rather than sit in Djibouti harbour for two days, we took off on a bit of unplanned exploration. Just outside the Red Sea, marking the southern border of Djibouti, there is a long narrow fjord-like inlet where strong tides can occur. Alex and Tamara guided us on a thrilling drift dive that finished up with divers scattered over a wide area of the bay. It felt good to get wet again, not to mention diving in what might be described as a war zone in terms of personal security. Heading back towards the port to pick up our late-coming guest diver, Alex spoke over the VHF and arranged for a Zodiac to meet us offshore so we would not waste time clearing customs and so on with the harbour authorities. With the transfer completed, we were on our way, heading up the African coastline of the Red Sea, with Yemen on our right and Ethiopia on our left.

Alex and Tamara had explored this area before. Indeed, there was one reef they were particularly keen to revisit, which they referred to as 'Giant Spanish Dancer reef'. Spanish Dancers are nudibranchs, molluscs without shells. The name means 'naked gills', and they are uncoiled gastropods, famous for their brilliant colours and graceful swimming movements. We were keen to be introduced to Tamara's giants.

The reef lay to the south-west of the Hanish Islands and was in an area where local fishermen sometimes augmented their earnings with a bit of piracy. Arriving at the reef location, Alex checked his references before declaring that we could drop anchor. There was a strong current flowing, and it became clear that it would be a challenging dive, hanging on to the anchor chain until we reached about 25 metres, and hoping to catch a glimpse of the impressive animals, which we thought might be a new species of a Spanish Dancer. I followed Tamara down the mooring line and was surprised to find one of these beautiful nudibranchs performing in front of Tamara's mask, almost on cue. For once, the camera and flash were working, and I took a few photographs.

Shortly after the dive, as we were cleaning off our gear and warming up, a Yemeni fishing boat approached us. Both Alex and I had come to know these hard-working sailors, who had never posed a threat. But this encounter had an edge to it, with our own crew adopting a defensive, almost military formation around the boat. Alex defused the tension with some cigarettes, and they eventually left us. 'They'll be back,' Alex said. 'Time to pack up and leave.' The sun was setting, and darkness was approaching – our electric windlass hauled our anchor and we headed north again, hoping for more rewarding encounters on Sudanese reefs.

Our next stopover was at the Sudanese offshore island of Dahrat Abid, a small sand cay surrounded by richly productive reefs. There was no safe anchorage, however, so our visit was quite brief. Fascinated by how Greek and Roman sailors had used such offshore islands as staging posts for their numerous trading missions up and down the Red Sea, I took the chance to look at the centre of the island rather than my usual mode of exploring surrounding waters. Not only was this a strategically placed islet but it also had fresh water, evidenced by the ground cover of xerophytic vegetation that took over the centre of the island. I also noticed a low sandy mound close to its centre, and it was here that I headed to do some archaeological hand scraping aimed at revealing what lay beneath the surface. I did not need to dig deep, nor for long, before revealing copious quantities of broken pottery. Indeed, I got quite a shock, realising that this must be an archaeological site that should be professionally studied and protected. I quickly covered over the cache of what looked like ancient black pottery and took a small sample so that I could have it identified. I returned to *Lady Jenny* as excited as if I had discovered a new species. Wrapping the two shards in an old T-shirt, I put them into my dive bag.

We were anxious to get back to our favourite reefs of Sanganeb and Shaab Rumi and so headed north to a much busier diving area than we had been experiencing to the south. Indeed, the reefs lay close to Port Sudan, which had been my home for five years, and where Alex and Tamara had been dive guides for several seasons. We had all earned reputations for establishing sustainable diving practices and had been active supporters of Sudan's nascent dive tourism business. I had been responsible for establishing the Port Sudan Coral Conservation Committee, whose members included the harbour master, head of police, admiral of the navy, heads of industry, and local scientists, whilst Alex had turned principles into action by setting fixed moorings at key dive locations, thus avoiding damage to corals from repeated anchoring at prime dive sites – a practice that had already turned several sites in Egypt into essentially dead reefs.

Thus, on arriving at Sanganeb late that afternoon, I was not surprised to see Alex dive in with a thin line that he tied to the end of his old mooring lying on the seabed, abandoned about five years ago on his departure from Sudan. Once we were hooked up to his old warp, we were safe for the night and could sleep peacefully, anticipating our reunion with some old fishermen friends that we were sure would be there to greet us after breakfast. But the morning brought angry German divers, on a local dive boat, protesting our assumed anchoring on what was Sudan's prime dive site. To say they were incensed would be an understatement, and the next thing we knew the VHF radio sparked into life with complaints that we could hear them make to the harbour authority, and threats made by some familiar voices who had no idea that their old friends Pete and Alex were on board an innocent *Lady Jenny V.*

But as Queen Gertrude declares in *Hamlet*, 'the lady doth protest too much, methinks' – our innocence was far from clear. The correct procedure would have been for us to enter Port Sudan and to 'clear in' before doing any diving in Sudanese waters. I was unaware that our dive boat had form when it came to ignoring maritime protocol. Apparently, Alex had no intention of losing valuable diving days whilst tied up in the port – a decision, I soon learned, that was influenced by the fact that eight of our crew were Israelis, five of whom also held Argentinian passports, leaving three no choice but to declare themselves as Israelis. What had started as a bit of cheeky rule-bending was turning into something with much graver potential consequences. We had been diving without permission in Sudan for several days, were not flying a Sudanese courtesy flag, and had not cleared customs; our crew had not had their passports checked, not to mention that most of them belonged to what was regarded as a hostile nation. We were in fact in flagrant disregard of standard maritime procedures and Sudanese laws, and would be at the mercy of the Sudanese authorities if arrested.

I dared not imagine what might happen to the female Israeli crew members who, like their male colleagues, I now learned had recently completed national service in the Israeli Defence Forces (IDF). The situation was complicated by the special relationship at that time between the Sudanese government and Hamas, many of whose members were in Israeli prisons. A conference was held on the bridge, with the VHF radio conversation between dive boats and the shore in the background continuing to remind us that all was far from well. 'We'll go ahead with our dive,' Alex announced, 'but be back on board by ten a.m.' Unsure of his plans, we enjoyed our dive, sliding down the old mooring towards the reef terrace at 45 metres or so, and watching a scalloped hammerhead school break up as the sun rose overhead. Once we were all back on board, Alex dropped the mooring back to the sea bed and turned *Lady Jenny*'s bows to the north. We would give them the slip before they had a chance to arrest us, seemed to be the plan, and we settled down to some serious sunbathing as our old vessel kept up a steady 8 knots or so towards the northern reefs.

Our second dive of the day was to be at a wreck site close to Shaab Suedi. Launched in 1950, the *Blue Bell* was a Saudi Arabian mixed-cargo freighter, used to transiting the Red Sea between Jeddah and Port Sudan. On 2 December 1977, when she hit the Sudanese reef 75 kilometres north of Port Sudan, she was carrying Toyota cars and spare parts – hence her popular name, the 'Toyota Wreck'.

Once we arrived at the wreck site we prepared to dive, but just before we jumped in, a gunboat's sinister profile appeared above the horizon. The Sudanese navy had chased us almost 100 kilometres, determined to arrest us. *Lady Jenny*'s laissez-faire legacy was about to catch up with us. As the gunboat approached, we were frightened by the sight of soldiers with their guns trained on us. The ship's commander ordered us to follow him all the way back to Port Sudan. Events had taken a turn for the worse, and decisions needed to be made: this was an unfortunate snarl-up that was going to require diplomacy to solve. It would have been easy, in hindsight, to do things differently and to have avoided the risks that we now faced. Alex, after all, was apparently only adopting habits reputed to have been followed by previous skippers – to minimise bureaucracy whenever possible, and to avoid rigid check-in rules if it was thought that diving activities could be classified as recreation by crew and passengers during transit passages, rather than as diving tourism, which unquestionably required government permission.

On our return passage to Port Sudan, under armed escort, there was a brief discussion about declaring only the five Israelis who had Argentinian passports. It did not take long to decide that this could have serious consequences, and it was decided to play it straight. We arrived in Port Sudan around 10 p.m. and tied up in the naval wharf alongside the harbour master's office. Soldiers came on board to guard us, blocking our exit via the wheelhouse, disconnecting our communications equipment, and restricting our movements to below decks. We were treated politely but sternly and were left in no doubt that we would face the full power of the law. In the meantime, most of us took to our beds and slept as best we could. It had been a long day.

A multitude of dark thoughts flooded my mind that night. Would the boat's crew deny diving or stopping in Sudan waters until Sanganeb? Would we claim that we had intended to come into Port Sudan for clearance? How could we explain having eight ex-military Israeli crew members on board? Would Hamas get involved in our fate, using us as bargaining chips? How would the Israeli military respond to detention of their citizens? Would they try to intervene? What would be the response of my Sudanese friends? And, most important of all, how would we communicate our plight to our families without causing them to panic?

The following morning, after a very disturbed, fitful sleep without the comfort of air conditioning – it had broken down again – I even contemplated destroying the two small pottery shards that I had picked up as samples on Dahrat Abid. Confused and wracked with guilt, I feared that the pottery would compromise our alibi of not having stopped in Sudanese waters. As it turned out, there never was a search of our cabins, and we were not forced into using a concocted alibi. It seemed, however, that the Port Sudan authorities were waiting on instructions from senior officials based in Khartoum.

Much to my surprise, we had satellite communications via a kit that Michael had brought with him. Michael had already called his wife, Fawzia, explaining our plight and asking her to request influential friends to pressurise the Sudanese to release us. Once the word had reached Fawzia, wheels began to turn in Europe, Arabia, and Israel. The Saudi foreign minister was apparently informed, as was the British ambassador and the UN representative in Khartoum. We were detained on *Lady Jenny*, but, thanks to the satellite phone, whenever we had news of negotiations for our release, this was quickly spread among us by 'bush telegraph'.

It is worth explaining how the Israeli government became closely involved. Their own intelligence network ensured early knowledge of the situation, but they had made no direct contact with us. However, following Fawzia McKinnon's call to Paula in Ireland, Paula had in turn spoken to her friend Kathleen, whose husband, John, was manager of the plushest hotel in Dublin, the Berkeley Court. Rooms on the top floor of the hotel were occupied by the Israeli ambassador to Ireland, Zvi Gabay. John and Zvi were close friends, so when John came looking for help, Zvi was inclined to do what he could. He called the Israeli Defence Forces' head of security in Tel Aviv to tell them what was unfolding in the Red Sea's Port Sudan, involving a mixed batch of expatriates including eight of his fellow countrymen. 'How do you know all this? We're working on a rescue plan,' the IDF commander told Zvi. There is no record of how Zvi explained the situation, but word came back to John, Kathleen, Paula, Fawzia, and finally Michael that we should sit tight and await developments.

At this point our imaginations ran wild with talk that 'rescue' might mean a limited military operation of the sort enacted in 1976 in Entebbe. This involved specialist trained commandos taking control of an area, evacuating their colleagues, and extracting themselves with as few casualties as possible. Alex recalled some details of the Entebbe raid, and his story did nothing to calm us. On that occasion Israeli transport planes carried 100 commandos over 4,000 kilometres to Uganda for the rescue operation, which took a week of planning and lasted 90 frenetic minutes. Of the 106 remaining hostages, 102 were rescued and three were killed in the operation and one died later in hospital. Suffice it to say we did not like what we were hearing or imagining. It became our top priority to dissuade the Israelis from any possible military action.

In the meantime, word had spread in Port Sudan that Alex, others, and I were being held for ignoring conservation rules – rules that I had helped to draw up. There was the feeling of faceless people in the capital calling the highly politicised shots. 'I don't know who these people are,' one of my friends told me. One by one, members of our crew were being taken ashore for questioning and then returned to our boat. Female members felt particularly vulnerable, and I did my best to reassure them of the high moral standards of my Sudanese friends. It was a bizarre situation, made all the stranger by the friendship established between us as we faced an uncertain future. Cooking became one of the distractions to take our minds off the situation, and I became a cookery class pupil with two eager instructors.

Our spirits rose or fell with each new rumour. Calls to prayer, drifting across the harbour, punctuated the interminable hours of hot, humid, soporific air. Sunsets brought some relief, since the interviews would end and there was a welcome release from the cauldron that was slowly cooking us alive. Eventually, after a week or so of incarceration and garbled communications, we learnt of a planned visit from Khartoum by the UN representative, which coincided with an internal deadline of 4 p.m. on the next day for the Israelis to cancel their plans to 'come and get us'. If the Israelis did not receive news of our release by that time, we should expect an unannounced visit from the IDF.

Alex and I attended the meeting in the harbour master's office at 2 p.m. the following afternoon. Traditional hospitality was clearly on the agenda, with coffee and tea on offer together with plentiful succulent dates. The UN representative had just endured a two-hour flight from Khartoum and was doing his best to catch up with the situation. 'I understand there are eight Israelis on board,' he said, straight after sitting down.

'Three,' I said.

'No, it says here' – he pointed to a brown foolscap folder – 'eight.'

'Three,' I repeated, as I kicked him under the table. 'Shall we move on?' I proposed to the harbour master.

Alex then explained that we had not dropped our anchor on the delicate reef off the south-west point of Sanganeb, as we were accused of having done. Instead, we had picked up his own mooring from the sea bed.

'And what about your flag?' the chief of police asked.

'We are not flying one,' Alex said.

'That's my point,' the officer said. 'You should have come into port to clear customs. For all we know, you're a shipload of spies.'

'I think we can find a diplomatic solution,' our new friend from the UN said. 'What is the penalty for not flying your flag?'

And so the meeting progressed until, at ten minutes before our 4 p.m. deadline, it was agreed that we would pay a $100 fine and leave Sudan with no further diving or landings. But we were not out of the woods yet. Somewhere beyond the horizon, possibly closer than we feared, was the guts of an Israeli rescue mission – on what scale we dared not contemplate. Michael had said to me that any such mission might focus on the Israelis, and the rest of us would be at great risk of becoming collateral damage. 'They'll suddenly appear in the harbour and warn everyone to keep down,' he said. 'It will be over in minutes.' I realised he wasn't joking.

Time was not on our side. The deal was that we would let our contact know by 4 p.m. or else they would press Go for a new operation – perhaps Operation Deep Blue or Mission Hammerhead, after Sanganeb's famous sharks. Whatever its name, I needed to get back to our satellite phone and give the all-clear message. I also needed to reassure the crew that we were safe. Their anxiety levels had been heightened by the questioning and by the realisation that their answers did not all tally with each other.

'We are most grateful for your understanding,' I began. 'It has been a trying week for all of us, but you have been most courteous in your handling of the situation, and we do apologise for not flying the Sudanese flag. I, for one, am happy that the mistake brought about an opportunity to renew my friendship with the remarkable people of Port Sudan. We only discovered the boat was not carrying this flag as we went to raise it, on entering Sudanese waters. It was a genuine oversight. Now that it's all sorted out, I'm sure the crew would appreciate hearing the good news. May I excuse myself and go to tell them?'

As I completed the last sentence, I rose to my feet, not waiting for (or else doubting) their response, and excused myself. I marched out, past armed guards, to the nearby *Lady Jenny*. Back on board, I headed straight down the companionway to the cabin where the phone was stored. It took a few moments to warm up, and we felt the clock ticking. How ironic it would be if, after such successful diplomacy, a technical issue would fail to prevent the carnage that I was convinced would result from an Israeli raid. Something was wrong, however. The satellite phone had worked perfectly up until this point, but now it was failing to connect with a satellite. Five minutes to go and no one hearing us. We abandoned the phone and dashed back into the cockpit, where an armed soldier was quizzically observing our agitated behaviour. We studiously ignored him as Alex plugged back in the power lead of the long-range shortwave radio.

'All stations, all stations, all stations. This is *Lady Jenny V* requesting a patched telephone call for urgent communication. All stations, all stations, all stations. Come in, please. Over.'

The radio crackled and hummed whilst Alex tweaked the knobs, taking me back to the Mayday call I had heard on *My Fair Lady* in the North Sea. Crackle, hum, crackle, hum, nothing, crackle, hum. Two minutes to four, tension running high and tempers fraying. 'Come on, Alex, there must be somebody listening.'

'All stations, all stations . . .'

And then suddenly, across the ether: '*Lady Jenny V, Lady Jenny V, Lady Jenny V.* This is Monaco Radio, please repeat your message.'

I have since learned that Monaco Radio operates an HF SSB radio station with long-range transmission, depending on ionospheric conditions. Its call sign is 3AC. Nevertheless, its operator on that Saturday afternoon was quite impressed by the call distance. 'Where are you calling from?' he asked Alex.

'Port Sudan. It is very urgent. Please help us.'

'What number do you wish to call?'

Alex gave him Fawzia's London telephone number.

'Connecting you now, sir.'

It was nearly five minutes past four. Would they give us some leeway? We held our breath.

Fawzia came on the line, and Michael took the microphone from Alex.

'All clear,' he said. 'Pass it on immediately—' and then the line went dead . . . crackle, hum, crackle, hum. And we waited, unsure of our future.

Later that evening, as we steamed slowly northwards, hugging the coast, a call on the satellite phone conveyed the excitement of friends and relatives at our release. 'They were ready to do it' was the codified message, 'but they turned back.' Good news indeed, and cause for even more celebration. These celebrations had begun as we slipped our lines, with friendly waves from all on board to the harbour master as he stood on the quay and we all clung to the rail of the upper deck, gazing, slightly dazed, as the harbour receded over the stern, unimpeded by armed soldiers. Hannah, one of the Israeli crew, held my hand and thanked me for keeping them safe. We both wiped tears from our eyes, and I told her that, at the end of the day, we were all just simple human beings trying to do what was right.

We admired the deep glows of sunset, lost in our thoughts. We steamed right through the night, making about 7 knots and getting closer and closer to our destination of Eilat, but we were still in Sudanese waters when day broke on Sunday morning. With it came news, over our phone, that our story was being carried by all the main Sunday newspapers in Israel. One headline alarmed us: 'Eight Israeli Hostages Released by Sudan' was the gist of it. I began to panic again. We had always claimed three Israelis and the others as Argentinians. Would the Sudanese regret they had been so lenient towards us? Thirty kilometres to go. Three more hours of tension. More deep breathing. But we eventually made it safely out of Sudan and headed for the marine capital of Israel.

We were met there by a large gathering of press reporters and photographers, but we kept our heads down, fearing that the story would be misrepresented and that Alex would suffer consequences. At the back of the media circus stood two Israeli scientists who came to meet me and show me their work on corals. This turned out to be very impressive: they characterised a wide range of conditions, temperature, salinity, turbidity, current, shade, and so on, favouring growth of different species. It was pioneering research in support of the coral reef regeneration that we all felt would become important in the future. I was happy to be engaging again with science rather than survival.

12 Nightlife

I began writing this particular recollection from the 1970s with the intention of explaining how an underwater film that I helped to make in the west of Ireland over forty years ago, featuring Salt Lake, Killary fjord, Achill, and Inishbofin islands, earned top recognition in Hollywood. My own experience, together with Internet research, revealed a tale of love and art that surprised me. It began in late summer 1973 with the appearance of two travel-weary, tetchy expatriates – one laconic American and the other quintessentially British – into the backyard of the Eastern Telegraph Building in Port Sudan, where our expedition to study the crown-of-thorns starfish and other aspects of the Red Sea's mesmerising coral reefs was in full swing.

'Did you get our telegram?' the Brit asked me.

'Who are you? And no, I didn't get any telegram.'

I soon learnt that the Brit – who seemed somewhat uncomfortable with finding himself in fly-infested Port Sudan and was paranoid about having an anaphylactic reaction to insect bites – was helping to organise a filming trip for the American, whose name was Robin Lehman. This enigmatic young man's main claim to fame, we were informed, was that he made avant-garde documentaries that fitted into the motion picture film industry's definition of action documentary shorts: none of them exceeding 15 minutes. Robin explained that they were depending on using our expedition's compressor, diving bottles, and boat to make a new film about sea life. Hadn't he telegrammed us accordingly? It was the first that I had heard about it.

Over the next few weeks, after Robin's colleague had returned to London, I gradually got to know and like our unexpected guest. He had a wiry physique and a sensitive, sometimes anxious demeanour together with a work ethic that demanded the focused support of all present. His main aim in life at that time seemed to be to make better films than anyone else. This involved much more than just diving, since much of his equipment had to be custom-designed and specially built. He had developed his own housing for a large-format 35 mm Arriflex cine camera – the sort of beast that was used to make cinema films. Once attached to all the wires for underwater lights, it was like pushing a weightless Mini car around underwater. It was so heavy and cumbersome out of the sea that it was at least a two-person job to handle on deck.

Once the camera was loaded and the housing sealed and bolted, only five minutes of film could be exposed before we had to return to the surface, haul the camera on deck, and change the reel. It was hard work – doubly so if Robin failed to shoot any good footage. My own role was to change reels and to create the underwater scenes for Robin to shoot: finding ways to direct our subjects to perform, on demand, in front of Robin's lens, be they fish, crabs, lobsters, scallops, or whatever exotic creatures we encountered.

Robin's previous marine film *Sea Creatures* was creatively edited by Robin in partnership with French editor Jacques Lecompte – a most imaginative team for whom nothing was quite as it first seemed. Thus, for example, a pair of crabs that we encouraged to fight by placing them close to each other became professional wrestlers in the editors' eyes. All they needed was a cheering soundtrack with a few gruesome cries of 'Off with his arms' or 'Tear his eyes out'. Less controversially, a burrowing mantid shrimp with its pulsing tail was shown to the accompaniment of the sound of a pneumatic drill cutting up a London pavement; and an exquisite Spanish Dancer (nudibranch mollusc) gave an elegant performance to music which conjured up images of a mesmerising tango by a lady in red.

The first film I helped Robin to make was titled *See*, and we 'trained' hermit crabs to write out its name on the sand. Or, to be more truthful, we collected hundreds of hermit crabs, squashed them into the sand in the form of the word *SEE*, held them in place with a piece of plywood, and then suddenly released the pressure, filming the crabs as they all dispersed. Reversing the film later created the impression that the hermit crabs were scurrying together to create the title.

The more time I spent with Robin, the more I dreamed of bringing him to my home diving grounds off the west coast of Ireland. All I needed was an enticing subject and the certainty that we would be able to film it. Robin was finally persuaded by the opportunity to dive with basking sharks on their spring migration up the west coast of Ireland. We would be most likely to encounter them at a focal corridor of their 1974 annual spring migration in Keem Bay, Achill Island, County Mayo. Armed with Robin's instructions to put together a professional film crew to undertake this venture, I headed back to Clifden in Connemara and set about calling up my friends. Andy, my brother, would be cook; Padraic, my university colleague, would provide the scientific support; Robert would lend underwater support; and our mutual friend Stan would be in charge of film set-ups on land. Our boat would be a local fishing boat hired for a month, and we rented a local cottage close to the famous Keem Bay.

Our confidence that we would meet these 'sunfish' (the second largest fish in the world) at this remote location was based on more than hearsay. Joe Sweeney, the local garage/shop/pub owner whose premises were strategically located at the bridge onto the island, had been engaged in shark fishing for many years, tapping into a buoyant post-war market for shark's oil. Joe had kindly shared with me his records for shark catches over the previous few decades. Peak months were April and May, when hundreds of these docile giants made their way into the bay on a northerly passage. As they encountered the shallows they adjusted their route, keeping about 50 yards offshore, following the curve of the bay towards its headland. It was along that last stretch of steeply sloping bay line, beneath an equally steep hillside, that Joe's men would set their nets and wait for the sharks to bump into them.

Our seasonal timing was right, but we were several years too late. I soon learned that Joe's decision to retire from the business had been based on a steep decline in numbers probably resulting from many years of big catches. On our trip, we waited and waited for sharks to swim by our boat and then skirt around the headland. We had not realised that a monofilament net had been set to catch salmon in just the location where we expected to see the sharks. After several days of watching and waiting there was a sudden commotion. A shark had swum into the salmon net and was struggling to free itself. It was during our coffee break, and by the time we had kitted up and dropped into the water, the shark had disappeared and Robin's patience had reached its limit.

We needed a plan B. Given the fact that we were burning money on a production that lacked the promised performers, I suggested that we should use our talents and equipment to tell a different story. At that time there had been little, if any, professional underwater filming off the west coast of Ireland. We would change that, bringing the wonders of the cold Atlantic to a wider public. 'I still need actors,' Robin told me.

'And you shall have them,' I replied.

We decamped from the exposed shores of Achill and headed for the protected waters of Killary – the only fjord in Ireland. Deep down below the kelp, this narrow glacial rift harbours some rich habitats brimming with life, including scallops, sea anemones, brittle stars, Dublin Bay prawns (*Nephrops*), and other species. On our first dive there I introduced Robin to our leading actor, a large starfish appropriately on the hunt for a tasty scallop. It was a case of 'Lights, camera, action', as the starfish was placed slightly up-current from the scallop. When the scallop sensed the presence of its ravenous predator, it took off as only scallops can do, clapping its valves together and bouncing up from the sea bed, out of reach of the starfish's probing tube feet. Robin's camera rolled on cue and act one, scene one was in the can. We were elated.

'What's next?' Robin asked, and I suggested a tussle between our leading actor, the starfish, and a tangled mass of brittle stars. The seafloor at 24 metres down was a seething mass of waving brittle star arms with occasional clean patches of sand where giant anemones were stationed. The anemones were keen on eating the brittle stars, which did their best to keep clear. Just as Robin began filming, a large jellyfish drifted past an anemone, which curled its tentacles around the pulsating bell. It was a bizarre underwater battleground, and Robin's finger squeezed the shutter until our five minutes were up. With this second sequence in the can, we gathered momentum.

We maintained this productivity for about a week before we turned to some macro filming of plankton in aquaria that we had set up in our new rented cottage in the heart of Tullycross village. We collected our performers during dives off the coast, and Stan set things up to receive the tiny animals. Contained between invisible glass panels within the aquaria, sea gooseberries and other delicate creatures performed for Robin in a manner that we found mesmerising, flashing their iridescent colours and spinning upwards as their long tentacles tested their surroundings. Robin had the Arriflex camera mounted on a large tripod, and his head was covered by a black cloth, giving the appearance of a robot ready for a moonwalk. Confined within this unworldly frame, he seemed to be at his most contented – quietly recording delicate planktonic creatures in shots that had never been seen before on television. We tiptoed around the room, adjusting lights, scooping other species into aquaria, praying that the footage would satisfy his demanding standards. It was almost 10 p.m. We had been working all day, between the diving, transporting our live catches, and creating the set-ups.

The sense of being in the middle of a space odyssey film set was unexpectedly broken by a knock on the door. Stan opened it to reveal Mr Curley from the shop next door. Our visitor, seemingly reluctant to enter beyond the open doorway, informed Robin – and the rest of us hovering around the lights, aquarium, tripod, camera, and buckets of seawater – that there was a phone call for him. 'You take it, Stan,' Robin said, without skipping a beat in his filming, and leaving Mr Curley with the strange vision of a black cloaked head hovering over a brilliantly illuminated fish tank. Stan ran out to take the call. Returning several minutes later, he told us, 'It's Claire. She wants to talk to you.'

'Ask her what she wants,' said Robin, still filming a sea gooseberry. Stan ran back to Mr Curley's shop and reappeared in record time.

'She says she loves you,' he told Robin, still cloaked in black.

'Tell her I love her too,' he instructed Stan, who once more ran out the door. To the best of my memory, that was the end of the call, and the sea gooseberries made it to the final cut. That was the last time I heard of Claire until I sat down to write this story.

Fortunately for all of us involved, our plan B filming turned out to be more successful than we could have hoped. The finished film was called *Nightlife*, primarily because we had used lights to illuminate virtually everything we shot, giving the impression that it was all at night, since the surrounds appeared dark in comparison to the well-lit subjects. More than two years after our exciting days with Robin in Ireland, while I was still working in Port Sudan, a telegram arrived congratulating me on the nomination of *Nightlife* for an Academy award. I was unable to attend the Los Angeles event the following January in 1977, but Robin was there – disappointed that we did not turn his double Oscars into a hat-trick. But we were all thrilled that it had even been nominated.

From time to time I would hear about Robin's work. The BBC put together *The World of Robin Lehman* as a series of short films, and I showed my film copy of *Nightlife* to local audiences in Ireland, who could not be convinced it had been filmed in local waters rather than in some exotic tropical location. Throughout the years, I have wondered what happened to Robin. Recently I turned to the Internet for an answer and was reminded that Robin and his producer, Claire Wilbur, had won an Oscar for *Don't* in 1975 and for *End of the Game* in 1976. I even discovered a short film clip of the pair making their acceptance speech at one of the ceremonies. In addition to its Oscar nomination, *Nightlife* also gained fame in Europe, where it was widely praised for its originality and quality of cinematography. It won the Jury Prize for Best Short Film at the Cannes Film Festival and was nominated for the Palme d'Or, also under the category of Best Short Film. The IMDb website records it all. My research on Robin's more recent life led me to an article by Francesca Genova, who interviewed him in 2012. It was here that I learned of his impressive creative work involving glass.

It became hard to let go of my quest to better understand the enigmatic character with whom we had created some extraordinary films in the Red Sea and the west coast of Ireland. In addition to the impressive background information on Robin, it was the first time that I had found any written references to the unique accomplishments of Claire, who had so poignantly declared her love for Robin. Who was she? Despite my credited role as camera assistant, I had no idea at the time that Robin was working with her as producer. To my great surprise I learnt that she had played a significant role in our filming ventures with Robin, and she had a successful career as actor on stage and screen. Claire had a deep interest in Robin's artistic filming, and it has been suggested that her earnings went to support his wildlife productions. Working alongside Robin, she co-produced *Nightlife* and *The End of the Game*. In her acceptance speech for *The End of the Game* Academy award, she said that since a producer's job is to create the best team, she figured she had proven her ability in picking the talented Robin. Robin then told the audience that Claire had shown him what was wrong with the film, something that he valued greatly. Claire was diagnosed with lung cancer in 2003 and died peacefully aged seventy in her apartment in Manhattan on 20 May 2004.

13   Brotherhood of the Sea

My good friend Padraic de Bhaldraithe, marine biologist, musician, historian, sailor, and fluent Irish speaker, was also instrumental in the making of *Nightlife*. Padraic accompanied me on many other adventures. He joined me in the Red Sea to assist with plankton research with the Cambridge Coral Starfish Research Group (CCSRG) and sailed with Paula and me on various yachts (*Silver Dipper*, *Harmony*, *Suaimhneas*, and *Saoirse*), always ready to help in deliveries between the UK's south coast and Ireland. When it came to organising Irish hooker–Arabian dhow exchanges between Galway and Abu Dhabi, as part of the 2011/2012 Volvo Ocean Race cultural programme, it was to Padraic that I turned for help.

Journalist Lorna Siggins takes up the story in the *Irish Times* on 6 January 2012:

> A near-century-old *gleoiteog* is due to make a small piece of history in the Middle East today, when it becomes the first rigged Galway hooker to ply the Arabian Gulf. The *Nora Bheag*, owned by Cóilín Hernon, has been shipped to Abu Dhabi as part of a Volvo Ocean Race cultural exchange, which could also see six Arab dhows racing against six hookers in Galway Bay later this summer.
>
> The *gleoiteog* . . . will participate in an Irish Day of festivities today as part of the Volvo race Abu Dhabi stopover programme in the United Arab Emirates (UAE). The vessel was shipped out eight weeks ago. Mr Hernon and family, including Cóilín jnr, Mary and Einde, along with crew Mike and Sue Fahy and Galway Hooker Association founder Pádraic de Bhaldraithe participated in the unloading. The *Nora Bheag* has been given a berth along with the Volvo Ocean race fleet in Abu Dhabi, occupying the pontoon that would have been used by the Team Sanya entry in the 39,000 nautical-mile race.
>
> Team Sanya, the Chinese entry with a Discover Ireland logo, was forced to retire last month due to gear failure for the second time. It is expected to rejoin the contest for the

246 Brotherhood of the Sea

next leg to its namesake port, Sanya in China. There is no Irish entry in the 2011–2012 Volvo race, which finishes in Galway in July, but the *Nora Bheag* is proving the next best thing in terms of the goodwill it has already generated during its star turn in the UAE.

The original idea came out of a conversation between Galway sailor John Coyle and Dr Peter Vine, who runs a media company in the UAE. Dr Vine then contacted Mr de Bhaldraithe, who also shipped out a currach for the event.

Irish Ambassador to the UAE Ciarán Madden, the Abu Dhabi Tourism Authority, and Tourism Ireland supported the project and helped Padraic and me to organise the return bout: Arabian dhows sailing in Galway. Thanks to some last-minute behind-the-scenes arrangements, the hookers eventually arrived, along with their crews, on a flight from Abu Dhabi to Shannon, with literally hours to spare.

I had given up on their chances of being air-freighted and was onboard our yacht *Suaimhneas* when I heard Padraic making a call to Galway Lifeboat on the VHF. One of the two dhows had disappeared somewhere off Spiddal. It had been sailing in a stiff breeze, outpacing its safety boat, which had turned around. The lifeboat launched, searched the area, and reported nothing amiss and no dhows. Padraic checked with me, and we agreed to push for a second search. The lifeboat headed back out to sea and eventually found the boat with mast down and three very cold sailors, glad to greet their rescuers. As usual, the quietly efficient, resourceful Padraic had saved the day.

14   Opening Doors

It was a December evening in 2019 and some family members were having a get-together in Galway. The conversation turned to the art of storytelling and my own efforts to write about my life. 'I remember you summed it up for me,' said my youngest daughter, Megan. 'You have to dive straight in to the middle and then pull back slowly to create context and narrative.'

Suddenly remembering one particular story, I tested her memory: 'Did I tell you about one of the most coincidental of events that changed my life?'

'I don't think so' came the loyal response of a daughter who had forgotten how many times she had heard the tales of my youth. So I began in the middle.

It happened in 1980 in Clifden with a chance meeting in a doorway, the Alcock and Brown Hotel entrance to be precise, when I got half stuck by an American gentleman on his way out, as I was entering, holding a box of fish.

'What you got there?' the large American asked me in his slightly Southern accent. It was a brand-new red fish box, stamped with the name Ardbear Sea Farms, with about forty sea-farmed trout in it. We hadn't started raising salmon at this stage, but the hotels and restaurants were keen to use this new local supply of fish – especially when bad weather prevented local fishing activities by traditional inshore craft or larger trawlers.

'Fish from my fish farm,' I proudly answered.

'Uh-huh,' my new American friend said. 'We're looking for a fish farmer.'

Sensing a potential customer, I offered my hand. 'Bill Thorpe' came the instant introduction as we continued to block the doorway.

'What kind of fish farmer?' I asked.

'Oh, it's for a project we'll do in Libya,' Bill told me, and I realised that there could be more to Bill than met the eye.

'I just might be able to help,' I said. 'I've just returned from Saudi Arabia, where I was scientific director for a fisheries development project. We were perfecting new sea-farming techniques for Middle Eastern countries.'

'Hot dog! We need to talk to you.'

And as I finally struggled past Bill, carrying my fish to the kitchens, he slipped me his card. 'I'm at Ballynahinch,' he said.

The subsequent meeting changed my life, leading to a major investment in my own fish farm and to the establishment of an international mariculture company that I headed up on behalf of the Charter Company, based in Jacksonville, Florida. 'If I had not been delivering fish that day, my life would have taken a different turn,' I told Megan. It was a 'door-opening experience', both figuratively and literally, and was fairly typical of how my life panned out, both pre- and post-Charter. The main conditionality of my involvement in any project was that dependent family members had to fit through the doorway with me. As time passed and my three daughters grew up, that became less and less of an issue.

15 Fish Farming

Saudi Arabia

If my jobs in Suakin, Port Sudan, and Khartoum were my idea of heaven, the same could not be said for my work in Saudi Arabia with the British Whitefish Authority on the Joint Saudi–British Fisheries Development Programme. In a letter to my parents dated 26 July 1976, I wrote:

> Things have been chaotic and disorganised and work has been quite a strain. There have been so many uncertainties that it is only now that I am getting organised enough to write. Until now the only letters I have written are to Paula who is back in Ireland.
>
> Jeddah is an atrocious mess of a city. It is undoubtedly one of the worst that I have seen. Its only redeeming feature is that the shops are stocked with virtually anything one wants. It is quite fantastic – Paris fashions, latest electronic gear etc... and the food supermarkets are the best stocked that I have seen anywhere. Our accommodation is of a reasonably high standard – a villa standing within its own walls, well air-conditioned and furnished within but surrounded by all the chaos of a dysfunctional building site.

Fish-Farming Research

My interest in fish farming began at an early age, but there were few if any opportunities to learn about the practice of growing fish in captivity in volumes great enough to feed one's family, village, country, or the world. And yet I persevered in my belief that all these things were possible, poring over images of villages in Asia or Africa where fish were cultivated in ponds – mainly freshwater species such as carp or a seemingly ubiquitous fish called *tilapia*. But freshwater fish were dependent on finite supplies of that most valuable of commodities: fresh water. I needed to find marine fish that could be farmed like some of their freshwater cousins.

I had read about milkfish that were cultivated from wild caught juveniles, as were mullet and sea bass, but these species depended on available supplies of wild caught fry or the ability to breed them in captivity. The former restriction was highly unpredictable, whilst the latter was accentuated by the fact that most marine fish have small eggs and larvae that feed on drifting plankton – difficult to arrange in purpose-built hatcheries. In cases where large eggs came with enough of their own food to take them to juvenile stages, establishment of commercial farms was less problematic. This was the case with salmon and trout that were raised from fertilised eggs and fattened in concrete raceways or released into the sea for ranching and harvested as adults when they returned to their spawning locations. The problem I had, notwithstanding fictional accounts of farming salmon in the tropics (e.g., *Salmon Fishing in the Yemen*), was that salmonids are cold-water fish that would not survive in the Red Sea or Arabian Gulf.

When I looked at all the combinations, I was drawn time and time again to the great family of fish known as cichlids, which included the genera *Tilapia* and *Sarotherodon*. These were farmed elsewhere in fresh water in semi-intense systems, as well as in more commercial systems where high stocking densities were employed. Their greatest asset was their reproductive system, which involved parent fish brooding their eggs and babies in their mouths. There was seldom any shortage of young fish for stocking into tilapia fish ponds. But tilapia were freshwater fish, and I needed a marine fish that did not eat up valuable water reserves. Mullet were a possibility, since they could survive at quite high salinity levels, but captive breeding at commercial levels remained problematic. Then came my lightbulb moment. I had been reading a paper on coastal fishes of the northern Red Sea and Gulf of Suez and was surprised to find that *Tilapia zilli* was being caught with hook and line in Egyptian waters. If they swam freely in the Red Sea, then surely we could devise a farming system with huge potential for expansion. So began my pilot fish-farming experiments in the Red Sea.

It may not seem that unusual or exciting, but remember that this was 1978: a time when there was no commercial farming of tilapia in seawater, worldwide, and no sea-cage farming of any kind in the Red Sea. In cooler climes, salmon farming in sea cages was beginning to take off, and with it a steady refinement in designs of nets, flotation collars, feeding mechanisms, diets, pellet formulation, and so on. I found it hard to restrain my excitement. If we could apply these lessons to tilapia farming, countries like Saudi Arabia would have potential to grow large quantities of fish in offshore farms and on land-based coastal tanks served by pumped seawater. I set off to find some tilapia to try out my theories. First stop was Egypt and its famous salty Lake Qarun in the Fayoum Oasis.

I flew to Cairo, hired a car and driver, headed out to Fayoum, stopped briefly to admire the horse-drawn carts and town waterwheel, then continued down along the narrow farm road, passing prolific fruit orchards, to the shores of the enigmatic lake, whose waters almost matched those of the Red Sea for saltiness. Greeted and followed by a horde of young boys, I handed out some jars and asked them to bring me a few tilapia. I did not have long to wait. Within minutes a dozen boys were standing in front of me with jars so jammed full of fish that they all died quickly for lack of oxygen. I selected six boys and asked each to bring me one fish, and then I put these in polythene bags before blowing up the bags with pure oxygen.

Within half an hour of my arrival on the lake shore, I was back in the car and the driver had been instructed to get me back to the hotel. Once in my room, I released the fish into the bath for overnight storage. I flew back to Jeddah the following morning and managed to move through customs without being held up. All the fish made it back to Jeddah, where two floating cages awaited them. I drove out to the creek and the Ministry's field station, where I released about thirty fish, all in healthy condition.

After successfully raising these fish for a month in floating sea cages, I had the feeling that my stock were of a species that did not grow particularly big and that I might get better results with a different species. With this goal in mind I headed down to Mombasa in Kenya, where I took a tour of the coast around Malindi, on the lookout for estuarine fisheries and any evidence of tilapia. I spent several days at this without achieving any results, and time was running out. In a last-ditch effort I drove north of Malindi and began checking in to a local resort. The receptionist, a Kenyan girl full of charm, was intrigued about what a single guy was doing on this family-oriented stretch of the country's tourism development.

'I'm actually searching for a special fish,' I told her, not expecting much of a response.

'What fish?'

'Tilapia – hopefully from brackish water.'

'Oh, you must meet Rene Haller. He's at Bamburi Quarry and is breeding them there.'

I nearly fell off my stool. 'Where is that?' I asked.

'About a hundred and sixty kilometres south of here.'

'Do you mind if I cancel the booking? I have to go now.'

She gave me a friendly wave as I drove out of the resort, one less guest during an already quiet season.

Kenya, Tilapia and Rene Haller

Bamburi was easy to find, since it was a massive stone quarry, reminiscent of a meteor crater. My visit and meeting with Rene Haller were inspirational, in more ways than one. Today the quarry has been transformed into a nature park named after its founder, and demonstrates the transformation of a cement quarry wasteland into a richly productive ecological area. It holds a variety of plant and animal species, serving as a tourist attraction.

The original quarry and scar on the landscape, located 10 kilometres north of Mombasa, was created in 1952 by Cementia Holdings. In 1959 the Bamburi Cement Company started to plan the rehabilitation of quarries associated with their cement works. They appointed Dr Rene Haller, a Swiss scientist and trained horticulturist, to transform the land scars into a variety of natural habitats – eventually creating a unique nature reserve. He did this by increasing the mineral content of the soil, planting casuarina trees and establishing a fish farm in the base of the quarry.

After five years, the casuarina began self-seeding and was colonising the surrounding area. After ten years the casuarina trees reached a height of 30 metres. At twenty years old, some of the trees had a trunk circumference of 2.4 metres, and the humus layer was 10 centimetres deep. At this stage many of the trees began to collapse, but they had accomplished their task and created an amenable environment conducive to new plants.

The tree trunks were used as building timber and firewood. Distributed by wind and animals, more plants established themselves in the quarry, which slowly developed into a sanctuary for endangered species of plants. Over the years, more than 180 species of indigenous trees and bushes have been planted there, and it was not just plant life that benefited. Rene Haller believed that animals played an equally important role in the forest ecosystem. Creation of new habitats attracted birds, insects, and mammals. Some larger mammals were introduced, while others were naturally attracted to the richly diverse habitat.

Water was an essential resource for the development of the plant life in the quarry and played an important role in its economic and ecological development. Rene was in the early stages of establishing a tilapia farm when I visited in 1977. Like most of his initiatives, it was a success, not just in achieving significant production but in showing others what can be achieved and how to do it. His fish-farming project started in 1971 alongside the reforestation project and was typically innovative, employing higher stocking densities and carefully prepared diets that were not typical of other traditional tilapia farms. I was surprised not just by the healthy-looking fish that were clearly thriving, but by his circular fish tank system that induced the fish to swim in constant current. Within ten years the farm was producing 30–35 tonnes a year and was demonstrating the potential of large-scale tank farming of tilapia – a practice that was being developed in many sub-tropical and tropical countries with freshwater resources.

I was full of questions for Rene Haller. First and foremost, would his fish grow in seawater?

'Certainly,' he told me. 'I wish I had access to it.'

'And could we raise them in floating cages instead of tanks on shore?' I asked.

'I don't see why not. Suck it and see. Do you want to take some of my fish back with you?'

'There is nothing I would like more.' My heart was already beating at twice its normal rate. Not only did I have a source for future stocking, but I had found someone who believed in seawater farming of tilapia and had the track record to underpin his credibility.

So my second fish-collecting trip took place the next day, complete with healthy tilapia (*Sarotherodon spiluris*) juveniles whose adults were already in local fish markets. My sea cages in Obhur Creek were small, but they demonstrated the feasibility of a new form of mariculture that had, and still has, huge potential. When I Google today for 'Seawater Farming Tilapia', I am fascinated to read that scientists are still claiming studies on saltwater breeding and growth of tilapia as 'new'. The Malaysian News Agency offered one such example in 2018:

> Universiti Malaysia Terengganu (UMT) has made another achievement when it came up with a tilapia species that can live in salt water. The director of the Tropical Aquaculture Institute (Akuatrop), Prof Dr Faizah Shaharom, said the success was achieved after more than two years of study. 'The salt water tilapia fish tastes like seawater fish and does not smell of earth like the freshwater tilapia fish,' she told reporters here, Wednesday. She said the salt water tilapia fish was bred in seawater. According to Prof Faizah, UMT planned to carry out the breeding project on a large scale soon. As such, Prof Faizah said companies that were keen to carry out the project were invited to implement it on a commercial scale.

It all sounded quite familiar, reminding me of my research forty years earlier.

Back in Jeddah, I arranged for a local laboratory technician, already employed by the fisheries department, to feed the caged fish, and I made weekly measurements of their growth rates. Despite salinity levels of 42 ppt (normal seawater is 36 ppt, or parts per thousand), the fish from Kenya thrived. Rene had been right – the only way to test this system was to 'suck it and see'. It was a lesson that I applied just over a year later in Ireland, where freshwater cage farming of young salmonids was discouraged by scientists, who were used to raceways for these fish nurseries.

My role as senior scientist to the Joint Saudi–British Fisheries Development Project (1975–79) brought me in touch with a number of Saudis who were busy making hay whilst the sun shone, some literally, others figuratively. This was how I met three young Saudi men who were riding the wave of innovation and development that was driving the country forward at breakneck speed. The first of these, Adnan Bakhsh, had applied to the fisheries department for a licence to catch and sell coral reef fishes for the aquarium trade. I went to visit Adnan in his busy office and met several young British guys there, delivering reports to Adnan and taking instructions. One of them told me the story of how they met Adnan and how his company, thanks to their efforts, was growing at over 300 per cent per month.

'His car was broken down on a desert road, so I stopped to help him. After I fixed it he asked what I was doing in Jeddah. I told him I was just visiting, delivering goods on my truck. "Stay here and work for me," he said. Now we are running over a hundred trucks in and out of Jeddah port daily, and there's no stopping us.'

'When did you start?'

'Two months ago.'

Adnan went on to create one of the country's successful land transport companies.

Adnan was surprised when I said I could not support his application to catch aquarium fish in local waters. 'We should be protecting the reefs and all their inhabitants, not exploiting them for profit,' I told him. But he wasn't someone who took defeat lying down. He invited me to sit down, and I became a regular visitor to his office in the evenings. He wanted to learn about my work and Saudi Arabia's hidden wealth of fish and corals, whilst I enjoyed his enthusiasm and infectious ambition to be the first and best at whatever he tackled.

Between us, we cooked up the idea for an underwater observatory. Our imaginations ran wild, and before long it was to be an underwater restaurant. I was to investigate the feasibility of this, and Adnan would pay my expenses. It was apparent that I needed to show Adnan how underwater observatories worked in practice. I had a few structures in mind, but one in particular seemed relevant – the Green Island Observatory on Australia's Great Barrier Reef. As I drove home that evening, to Paula and our toddler, Catriona, I pondered the feasibility of Paula making a trip to Australia to gather information and images for Adnan. I walked in the front door, hugged my wife and young daughter, and asked Paula if she would like a quick trip around the world, starting next week. She said yes and flew to Ireland to leave Catriona with her mother, then flew on to Hawaii, New Caledonia, Australia, and back to Jeddah via India.

The perceived wisdom at that time was that a ticket on Saudia Airlines entitled one to fight for a seat. By the time Paula reached Calcutta, she was in fighting form, not willing to relinquish her seat to anyone. I picked her up at Jeddah airport and took her home. She went to bed and slept for two days and nights, barely conscious of her surroundings. It was just ten days since she had set off, and she had visited every significant underwater observatory that we knew to be in operation at that time. With my report complete and our accounts settled up, Adnan started to approach qualified engineering companies to turn his dream into a reality.

The other young dynamic Saudi Arabians that I met were Osama Zainy and his brother Gazi Zainy. Part of the Abbar and Zainy group, they were involved in a wide range of enterprises, especially farming, food wholesale and retail, cold storage, and anything else that captured their interest. They had been trained in business schools in the US, and believed that anything they tackled should be to the highest possible standard. Their farm outside Jeddah, for example, was a showcase enterprise that often hosted government visitors.

I introduced Osama to the prospect of commercial tilapia farming, especially in seawater. He in turn started firing questions at me – many of which I found hard to answer. In talking enthusiastically to companies like Abbar and Zainy, I felt we were beginning to stand on thin ice. Yes, the science was sound, but what about the nitty-gritty detail, costs, physical infrastructure, commercial structure, environmental impact, market price, labour needs? We were scientists and lacked first-hand experience of what we were suggesting our Saudi friends should put their money into. As the summer of 1978 dragged on, I became increasingly excited about the idea of becoming a real fish farmer.

I wrote my resignation letter, let it simmer for a few days, and eventually summoned up the courage to hand it in to the project manager,

Peter Chaplin. I told him that I would return to Ireland to establish my own salmonid farm in Ardbear Bay, close to our home. He responded with a gracious acknowledgement of what I had accomplished, and I hoped that someone from the team would pick up the pieces and set up a pilot-scale sea farm. I had no idea that I would soon be back in touch with the commercial farming of sea-cage tilapia or other warm-water species. My focus shifted to setting up the new venture in Ireland, and I was back in Clifden in February 1979, ready to take up the reins of the newly formed Ardbear Sea Farms.

Ardbear Sea Farms

Fish farming is a business that has attracted a host of entrepreneurs who see the potential for rapid growth and large profits without realising the difficulties of establishing a successful aquaculture enterprise. There have been more failures than successes, but those companies that do succeed are recognisable for their combination of technical expertise and applied skills together with sound business planning. Inevitably, each company experiences a different learning curve, but the successful companies are distinguished by the speed with which they learn lessons the hard way.

Marine fish farming in Ireland was first established in the latter half of the 1970s. It came with a fanfare of publicity, describing the potential for new jobs and investments in the west of Ireland. As part of that new wave, it is interesting for me to reflect on whether it lived up to its promise. It was a slow start, and a steep learning curve, but the overall figures for the venture that I started, before later handing over my shares to Eugene Casey and Gerry O'Donoghue, are quite impressive:

1979:	5 tonnes sea-farmed trout
1980:	18 tonnes sea-farmed trout
1981:	25 tonnes sea-farmed trout
2010:	c.1,000 tonnes organic salmon
2018:	c.1,500 tonnes organic salmon

In a report in 1983 for our investment partner, Charter Resources, I wrote:

> Now that the initial euphoria has died down, somewhat
> more realism has entered into Irish mariculture planning and
> development. There are still great hopes that it will continue
> its growth and become a major industry on the west coast of
> Ireland but there is more realisation that this will take good
> planning, substantial investments and a lot of hard work.

Looking back, it was a fairly accurate prediction.

When I encountered Bill Thorpe in the doorway of Alcock and
Brown Hotel, my feet were set in a new direction. Here is what happened.
At our meeting in Ballynahinch Castle in 1980, Bill told me he was part
of an oil company conglomerate called the Charter Company, and that
Charter Oil had been buying oil from Libya before it hit a politically
instigated blockage based on the Libyans post-dating the price of their
oil supplies to Charter.

'There's a lot of money involved,' Bill told me.

'What has this got to do with fish farming?' I asked my new
American friend.

He explained that during their mostly tense negotiations regarding
the unexpected cost hike, one of the Libyan team picked up a brochure
about the Charter Company from the table. His attention was drawn
to photographs of salmon jumping up a raceway alongside a river, and
of fish being captured from a pond. These fascinating images showed
the activities of Anadromous Inc., a recently acquired salmon ranch in
Oregon. It raised salmon eggs in faintly scented water, and when the
young fish (parr) reached a stage ready to go down to the ocean (smolts),
they were released to swim freely for two or three years before returning
of their own free will to the river of their birth and ultimately, thanks
to the rose-flavoured water, to the harvesting tanks, where they were
selected for breeding or eating.

The Libyan negotiator interrupted the discussion about how many
more millions of dollars they could extract from Charter. 'We want one
of these,' he told his most cooperative of business counterparts, pointing
at the Anadromous images. Jack Donnell, Charter Company general
manager, was pleased with the turn of conversation, not least because his

son, Mike, had aspirations to become a marine biologist and eventually a fish farmer. But anything that steered the conversation away from post-dated price hikes was a welcome intervention. They had been round and round the houses for several hours already. 'I think we can help you with that,' Jack replied. 'We'll build you a fish farm.' He had little if any idea of how he would fulfil such a promise. The meeting ended soon thereafter, with no resolution of the contentious debt, but great expectations for a high-quality fish farm.

Bill turned to address me in a hushed, confidential manner: 'When I met you I figured you were one of the few people on the entire planet that could deliver what we needed. Not just for your fish-farming experience but for all that work you told me about in Saudi Arabia. This could be really big, and I want you to manage the project. We do things big in Charter – you will create the largest commercial mariculture enterprise in the world.'

It had certainly been a fortuitous meeting in the doorway, and I was excited by the prospect of working with a large corporation that could make my own dreams come true. I invited Bill to visit our fish cages and to taste our sea-reared trout. He was impressed by the project and its potential for scalability, but I realised there was a problem looming. If I was to follow Bill's vision and my dream, we had to keep Ardbear Sea Farms going from strength to strength. I needed to find a replacement for myself, and I needed to strengthen the company's finances. It seemed likely that I might kill two birds with one stone. The birds were management and money, whilst the stone was Charter's need to create instant credibility in commercial fish farming.

Over the following days I sent messages to Paula's brother, Eugene, who was touring Australia with his friend Gerry. Would he come back and take over running the farm, I asked him. The answer was yes, and Gerry would come too. Next there was the money issue. Would Charter buy around 40 per cent of the company for approximately 100,000 Irish pounds? Again, subject to the usual provisos, the answer was yes. It was time to look to the future and create what Charter's chairman, Raymond Mason, had greeted with a loud exclamation of 'Hot dog' when Bill told him of our plan. It was pretty earth-shattering for those of us who thought we had many years of hard slog ahead to establish a successful fish farm. Now I was to build the biggest aquaculture conglomerate in the world.

The first step was to find a team of experts with knowledge of sea bass, sea bream, salmon, turbot, mullet, tilapia, etc., together with prawns and oysters. Whilst I began to draw up lists of viable facilities and their staff right around the world, Bill invited Paula and me to the States to view their existing operations and to meet some of the Charter team. We flew to New York and then down to Jacksonville, where we were escorted down to the company guest house at the beach. The next day we were driven to Charter's HQ and introduced to its senior management team. Bill had told us to bring our luggage, since we were going on a 'little trip across America'.

The little trip took place in one of Charter's private planes. It was waiting on the tarmac at Jacksonville airport after our quick tour of the Charter Company's cluster of companies. I remember being fascinated by what appeared to be a drinks menu displayed on a reception table. On closer inspection it was announcing a billion-dollar 'note', reaffirming the fact that the company had recently raised a billion dollars to fund some of its bold development and diversification programme. Bill also pointed me to some reports that identified the company as one of the fastest-growing in the States. There was huge pride in what they had achieved, and a feeling that there were no barriers to future growth. 'Your fish farming can be part of all this,' Bill told me, and I began to wonder whether we were living on the same planet. I determined to keep both feet firmly on the ground, whilst embracing the opportunities that were being presented.

It turned out that 1979–1982, the years in which I worked with Charter, were some of its peak years, with revenues ranging from 4.3 billion to 5.7 billion dollars. I soon learnt that Charter loved its private jets and that the trip to Oregon and back was a gentle way of easing me into how the company operated. We were six people, plus a hostess and two pilots. Having never even flown business class, I skipped two levels, from economy to private jet. I was impressed and amused – before the era of carbon footprint awareness.

On that trip, we visited a seafood company, Captain Chuck's, in Coos Bay, Charleston, and the Anadromous project. Captain Chuck's specialised in shrimps, which Bill Thorpe told me were 'the best in the world'. They were good, but I had tasted better, so when Bill came to me on our way back to Jacksonville and once more sought affirmation that Captain Chuck's was unbeatable, I was ready for him.

'So what did you think of Captain Chuck's?' he asked.

'Great, very impressive.'

'And what about their crab?'

'Great, yes, very good.'

'And the shrimp? Weren't they just divine?' Bill pressed me.

'Yes, they were very good, but I have tasted better.'

Bill's smile vanished. 'I don't believe you,' he said.

'Well, where I come from in the UK there's a little village called Parkgate, and there you will taste the best shrimp on our planet.'

'Have you tasted Gulf shrimps?'

Realising he meant Gulf of Mexico, I told him I had not. Without a moment's hesitation, Bill called up to the pilot, 'Craig, where are we?'

'We're fifty kilometres east of Houston and will be landing in Jacksonville in about ninety minutes.'

'Well, please divert for a short stopover at Houston. Have them bring a plate of Gulf shrimps to the plane, and then you can get back on track for Jacksonville,' he instructed, as I sat back in my seat wondering which of us was the craziest.

As promised, we made the unscheduled landing in Houston. A plate of shrimps was brought on board, and I was first to taste them. They were truly delicious. 'Not as good as Parkgate,' I insisted, without a grain of evidence to back me up. Bill, however, got the picture. Back in Jacksonville, details of my employment with Charter were ironed out and the scope of Charter Aquaculture was agreed. I would leave Ardbear Sea Farms in the capable hands of Eugene, whilst I put together a multi-skilled consulting team with hands-on knowledge of farming a variety of fish species.

Once back in Ireland, I planned a round-the-world trip to meet potential candidates on their own ground. One of the most memorable stopovers was at the Oceanic Institute in Honolulu, Oahu. A biologist there showed me his tank of young mahi mahi (dolphin fish, *Coryphaena hippurus*), the most popular fish in the market. These are pan-tropical, in both the Indo-Pacific and Atlantic oceans, and I was initially interested in them because they had been hatched from laboratory-reared eggs, potentially opening the way for commercial hatcheries to be established.

'How old are these fish?' I asked the biologist.

'What's your guess?'

I quickly made a comparison with my sea-farmed trout in Ireland.

'About eighteen months,' I ventured.

The biologist smiled. 'They are eight weeks old from post-larval stage,' he told me. It was one of the biggest shocks of my life. That was the moment that I realised mahi mahi could become a commercially farmed marine fish, and I determined to learn more. A call to my old friend Jack Randall, who lived on Oahu, confirmed the story and added a new tilt.

Apparently Miami Aquarium had kept two mahi mahi in captivity for a while. First, one of them got stuck trying to swim through a gap that formed part of its regular route through the aquarium, then the same thing happened to the other. Both fish died. They had grown too big for their tanks – overnight. Determined not to let this one get away, I decided we would build a pilot-scale mahi mahi farm at Harbour Branch Foundation in Florida. Randy Hagood came on board to run that project and confirmed the remarkable statistics, demonstrating that juveniles gained roughly 30 grams a day in laboratory settings and grew up to 9.5 kilograms in the first year. They reached sexual maturity in just four to five months in the wild and spawned up to 180 days of the year. There is still great interest in mahi mahi farming today, but techniques are not fully established. However, in 2018, the University of Miami reported success in rearing large quantities of juvenile mahi mahi.

At the end of the recruitment drive and the glut of international travel, we decided to set up offices in Athens and to start focusing on (1) commercial tilapia farms for the Arabian market, (2) sea bass and sea bream farming in Greece and Italy, (3) salmonid farming in Ireland, and (4) shrimp farming in south-east Asia. We conducted feasibility studies in

Dubai, Saudi Arabia, Greece, Italy, Nigeria, Gabon, Antigua, and several other countries. The choice of Greece as our base came with a variety of attractive advantages, from tax exemptions to social living conditions, climate, and suitability for commercial-scale fish farming. I was busy making life-changing decisions on a daily basis, from issues of housing, schooling, and family affairs to company management, liaison with government officials, and staff safety. It was difficult to be everywhere that I was needed, and the Internet had not yet arrived. Air travel was normal for a host of purposes where alternate communications could have been used to a much greater extent. Carbon footprints were unheard of.

Paula put her foot down on one issue – the choice of house in Greece that we would rent to live in as a family. After I found what I thought to be a convenient residence, Paula needed to come and give it her approval, so Charter did what oil companies did in those days – they sent one of their Boeing 727 corporate planes to pick us up at Shannon Airport, and the two of us drove down from Clifden in our ageing car. Upon arriving at the airport, we made our way to the door marked Shannon Repair Services. Pushing the door open, we were greeted by our pilot, who introduced us to the hostess and escorted us to the huge airliner sitting on the tarmac in full view. We were its only passengers.

Once on board, we took in the extraordinary scene of corporate extravagance, more reminiscent of a luxury hotel suite than the interior of a commercial airliner. With a conspiratorial smile, the hostess presented us with a large plate of delicious cherries and asked whether we were ready to take off. 'Yes please,' we replied in unison, and so they did – next stop Athens. Apart from a moment of panic when Paula could not locate the toilet bowl in the toilet, due to floor-to-ceiling carpeting and an interior decorator who believed in camouflaging embarrassing 'rest room facilities', all went well, and we managed not to blot our copybook with the crew.

We were met at the base of the plane steps, inside the security cordon at Athens Airport, by three black limousines, an immaculately attired young man named Stavros, and the pilot, who had whisked himself down the plane steps ahead of us so he could join the reception committee as we emerged from our 727 corporate jet – normally

configured to carry 189 passengers but actually just fine for the two
of us. I tried to tell Stavros that there was no need for ceremony and
that one car would be fine, but the words would not come out of my
mouth. Meanwhile Paula's embarrassment was accentuated by the sight
of mothers struggling through immigration queues with babies in arms,
children in tow, and a few invalids in care. We were quite uncomfortable with this blatant exaggeration of the privilege gap, but there was no
time to debate the issue; our limousines were ready to leave. On our way
through the Athens city smog, we reflected on the fact that this was a bit
different to the lifestyle we had expected to have as rookie fish farmers.
We had some adjusting to do.

Later, when we met Bill Thorpe at our hotel, he confirmed to
Stavros that we were on a tight agenda. 'House first, then Acropolis,
then dinner,' he said. At first his familiarity left me thinking that he
and Stavros were old friends, but I soon realised that this was their first
meeting and that before today, neither even knew of the other's existence.
While Bill plied Stavros with questions about Greece, and the smart,
charismatic young man charmed his way into our lives, we managed
to get Paula's approval for the house, which was almost adjacent to the
prime minister's residence. Halfway through our walk to the top of the
Acropolis, Bill turned to me and said: 'Stavros is just the kind of guy we
need as office manager.' Within minutes they were negotiating his new
appointment. Fortunately Bill's intuition was correct, and Stavros lived
up to the potential that Bill had spotted. We had arrived in Greece in
American style; now all that remained was to find a fish farmer who
could take me on a tour of their facilities.

When people describe me, they sometimes use the phrase 'a bit
ahead of his time', and I have to admit they are sometimes right. Despite
the lack of any written evidence for a fish-farming industry in Greece,
I had formed the fixated opinion that a country with so many deep-
water bays and such clear water simply must be crawling with cage
farms. Norway on steroids was more or less the picture I had in mind.
Soon after Bill departed Greece, leaving me to start putting the jigsaw
together, I visited the Department of Fisheries in downtown Athens.
'I'm sorry we cannot help,' I was told. 'We are not having floating cage

farms or hatcheries for sea bass or sea bream. Maybe next year.' At first I panicked, and then I thought of Ireland five years ago, when there were no salmon cages. 'Maybe I am a bit ahead of my time,' I told the bemused fisheries officer.

How things have changed. Today, almost forty years later, gilthead sea bream and sea bass are the most intensively farmed fish species in the Mediterranean, according to Chris Dove at SeafoodSource. Since the early 1980s there has been exponential growth in Greece, Turkey, France, Italy, Spain, Malta, Croatia, Cyprus, North Africa, Egypt, and Israel. Dove cites a Eurostat report that says total aquaculture production in Greece amounted to 114,888 metric tons live weight in 2008, and Greek aquaculture output between 1998 and 2007 surpassed its four largest European Union competitors – Spain, France, Italy, and the UK – increasing 90 per cent by volume.

Notwithstanding the birth pangs of a new aquaculture industry in Greece, circumstances turned against Charter Aquaculture becoming the pioneer of sea bass and sea bream farming there, despite efforts to form a joint venture with the Greek construction company Archirodon. But others took up the task, whilst our attention became focused on applying our knowledge to tilapia and systems that might work in the Middle East. Ironically, the embargo on American companies doing business with Libya dictated against us building them a sea bass farm in their Mediterranean seas. Looking back on what could have happened in different circumstances, we now know that environmental conditions in that war-torn nation are less conducive to sea-cage farming than in Greece and other nearby nations, but they are nevertheless gradually establishing commercial production of tuna, sea bream, and sea bass, together with some tilapia.

The Charter Years
Kifissia, up the hill out of Athens, turned out to be a wonderful place to live and bring up our family: Triona, who was born in Khartoum, and Sinead, who was born during our time in Jeddah. Consultancy work was growing, and we were opening up opportunities for Charter Resources to partner in various new fish-farming ventures. Then disaster struck. In the

foggy early hours of 29 July 1982, four senior executives of the Charter Company, together with their pilot, were killed when their helicopter crashed en route from Ballynahinch Castle to Shannon Airport. Aside from the personal tragedy that this represented, it shattered Charter's management team, which had been riding high in the American stock market. The Charter team who lost their lives were Jack Donnell, 53, Charter's president and chief operating officer; and three from Charter Oil: Dudley K. Parker, 49, president; Barry L. Green, 34, executive vice president; and Jay L. Lammons, 43, senior vice president.

As soon as I heard the news of the crash, I thought of Jack Donnell and Barry Green, who were the members I knew best. Jack had been a keen proponent of Charter Aquaculture, and we had made a special trip together to Abu Dhabi to bring modern fish farming to the UAE. Barry, the youngest of the group, was equally excited about the buzz of working for Charter. On one occasion we shared a lift together. 'Ever wondered what a million dollars in cash looks like?' he asked me. Not waiting for an answer, he tapped on his rather bulky briefcase. 'There you have it,' he told me with a wink. With approximately four billion US dollars in revenues, Charter was approaching the pinnacle of its growth, but now the brains behind much of that success were no longer present. Instead, the Boston Consulting Group were sent in to restructure the company.

One of their first ports of call was Athens and our operation. 'What is an oil company doing running a fish farm?' they asked me, and I argued the case for being part of one of the fastest-growing industries in the world. They weren't impressed, and I was instructed to close things down, go home, and accept the generous redundancy settlement. Unhappy with the decision and concerned that our staff should be properly cared for, I argued for considering them as employees while they found alternative postings. In a last-minute effort to save the sinking ship, I flew to the States and discussed selling the company to Heinz or Tony O'Reilly, its chairman. But Charter was impatient to divest itself of everything except core activities, and mariculture did not fit its new profile for the group. By the end of 1982 we were back in Clifden, looking for work.

The China Lectures

It had been a superfast ride with Charter, and I had some extraordinary experiences, too many to tell. Generally they went from the sublime to the ridiculous, like when I was sent to China as part of an Italian Communist Party delegation. I was Charter's wild card: the only non-communist and non-Italian in the group, playing a game of business whose rules were, to say the least, opaque. My official role was to lecture the Chinese on modern methods of fish farming. In order to overcome language barriers we created a dual carousel slide show synchronised with a Chinese commentary. It was, in theory, a 'click and go' show that would only require my presence for answering questions. There had been a delay in delivering the projectors and tape recorder to me. Eventually I got my hands on the three boxes of equipment at Rome Airport, just before we all took off for China.

The talk was to be delivered in a large hall in Harbin, and the delegation was accommodated in Chou en Lai's guest house. I was introduced to the local chairman of the Communist Party, and I asked for some time before the lecture to put everything together, since this was a first run. He gave me a nervous laugh and agreed to the request. On the following day I was driven to the lecture theatre, which can best be described as an indoor basketball stadium with seating for about 5,000 people. We entered from a back door that opened into the seated area. There did not appear to be an empty seat in the amphitheatre, and as I walked down the ramp towards a group of official-looking characters who stood at the very front, about 50 metres from where I was standing, I started to wonder what these people would make of our show.

Placing the three boxes on a table, and extracting the projectors and slide carousels, I assembled the kit. Everything was working, but I could not get the control unit to recognise two projectors at the same time. After struggling for about 15 minutes, and sensing the mounting tension, I decided that I would have to do it the old-fashioned way, slide by slide with a translation of my English commentary. The clock told me it was 11 a.m.: time to get started. Turning to the chairman, I asked how long they had allotted to my presentation. I will always remember the change of facial expression and his surprising response: 'All day.' It was my turn to go through a series of facial contortions. Seeing and sensing my unease with his bombshell, he added: 'Oh. Don't worry. We break for lunch.' Several thousand audience members were awaiting a slide show originally designed to take about an hour to run through.

We did indeed break for lunch, and I managed to string out the illustrated talk about modern technologies in aquaculture. My objective was to persuade them to insert an indoor hatchery or nursery into their existing production cycle, so that the capacity of the pond system would be almost doubled, due to improved management and avoidance of the virtual shutdown when the ponds froze up in winter. By the end of the day, I was quite pleased with how it seemed to have gone. After all, not everyone has the privilege of addressing such a large class of experienced practitioners for a whole day. A process of slow translation and me teasing out the fine details of the proposed system transformed our one-hour show into one lasting six or seven hours. Mission accomplished. Or so I thought.

I rejoined our delegation for a series of factory visits, and looked forward to any feedback. When I saw the chairman making his way towards us from the far end of a cotton manufacturer's shed, I suspected that I would not be waiting long.

'Thank you so much for the talk yesterday,' the chairman began.

'It was my pleasure.'

'It was very interesting, but there is one small issue.'

Concerned that I had offended someone, I let a few seconds pass before investigating what the issue was. The chairman continued without waiting for my response.

'Yes,' he said, somewhat sheepishly, 'they were the wrong audience.'

'What do you mean?'

'Well, they were the *agri*culturists and not the *aqua*culturists. I'm afraid there was a mix-up.'

'I don't believe it,' I said, losing control of my carefully nurtured diplomacy.

'I'm afraid it's true. But don't worry, we have lined up the *aqua*culturists for tomorrow, same time,' he said with a smile, before taking his leave.

And so I turned up the next day to a similar-sized audience who, in their uniform blue denim, were indistinguishable from my previous audience. I looked forward to some good feedback after the day's presentation, and this time, right on cue, the chairman visited us at the guest house. 'Everything OK?' I dared to ask.

'Oh yes. Very good.'

'Right audience?' I joked.

'Oh yes. Right subject, right audience, and very good talk. There was just one thing,' he said with a disarming grin.

'What was that?'

'Well, you see, they were the working staff, and now we need you to talk to our management team.'

What had been scheduled as a couple of hours eventually stretched to almost the full week of our stay, and whilst my colleagues got to know all about Chinese weaving, I became familiar with the interior of Harbin's basketball arena.

Abu Dhabi Fish Farm

Another of my memorable journeys with Charter was to Abu Dhabi in 1981, when one of the company's BAC 1-11 aircraft stopped to pick me up in Shannon on its way from Jacksonville. On board were Bill Thorpe, Jack Donnell, Barry Green, and a few other senior executives. 'They want to give Abu Dhabi one of your high-tech fish farms,' Bill had told me when, at very short notice, I joined the plane on a Friday evening.

Abu Dhabi was still in early stages of development. After driving over a sandy road into town, we pulled up at the Sheraton Hotel on the creek shoreline. There were just a few high-rises; most buildings were low, concrete-block shops and houses spread out around a beautiful old fort. After a quick freshening up, we were collected by three cars and driven to a nearby ten-storey building which, as the sheikh who owned it was keen to divulge, had one of the few lifts in the city. After being introduced to a small herd of camels that were corralled adjacent to the building, we took the famous lift to the top floor. Our senior Emirati host and Jack Donnell almost immediately withdrew to an adjacent room, where they sat on the floor, ate dates, and drank coffee before getting down to business.

I can only guess at the precise words used, since Jack's comments later that evening were pretty terse. It went something like this. 'Your Excellency, as you requested, I have brought a fish farmer with me so we can begin planning a fish farm as a mark of our gratitude.' (At that time Charter Oil Company was reported to be making over a million dollars of profit per day from its 50 per cent share in an Abu Dhabi oil well.)

'Fish farm? I don't need a fish farm. We need a dental clinic. Every time I get toothache, I have to fly to London.'

'We'll build you a dental clinic' came the quick response.

They dropped me off at Shannon on their way back to Jacksonville. I was home in Clifden by Sunday evening.

DR. HANS HASS
Opernringhof
A-1010 Vienna

TRIESENBERG,
Fürstentum Liechtenstein

Vienna, March 6th, 1973

Dr.Peter J.Vine
Marine Biological Research Station
P.O.Box 99
Port Sudan

Dear Dr.Vine,

Thank you very much for your letter of February 8th and for sending me the Conservation-Manifesto which you are placing with the Government of the Sudan in order to achieve an appropriate legislation for the protection of the costal areas and coral reefs.

Let me first of all express how highly I estimate and appreciate your activity at the Seychelles by which a total ban of spear-fishing in these islands has been achieved. I have only now returned from a visit to these waters and can tell you that this wise act has insured tourist development in these waters for a long time. The Seychelles Government,respectively the population of the Seychelles, will very much benefit by this legislation which is now attracting tourism in very increasing extent.

I equally congratulate you for your very clear and convincing Conservation Manifesto for protection of the marine environment of the Sudanese Red Sea and its Coral Reefs. I can hardly add anything to your excellent arguments except the fervant hope that the Sudanese Government will take up this urgent matter very seriously and pass a similar legislation as in the Seychelles which would be an extremely wise act in order to insure future prospering of tourism indeed. As I had been the first to dive and photograph in these waters and to publicize the charming beauty of these areas through my books and films my opinion may perhaps be of some value and influence. If you think that it can help your efforts that I write directly to the Sudanese authorities to further endorse what you are proposing, please let me know. But perhaps it is sufficient if you add a copy of this letter to your application because what has to be said you have perfectly described.

I do hope indeed that your effort is successful and enclose a manifesto of myself which you may perhaps also want to add to your application.

With kindest regards

sincerely yours

(Dr.Hans Hass)

TOP Paula with Rupert Ormond on the Cambridge Coral Starfish Research Group platform at Harvey Reef.

ABOVE The platform, photographed in 1972 from a fixed-wing remote-controlled model aircraft. The reef was our study area, where we came to know individual fish and started to understand the rhythm of their daily lives.

OPPOSITE Dugong *Dugong dugon* in the Egyptian Red Sea, where some have become accustomed to human company.   © Alamy

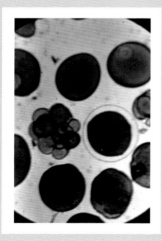
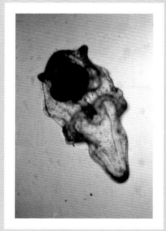

ABOVE Crown-of-thorns starfish *Acanthaster planci* in adult, fertilised eggs, and larval forms. With the help of Mike Barker from New Zealand, we succeeded in raising young starfish in the laboratory.

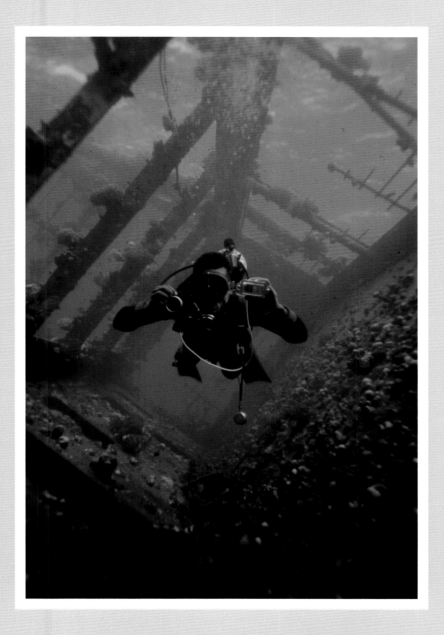

Dr Dirar Nasr is a close friend and colleague whom I taught to scuba-dive.
He went on to undertake important research on pearl oysters, whose larvae settled
in vast quantities in Dungonab Bay, and is Sudan's leading scientist on the Red Sea.
The picture shows a dive we did together on the wreck of the *Umbria* on Wingate
reef in 1973.

Jacques Cousteau's old underwater garage on Shaab Rumi reef is a
reminder of one of the great pioneers of underwater research and
provides a living laboratory to study the growth of corals.

TOP Eating a rare banana between dives at Mesharifa reef in the Sudanese Red Sea.
Doug Allan took the picture and accompanied me on this excursion in search of
manta rays.   © Doug Allan

ABOVE A manta ray *Manta birostris* feeding in the Mesharifa channel.

TOP Pete with Hassan Bodie, photographed in 1973. Hassan was employed by the Archaeological Department to guard the deserted buildings on Suakin Island, including Shafai mosque, where he made the call to prayers. Suakin people used to call him 'Sheikh Bodie'.

ABOVE Doug Allan's delight at raising the bell of the *Umbria* was tempered slightly by discovering she had changed her name to *Bahia Blanca*. The ship remains on Wingate reef, cargo holds still stacked with WWII bombs and other munitions.
© Doug Allan

Sanganeb Lighthouse, where the keepers gave us a bedroom and where we dived on some of the most beautiful reefs we had ever encountered.

ABOVE Tamara Double led a dive in the southern Red Sea, where we were shown these giant-sized Spanish dancers, *Hexabranchus sp.* There was a strong current. Diving was difficult, but I was lucky to get this shot.

OPPOSITE These pictures dramatically illustrate one of the most significant relationships on coral reefs: the sponge–coral interface. When I first realised the constant battle that was being waged between these groups of animals, very little had been published on the topic. Photographed at monthly intervals, the creeping, smothering sponges killed corals that they overgrew, advancing in summer, receding in winter. I soon realised that the grey *Terpios* sponge could be just as devastating to corals as crown-of-thorns starfish.   © Hans Sjoeholm

TOP Tilapia *Sarotherodon spilurus* that I brought from Kenya and raised in a floating cage in the Red Sea.

ABOVE *Ibn Majed*, the specially built commercial fisheries research vessel introduced by the UK Whitefish Authority to provide the hard data in support of a Saudi Arabian fisheries development programme. She seemed to spend most of her time under repair and was not much help in studying coastal fisheries among coral reefs. Under skipper Phil Skipworth, she did however manage a few deep-water trawls off Gizan, revealing both shrimp and fish resources that were still largely unexploited.

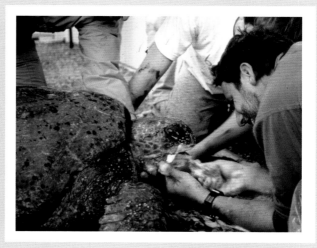

TOP Michael McKinnon and cameraman Tony Bomford amid the Gulf oil slick that we filmed for *Tides of War*.

ABOVE Biologists try to rescue a heavily oiled turtle in the Arabian Gulf. The oil slick was the result of war damage in Kuwait, but it remains uncertain how it was caused. The environmental catastrophe killed thousands of birds, turtles, and other marine species. It also threatened shutdown of key desalination plants in eastern Saudi Arabia. I wrote the book *Tides of War*, which was translated to German and won a gold medal at the Frankfurt Book Fair.

TOP This picture of two Sudanese boys, close to the border with Eritrea, reminds me of our honeymoon on a local fishing boat.

ABOVE Paula with baby Catriona at the Red Sea Club swimming pool in Port Sudan in the winter of 1975.

13th January 1975
Sisters Nursing Home
Khartoum.

Dear Mum + Dad,
                I hope that you received my
cable with news of the birth of Catriona Mary
who was born at 3·30 pm Sudanese time on
11th Jan — both Paula and baby are in perfect
health and the delivery was exceptionally
easy and natural. You will I am sure laugh
when I say that Paula was not sure that
labour had begun until she was told to
push the baby out — "On the next push you'll
see the head emerge". She had not had a "show"
or any other preliminary sign and although she
suffered back pains in the morning — there
were no rhythmic uterine contractions of which she
was aware — + the baby only moved down
on the morning of the "D·day" — thus I worked all
morning (leaving an English Doctor - Mrs Wainright with
Paula) — arrived home at 2·10pm — decided to take
Paula into hospital — they gave her a prelim. exam
- decided she was ready to deliver — I telephoned
our gynaecologist and within 10 minutes he arrived
+ the baby was born 10 minutes later! I was
present at the delivery — they did not even have
time to put any special clothes on Paula —
just pulled up her dress + told her to push —
3 pushes + the baby was out + crying. I was
reeling with the suddenness of it all — the "Oh Pete
its a little girl!" and Catriona turning blue —
clamps on the umbilical cord + my whole attention
on it as it is cut — I was supporting Paula's
back + like that we felt NIL embarrassment
or with the whole process — I watched the Dr's
hands as he eased out the after birth —
put a couple of stitches in Paula (he had not
made any incision but the baby caused a slight
tear) — always glancing at Catriona as she
lay there turning from blue to sun-tanned
pink — She gripped my finger slightly +
stopped crying — I was of course + still am -
in seventh heaven. Paula is now starting to
breast feed + we hope to go home in a couple
of days (I am of course sleeping in the flat but am
spending most of the day(s) with Paula). Pete + Paula
          All   love from the 3 of us.

Dr Hans Hass with his wife and diving partner Lotte, on an underwater filming expedition to the Caribbean in 1953. Hass later cooperated with me to instigate bans on spearfishing and other conservation measures in Sudan and Seychelles.   © Alamy

Tube worm colonies formed by the serpulid *Serpula vermicularis* build calcareous reefs in Salt Lake. Their bright red feeding fans, so sensitive to light changes, made them engaging stars of the Oscar-nominated film *Nightlife*.

A memorable and historic picture of Eugene Casey holding the first farmed salmon produced by Ardbear Sea Farms. It was the precursor of a significant and sustainable industry that provides scores of jobs and boosts the Connemara economy by millions of euro. The company's focus on organic salmon not only creates a superb product but also underpins environmental protection. Prior to its salmon cultivation in 1984, Ardbear Sea Farms produced sea-farmed trout.

OPPOSITE TOP Danny Vaughan, the first employee of Ardbear Sea Farms, brought his innate seamanship, together with a keen angler's insight into nature and the environment, to the task of building from scratch this pioneering venture.

OPPOSITE Preparing to harvest organic salmon in 2019.

16   Seychelles

My associations with this delightful country also ranged from the sublime to the ridiculous, taking in two expeditions focusing on reef conservation, my first book (really a booklet), authorship of a big book on the country, a news item in *Private Eye*, a case of libelling the Seychelles' previous prime minister, the fortunes of a Saudi–British publishing company, and a Sunsail yacht charter that reintroduced me to the Seychelles' wonderful wildlife and its unique people.

It all began with Roger Lubbock: a young man with a comprehensive knowledge of coral reef fish, who kept an impressive aquarium at his grandmother's house in Kensington, central London. I met him on our first CCSRG expedition to Port Sudan in 1970. Back in Swansea after that trip, Roger contacted me and asked if I would lead an independent expedition to Seychelles in the summer of 1971, as an alternative to another Sudanese trip. He and his two friends Miguel Nidal and Peter Etherington-Smith were all from privileged public-school backgrounds, but there was nothing pretentious about their diving skills or knowledge of fish taxonomy. I welcomed the opportunity to explore new reefs, and mentioned the plan to the British Conservative MP Brian Harrison, whom I had first met in Tarawa, five years previously, and with whom I had kept in touch. Brian offered to sponsor the expedition, and I agreed to lead it on the basis that we would focus on establishing baseline data in support of a coral reef conservation programme for the Seychelles islands.

I arrived on Mahe by one of the first British Airways commercial aircraft to fly direct from London. The country's chief minister, James Mancham, personally greeted the passengers as they came through the arrivals lounge. Excitement about the service had not yet died down, and each plane's arrival at the 'island of love' was an excuse for celebrations. It was 25 July 1971 and our touchdown at 4 p.m. was on time. Expedition preparations had been minimal due to slow communications and a general tendency to leave things to the last moment. To put it frankly, we had no arrangements for accommodation, transportation, boats, diving, or scientific facilities, and not surprisingly there was a mixed response from government officials, with the British ones largely uncooperative and the local ones strongly in favour. Freddy Williams, civil servant in charge of natural resources, was less than encouraging, offering little help. It was apparent that the governor, Sir Bruce Greatbatch, had already made up his mind to stay as far as possible from our project. Freddy's hands were effectively tied, but he took me to see Serge Savy, in charge of the Agriculture Department, who immediately impressed me with his enthusiasm and kindness. He offered us the use of a laboratory at his department and was keen to help with boat and accommodation. He was clearly bewildered by the British government's reluctance to help us. Eventually, however, I struck gold in the form of Kantilal Jivan Shah, the owner of a trading store in Port Victoria. He welcomed me with open arms and was keen to ensure we received support.

'Kanti' was not surprised by the official response but was angered by it. It was not the first time he had had such arguments with the governor. An ardent conservationist and knowledgeable amateur biologist, he had helped other expeditions to Seychelles. Despite the discouraging start, wheels did begin to turn. On 28 July I met again with Captain Sauvage and Captain Ferrari, who told me that our expedition would receive 'full Seychelles' government support', starting with free use of the governor's palatial guest house at Grand Anse. They also offered free use of the boat *Rosemary* and of a smaller dinghy. The only thing missing was land transport, and this we rented from Kanti in the form of a Morris Mini Traveller, at a nominal rate of 20 rupees (about £1.50) per day. Its only real limitation was the absence of any functional brakes, which did create challenges, especially when we crossed the mountain between Grand Anse and Port Victoria.

Other expedition members arrived the next day, by sea from Mombasa. They included Alastair Birtles, Roger Lubbock, Miguel Nidal, and Nicholas Polunin. Nicholas and Roger were contemporaries, with a passion for coral reef fish. Peter Etherington-Smith was Roger's dive buddy, in awe of his knowledge and quite well informed himself. Miguel was a friend of Roger with no particularly relevant skill other than to make us laugh. Alastair had worked with me in 1970 on our first CCSRG expedition, and was a competent marine biologist and Oxford graduate.

For two months, from the end of July to late September 1971, based at the governor's guest house, we recorded ecology of local reefs using the standard practice of marked-out quadrants, whilst Roger and colleagues identified the reef fish, catching some as samples or as live fish to send back to Richard Sankey, his friend in London. Sankey, an avid aquarist, started his business in 1970 as the Tropical Marine Centre. This has been Europe's leading supplier of quality marine fish and invertebrates to the ornamental trade since its inception, importing more than 1,800 species of livestock from twenty-six countries around the world. Sadly, Roger was killed in a car accident in Rio de Janeiro in 1981 at the age of twenty-nine. He would be proud of what his friend Richard has achieved.

As part of our own work, we built a number of aquariums, stocked them with reef fish, and opened up a display in the museum of Victoria, the capital, firstly to government dignitaries and later to the general public. Interest was so strong that we soon had to switch from afternoon opening hours to all day. There were queues almost constantly. A tribute on the first page of the visitors' book reads as follows:

> In full appreciation to the Cambridge Coral Conservation Expedition for providing to many on these islands a glimpse of the tremendously beautiful underwater garden that surrounds these shores . . . and in so doing has enlightened the Seychelles Government to the existence of a potential which could be the admiration of tourists from everywhere.
> —James Mancham, Chief Minister

The two summers spent studying coral reefs in Seychelles, and interacting with the small group of fish/coral enthusiasts who together formed the Seychelles Coral Reef Conservation Expedition, were exciting and rewarding. I also got to know the chief minister, James Mancham, quite well, admiring his enthusiasm and energy, not to mention a passionate love of his islands and their people. It came as a surprise therefore when he sued me for libel. I learnt of this most frightening turn of events on the Piccadilly tube train in London, en route for Heathrow Airport. Sitting, minding my own business, glancing through *Private Eye* magazine, my own name suddenly leapt off the page. 'Seychelles

Ex-Prime Minister Sues Author Peter Vine' went the heading over a story describing how Sir James Mancham had engaged the services of the country's most feared libel lawyer, Peter Carter-Ruck, whose last name had been hijacked by *Private Eye* by replacement of the letter R to spell, predictably: F-U-C-K, instilling even more fear and loathing than his true title. I soon learned that you don't mess with 'Carter –UCK'.

Sir James had taken the case to put a stop to the unsubstantiated rumour that he had 'announced his intention to declare himself President for Life' – which became the pretext for a bloodless coup against him and led to his subsequent exile in the UK. I had been fed this story from what I thought was a reliable source in Mahe whilst writing my book on the country for Immel Publishing, whose chairman, Sheikh Gazi Zainy, though morally supportive, did not let me off the great big hook from which our house and 'all worldly goods' were so precariously suspended. I could hardly be called a 'person of means' – but Gazi was worth millions, and I had signed a contract to indemnify him against any damages. A legal battle, fought on our behalf by Biddle and Co., soon established that there was no firm evidence to back up the new government's account of precisely what had occurred.

Angry that I had apparently been misled, I flew back to Seychelles and immediately requested a meeting with then-president *France-Albert René*. Within an hour I was sitting down with President René, himself a trained lawyer. He was careful and measured in his response, and I sensed that he had some sympathy for the position that James Mancham found himself in. 'You had better talk with the director general of information, Mr Berlouis,' he told me and picked up the phone to make arrangements for such a meeting. An hour later I was sitting with Mr Berlouis, who seemed somewhat reticent in terms of his ability to provide evidence that would stand up in court to support the 'official account'. I was beginning to wonder just how vulnerable my own position might be.

The conversations with Mr Mancham, as reported at the time by President René, may have taken place on a private level, but they seem to have been part of a general theoretical narrative, rather than an official statement or public declaration. No doubt Mr Carter-Ruck would drive a coach and horses through the new government's reasons for overthrowing James Mancham as president. I needed to tread carefully. The official government line, in a publication released on the tenth anniversary of the coup (5 June 1987), was described by the Ministry of Education as follows:

> At one stage after independence the SDP began to conceive plans to postpone elections and set up a feudal type of dictatorship with its leader becoming president for life. This was resisted by the SPUP.
>
> Within a year, the people having become concerned at the deteriorating state of affairs in the management of the country's economy and the dangers their young country faced, staged a revolution at dawn on 5 June 1977, liberating the land and its people from a leadership that was placing the country in a situation that would have kept them as house boys of foreign countries.

A speech given by France-Albert René on the day of the coup was reported as follows:

> The Meaning of Our Decision
> You have heard on Radio Seychelles since this morning that the people of Seychelles have decided to overthrow Mr Mancham's government, and they have asked me to form a new government. . . . I have agreed to form this new government because I too have been worried about many things that have been happening lately. Furthermore, Mr Mancham was trying to create a situation whereby he would remain president forever, and he was putting our country in such a situation that we would have found ourselves slaves of the capitalists and of foreign countries . . . he was adopting a dictatorial attitude, and naturally I shared my impression with as many people as I could. . . . I cannot blame anyone if the people have found it necessary to overthrow the government.

The negotiations continued on the basis that I would instruct our solicitors to obtain the best possible arrangement in an out-of-court settlement, which would involve: withdrawal of, or corrections to, existing books; republication and distribution of 'correct' versions; a printed apology; and £10,000 plus solicitor costs. Just when it looked as if agreement and settlement was possible, albeit at considerable cost, Mancham's team at Peter Carter-Ruck and Associates broke off communications. On 3 May 1990 we were told that we had to 'serve a formal defence' and take 'protective measures'.

Final settlement was achieved after considerable gut-wrenching, a year later, in May 1991, at a cost of around £20,000 – a small fortune to me and far from comfortable for Immel. However, relief finally came when Immel received notification that, true to the Seychelles government's word, a sum roughly equivalent to our costs was being transferred to Immel's bank account. Since November 1989, when I first read the news in *Private Eye*, I had been under the strain of potentially losing our home. It was finally time to celebrate.

Return to Seychelles
The next time I set foot in Seychelles was in 2005, when Paula and I chartered a yacht from Sunsail and cruised the islands in the company of Paula's brother John and his wife, Brenda Casey. My book was still on sale, with the offending passage excluded. It was a memorable reunion with the islands and with Kantilal Jivan Shah, who recognised me instantly when I entered his shop. His son, Nimou, joined us for a meal and a chat about old times.

17   Immel Publishing

In 1982, following the helicopter crash in Ireland that killed Charter Oil's CEO Jack Donnell and three of his colleagues, we returned to Ireland from Greece and I oversaw the closure of Charter Aquaculture. A corporate consulting group, Boston Consulting Group had been appointed to rationalise the tangled web of Charter's rapidly expanding empire. I was sorry to see our efforts being so coolly dismissed, but I accepted the logic of the situation.

Shortly after settling back in to life in Clifden, with Eugene and Gerry still running the fish farm, I received a call from Sheikh Gazi Zainy in Saudi Arabia. He recalled meeting me when I had presented him with the materials for Jack Randall's book *Red Sea Reef Fishes*, and he wanted me to write a more general book on the Red Sea. This was the beginning of ten years of intensive travel, authorship and, increasingly, publishing, with Gazi's UK-registered company Immel Publishing. In quick succession, at a rate of about two books a year, I wrote, often with Paula's assistance: *The Red Sea*, *Red Sea Safety*, *Red Sea Invertebrates*, *Red Sea Explorers*, *Pearls in Arabian Waters: The Heritage of Bahrain*, *Arab Gold: Heritage of the UAE*, *Kuwait: A Nation's Story*, *Jewels of the Kingdom: Heritage of Jordan*, *Heritage of Qatar*, *Heritage of Oman*, *New Guide to Bahrain*, *Bahrain National Museum*, *Natural Emirates*, *Caribbean Divers Guide*, and *Seychelles*.

The backbone of my published work was books on the Red Sea and my 'country studies': pictorial essays covering The Past, Natural History, Traditions, Art & Artists, and Modern Development of some Arabian Gulf countries together with Seychelles. The most substantial of the Red Sea books was *Red Sea Invertebrates*, which brought together knowledge of all the invertebrates that had been recorded in the Red Sea, including corals, sponges, crabs, and molluscs. Nothing like this book had been attempted before, but there were some beautifully illustrated monographs focusing on individual groups, mostly published in the nineteenth and early twentieth centuries. Knowledge about Red Sea invertebrates tended to lag behind knowledge about the fishes, and Immel had already published an excellent volume on the fishes, so a companion volume on other Red Sea marine life made sense. I was fortunate to have a publisher that was willing to finance such a sumptuous book, full of colour photos and illustrations. It should be apparent from the list of titles that I wrote on a wide range of topics. Occasionally I came across some surprising people with unique experiences to recount. The Kuwait book is a case in point.

Kuwait: A Nation's Story

On 2 August 1990, at the time of Iraq's final push into occupying the whole of Kuwait, I was in the midst of writing about Kuwait's history, traditions, natural history, and modern development. I put the book on hold during the occupation, and returned to Kuwait a few days after 15 January 1991, when the country was finally liberated. Keen to hear a Kuwaiti account of what had occurred during the invasion, I revisited the Ministry of Information and was sent to talk to someone who had a real first-hand story to tell. He had been in charge of the northern barracks on the day of the invasion in August 1990, and had put up the only significant resistance of the entire war, until the joint forces liberated Kuwait five and a half months later.

I shook hands with a stocky gentleman dressed in military fatigues, and placed my tape recorder in clear view. The room was empty except for the two of us sitting at a long table. Before he left the room, the officer-in-charge asked this brave soldier to tell the whole truth of what had happened to him and his men on that fateful day. Here is that story.

My interviewee, Colonel Salem Masaoud Saad Al-Sorour, told me how he rose before the sun after less than two hours' sleep. First he washed his face, hands, and feet with water from a container strapped to the back of his command vehicle. Then he knelt down to face the Holy City of Mecca, which lay just over a thousand kilometres to the southwest, and prayed. A quarter of an hour later, he stood up. Still wearing yesterday's battle fatigues, he pulled on his boots and went out quietly to check on his men. He was deeply proud of what they had accomplished but confused and angered by the events of the previous 24 hours. Amidst the fray of battle, with men dying before his eyes, not knowing whether he and his comrades in the 35th Armoured Brigade would survive the fierce onslaught by Iraq's Republican Guard, there had been little time for emotion. Now, however, as he walked among the tanks and other military vehicles, he began to reflect upon yesterday's events. Most of his soldiers still slept, many humped at the wheel of their vehicles, their faces unusually pale, lips cracked and dry, uniforms dishevelled and covered in dust. Every slumbering soldier hugged his personal weapon as dearly as if it were a loved one. Colonel Salem was still shocked by the loss of four of his men.

Admittedly they had been unprepared for such a battle. For many days, as they had watched Iraq's forces gather across the border, they had been expecting instructions to arm their tanks, artillery vehicles, and rocket launchers in order to prepare their defence against an attack. But the Kuwaiti government, overwhelmed at the enormous size of Iraq's army and the apparent impossibility of defending such a small country against a determined onslaught from its bellicose neighbour, had been engaged in urgent negotiations to find a peaceful solution to the mounting crisis. Whilst denying the litany of claims that Iraq had brought against Kuwait, and facing the threat of an invasion and the potential destruction of their country, the government had not given up hope that these talks would succeed.

Anyone who has bartered for goods in an Arabian market will understand that facial expressions and body language are almost as vital as the spoken word in communicating one's message. Iraq had been trying to force Kuwait to 'buy peace' at an extortionate price. Kuwait was in the process of trying to talk the Iraqis into behaving responsibly. In such a delicate and sensitive situation, they had been anxious not to send any signals to Baghdad which might be interpreted as indicating a willingness to participate in a military showdown. For the Kuwait government, the best chance to solve their differences was at the negotiating table rather than on the battlefield.

With the wisdom of hindsight, things might have been different. But at the time, not one person in Kuwait, not even Colonel Salem and his military colleagues, suspected that Saddam Hussein would send his forces all the way to Kuwait City, occupying the entire country. First of all, he had promised that he would not do so. Secondly, the extent of his recent territorial claims seemed to be restricted to the Kuwaiti section of the Rumaila oil field and Bubiyan island. The country's political and military strategists believed that, at worst, his forces might cross the border in an attempt to occupy these areas, and there would be an early ceasefire and military standoff whilst peace negotiations took place – under the additional duress of Iraq's temporary and partial occupation of Kuwaiti lands.

The secret of Saddam's plan to invade the whole country was well kept, not even revealed in full to many of the troops whom he sent in to do battle. Colonel Salem recalls that on the afternoon of 2 August they captured officers of the elite Republican Guard – young men in civilian clothes with pockets full of money. The Iraqi soldiers had enquired from him why his forces had blocked their way. Astonished by such a question, he asked them what they thought they were doing marching into Kuwait with battalions of armoured vehicles. 'We are on an exercise,' they said. 'It's part of our training.' Unimpressed by their reply, and unable to take them with him, he tied them up and left them in the desert.

It was not until late on the night of 1 August, after the Iraqi force had entered Kuwaiti territory, that the armoured brigades of Kuwait's army were given the order to arm their tanks and other weapons in preparation for a military response. But it takes time to prepare a full brigade for war. Six hours or more are needed to load all the necessary ordnance and munitions to enable the military columns to leave their barracks as an effective fighting force. Colonel Salem did not have six hours, and his men laboured all night without rest to prepare their tanks and other vehicles. The Iraqi army were advancing so fast that information was very difficult to analyse or verify. The Sixth Brigade to the north had not even been able to get out of their barracks, they had been so rapidly surrounded.

At 2 a.m. on the morning of 2 August, Colonel Salem received orders from army headquarters for their first mission. They were to take up positions outside of the camp 70 kilometres to the north and to spread out in an attempt to stop the enemy's advance. But there were reports that sections of the Iraqi army had already entered Kuwait City, and it was becoming increasingly difficult to obtain clear information.

Colonel Salem called in his company commanders and asked them how soon they would be ready for action. His tanks and artillery commanders told him that the earliest they could leave the barracks would be in four hours, at 6 a.m. By 4 a.m. all he could muster was an anti-tank Tube-launched, Optically tracked, Wire-guided missile (TOW) column of armoured vehicles, together with his command vehicle and a jeep. He ordered that these be lined up at the main gate and went back to his communication centre to clarify the situation. His officers there told him they expected an order to be 'moving soon'. Fearing that they too would be overrun before they were able to get away from the barracks, he again called the military headquarters in Kuwait city. It was now after 4 a.m., and HQ again told him they were awaiting more information.

As the first light of dawn began to show on the horizon, Colonel Salem went to pray at the small mosque in the barracks. On his return, there was still no clear information on the position of the advancing Iraqi forces, and he decided that he must leave with those forces that were ready. 'I'll be in touch with you on my way north,' he told his communications officer as he led his force out from the barracks at 4.30 a.m. Twenty minutes later, as they were speeding northward, his base informed him that the main headquarters in Kuwait City had been abandoned, that everything had been destroyed, but that the commanders were operating from a secret fallback position and his force had been issued with three new missions: to secure the Al Salem Air Base, to secure the Atraf junction east of the airbase, and to block the main north–south road at Mutlaa, close to Jahra.

Instructing his TOW company commander to use his forces to attempt to secure both the airbase and the junction, Colonel Salem continued towards Mutlaa with just his command vehicle and jeep. On arriving close to the camel market at Jahra, he stopped. 'To tell you the truth,' he told me, 'I knew the Iraqis must be in Jahra, since I could hear the noise of hundreds of their vehicles . . . waiting there for a moment.' He was unsure of what he could do. Then a Kuwaiti soldier came running up to his vehicle. 'The Iraqis are there in the school. They told us that unless we all strip off our uniform, they will kill us. How did they get there?' the soldier asked, totally bewildered by what had happened, deeply angered by this news, and incensed by the belligerence of the Iraqi army. Colonel Salem picked up his radio microphone and called his camp.

'Send me anything that you have ready,' he commanded. Fortunately, Seven Company commander was nearby: 'Yes, sir, I'm coming. Where are you?' Within minutes, twenty-five Chieftain tanks were on the road north, racing against time to support their brigade commander and to challenge the Iraqi army. Colonel Salem awaited their arrival with mounting anxiety. As soon as they reached Colonel Salem's position, at around 6.30 a.m., he discussed their task with the company commander.

'Our mission is to block the Abdali road, in front of the Iraqis. Let's go! Let's do what we have been instructed to do. Let us accomplish our mission,' he ordered.

Moving to take up position on the opposite side of the road, close to the Jahra Cemetery, a line of military vehicles appeared in front of them.

'Who are those vehicles, sir?' the company commander asked.

'Those are the enemy,' the brigade commander replied. 'So fire!'

It was the first time the Seven Company commander and his men had ever been ordered to fire in a real battle, and the order took a split second to fully register.

'Should I fire?' the commander asked.

'Yes, fire!' ordered Colonel Salem, and so began the longest and bloodiest battle of the day. It was a quarter to seven in the morning.

The advancing Iraqi force had clearly not expected this opposition. As the tanks of Kuwait's 35th Brigade began hitting and destroying the enemy vehicles, hundreds of soldiers dismounted. Within minutes the road was blocked by damaged vehicles and soldiers, halting the progress of a long line of tanks, armoured personnel carriers, trucks, and unmarked civilian cars. The Kuwaiti force kept up a relentless and highly effective barrage of fire against the invading army. It was not until later in the day that they discovered they had been fighting against the crack forces of the Republican Guard and that the men in unmarked cars were their commanding officers. After a while they were joined by sixteen tanks from 8th Company, whose commander was told to take the right flank. Instinctively understanding what was required of him, the Kuwaiti officer ordered his tanks to spread out, and they began firing immediately, hitting and destroying the first advancing vehicles in a new wave of the Iraqi attack.

Again the Iraqis dismounted from their burning vehicles, gathering on the road and along each side of it. As each tank or armoured personnel carrier approached within range of the Kuwaiti brigade, it was hit. 'We learned later that this new advancing force belonged to a division of the Republican Guard,' Colonel Salem explained. 'By late afternoon we could see that, despite our success against this particular force, the battle to save Kuwait had moved against us. We watched flights of thirty Iraqi helicopters flying towards Kuwait city and then returning before flying south again.' It was clear that Kuwait's armed forces had been outnumbered, and now the 35th Brigade was also at risk from an advancing mass of soldiers, this time on foot. 'I told my Artillery Company commander to stop shooting at the tanks, so that my infantry force could deal with the Iraqi infantry. We could not capture them, since we knew their tactics. They were moving to surround us before using anti-tank weapons against us.' Iraq's army officers were using their own soldiers on what amounted to suicide missions, since the Kuwaitis were left with no option but to halt their advance, killing large numbers of them.

By two in the afternoon, following almost eight hours of fighting by the Al-Shahid 35th Brigade, under command of Colonel Salem, the mission had been accomplished: the north–south road was blocked, Ali Salem air base defended, and the area from the junction to their northern position secured. But in the absence of a large back-up force, there was no chance of holding these positions. At what seemed to be the eleventh hour, it looked as if help was on its way. The observation officer of the force which had been seconded to secure the Atraf junction radioed to Colonel Salem that a brigade of tanks had passed along the road, coming towards his position from the south-west. Both men initially thought that these tanks were coming from a special force stationed in Saudi Arabia. 'Make sure that they are friendly forces,' Colonel Salem told the officer. He had reason to be cautious and spoke immediately on the radio to another officer at the new temporary HQ in Kuwait City. 'Nobody informed us about such a special defensive force from Saudi Arabia,' they told the colonel.

A complete brigade of this unidentified force managed to reach about two kilometres from where Colonel Salem had his troops deployed.

'They look different, sir. Their vehicles are different, and we can hear them on the radio – they are speaking differently,' his observation officer told him. By this stage Colonel Salem was used to the tactics being employed by the Iraqis, and without a moment's hesitation he replied, 'This is the enemy. Fire! Destroy the enemy.' It was an intense and close-fought battle, in which every type of available weapon was employed, from small arms to tank guns. The Kuwaiti force destroyed a complete brigade of what they later discovered was the Iraqi Al Madina Republican Guard.

By now the 35th Brigade knew that they had enemy forces advancing from the north and from the south-west. Repeated requests for air and artillery support were met by no response. 'At that time it seemed that nothing was available,' Colonel Salem explained. 'We were running short of ammunition.'

By three o'clock all the commanders notified me that their ammunition would be finished if we were going to continue fighting, and we had no means of replenishing our supplies. By this stage we had already finished our third supply of ammunition. The situation was such that I felt obliged to ask HQ for assistance in the form of air and artillery. I asked four times for assistance. Then the Iraqis began to realise what situation we were in, and I could see that they were gathering, moving in on us from both the left and the right.

They began to shell us with mortars. I lost four in my command, and ten were injured. We tried to stay, but the situation began to turn on us. It was no longer in our favour. I could see that the Republican Guard were stopped way behind the junction, and they started to spread from the west to the east. I knew that they were going to flank us from all directions, and they would then ask for the Iraqi Air Force to destroy us. I told the HQ about the situation. 'I am certain you should send me some help,' I told them. They said, 'You are the man in this situation. You have to decide what to do. To tell you the truth, it is impossible to offer you support from the air force or artillery.'

Within our area of the conflict, one Kuwaiti aircraft had been active, striking forces from the junction to the south-west. I took the decision and informed my commanders that we would retreat to the south. It was the only way. We had to break through the Iraqi forces to the south.

I am very proud of my officers. They appreciated the situation we were in, and the 8th Company moved with their artillery and missiles, covering our retreat and defending a new base. We retreated to an area called Al Haya, to be away from enemy fire, and we managed to break through and go there. But the enemy managed to damage two tanks. When we arrived at Al Haya, we found that the area was good for the track vehicles but too soft for the wheeled vehicles, which sank in the sand. In addition, there was no cover; we were in the open. Also, to tell you the truth, the Iraqis were on the same channel. I could hear them, and they could hear me. They thought that we were going to go to the broadcasting station, and they said: 'OK. . . let's have them going there, and we will encircle them and destroy them with artillery.' They didn't know that I was going south, and we went further, to get away from their mortar shells, and then we waited and regrouped.

I called on my commanders to make sure that everyone was there and to check on their situation. Whilst we were regrouping, six Iraqi fighter planes flew over us. We realised that if we stayed in the area, the enemy would follow us. It was going to be very difficult at night, and we had no logist-ical support. We had only the water, ammunition, food, fuel, et cetera, that we carried with us. We had thirty-one tanks … two had broken down, so I decided to move further south to the last point before the Saudi border.

We moved in formation, with the commander of the Second Company in the front tank as a guide. Then the artillery was behind, followed by the rest of the logistics. Whoever could manage. It was very difficult, with vehicles getting bogged down in the sand, but we had to keep going. I was concerned to protect my soldiers. We reached our destination close to the Saudi border, and after we reformed, I sent my last message of that day to our HQ, explaining where we were. Next, we discussed our situation with the Saudi border guards, and they were very understanding. I told them that we were expecting the enemy at any time, so I might be forced to cross into Saudi Arabia. I said that if this caused any inconvenience to them, they should let me talk with their senior officers. They sent a message to their command HQ, and after two hours, at 8 p.m., the commanding officer came and told us that he had orders to request us to move inside Saudi Arabia, since if we stayed on the border the enemy would come to us.

These preparations to move took a long time. At two in the morning we began to enter Saudi Arabia. I am very grateful to the Saudis for their efforts. They supplied everything – water, fuel, rations, tents, everything we needed except ammunition. We went south until we reached a new defensive location about twenty kilometres inside the border. We took up a defensive position, and immediately I told everyone, except those assigned to guard the place, to go and rest.

We had been going for a long time. We had struck the enemy at a quarter to seven the previous morning, and we fought until four o'clock. Just over nine hours, fighting non-stop. Then we drove from four o'clock, reaching the Saudi border at 6 a.m. We regrouped, and it took us a long time to gather our vehicles and forces. Some people went back to gather the broken-down vehicles. When they had become stuck, the soldiers had stayed with them, so we went back to bring them with us. Some even went back to our main base camp to bring rations and vehicles. The enemy did not actually find and enter our 35th Brigade barracks until Sunday, so we were able to save some equipment. At seven o'clock on the morning of 3 August, I heard loud explosions.

A bit later in the morning, some intelligence officers arrived, sent to me from the Saudi Arabian government. They told me that the Iraqi forces had been searching for our brigade and had crossed into Saudi Arabia, dropping four bombs. They had violated Saudi air and land space.

I told the Saudi officers that our country had been invaded, that we had not finished our battle, and that we were ready to fight to defend our land, if necessary until the last one of us was killed. For us, the battle was not over, and we said that we wanted to re-arm our weapons and return to fight. They understood our position, but we were told to await further instructions. After a week, I managed to get in touch with the Ministry of Defence in Saudi Arabia, and I was asked to meet with them in Dharan. I went there, and so began our cooperation with the coalition forces in the eventual liberation of Kuwait.

The Aftermath of War

When we returned from living and working in Greece, Paula completed a master's degree in international humanitarian law, specialising in the protection of civilians in wartime. She was therefore very interested in humanitarian issues surrounding the aftermath of the Kuwaiti war and accepted a commission from the Kuwaiti government to write a report, *Forgotten Victims*, primarily focusing on missing persons. This was initially based on research we were doing for *Kuwait: A Nation's Story*, and later on a series of one-to-one interviews she did with affected citizens. Many told poignant stories of their loss:

> Pinned to her black shawl, exactly over her heart, was a photograph of her own daughter who was still held in Iraq. Before we began the interviews, she brought out some large albums of pictures and slowly turned the pages. On each were several photographs of young people whose features had been recorded in happier times. Page after page of smiling young faces, each of them detained, many based on

the slimmest evidence. Some were tortured and killed. Some still alive and incarcerated in Iraq's jails. None of these people had been released.

'I have made these albums for the hostages,' she told us. 'These are two brothers. This is my cousin, he had a camera. They took him and no one has seen him. There has been no news of him since. This is also one of our family. Also this person is from our family.' Nearly all the pictures were of young men. 'This is an Egyptian, his mother is Kuwaiti but his father is an Egyptian. This one is the same, mother Kuwaiti, father Egyptian. This fellow, his mother is from the United States. He was outside, in the USA, with his father, so he came back, through Saudi Arabia, to see his family. They took him as he was passing from Saudi Arabia to Kuwait. These are also two brothers. They heard only that he is in Baghdad. This man has an Egyptian mother and a Kuwaiti father. These two and these two are brothers. This is a young Kuwaiti girl.'

She continued to turn the pages, page after page of missing people. It was hard to understand how she could endure her own obvious pain, let alone take on board all the distress of the many other people who were suffering a similar trauma. A woman of action, she was prepared to go to any length to ensure that the world did not forget her own missing family member, nor the other missing people. To this end she had produced posters illustrated with the photographs of several missing persons. 'This is not the government and not the National Committee,' she explained. 'We do it ourselves. I wanted a picture to show my own daughter's face, others wanted me to include members of their own families.'

Whilst we were in no doubt about the tragic suffering of many Kuwaiti families and their deep need to find out what had happened to their loved ones, we were also aware of reports of retribution against

Palestinians who had remained in Kuwait during the Iraqi invasion. Evidence of alleged 'summary justice' by kangaroo courts included the disappearance of some well-known Palestinians, one of whom was a hospital director who had tended to the wounded on both sides. As is often the case with war, propaganda also muddied the waters, and the international press became quite wary of taking news from Kuwait at face value. Having listened to the tragic stories of so many Kuwaiti families, we found it disappointing to see how this may have compromised the cases of the victims reportedly trapped or killed in Iraq.

The search for answers is ongoing: in January 2020 a news release issued by the International Committee of the Red Cross (ICRC) reported on findings of the Tripartite Committee under the heading 'Further discovery of human remains believed to be missing people from 1990–1991 Gulf War'. It said there had been a recovery of human remains in the Samawa district of southern Iraq. Pending results of DNA analysis, these were alleged to be of Kuwaiti citizens, including civilians and prisoners of war. This and other discoveries were reported to be the result of joint efforts conducted within the framework of the Tripartite Commission, involving Iraqi and Kuwaiti authorities, and experts from the ICRC. Hopefully the identification of these human remains will help bring closure to the families and relatives of missing persons.

Paula also drew on her expertise in humanitarian law to comment on the legal aspects of environmental warfare in the book *Tides of War*, which I wrote with Michael McKinnon about the environmental impact of the first Gulf War. Meanwhile, a combination of writer's block and the need to keep an ambitious publisher fed with new books led us into commissioning and publishing other authors, first for Immel Publishing and later for our own publishing companies, Trident Press Ltd in the UK and Trident Media Ltd in Ireland.

My career with Immel spanned the decade 1985 to 1995, during which time Paula and I guided the company from a 'one-horse show' to being widely recognised as a niche publisher specialising in natural history, the Arabian peninsula, and cultural studies. Immel maintained a steady rate of publishing new titles for almost thirty years, being first registered in November 1979 and dissolved in the UK on 18 March 2009.

Gazi Zainy was a colourful, enigmatic, passionate, enthusiastic person with an exceptionally gifted mind, whose kindness and compassion were sometimes masked by an inflammable anger and a sharp pride. He loved good food and good company, and was larger than life and fiercely independent. He developed the company's list of high-quality books, aiming to satisfy a growing market of readers who lived and worked in the Arabian region. He later added books on other countries, including the UK and Ireland. All of these titles are now out of print, but copies can still be purchased through Natural History Book Service or on Amazon.

Books

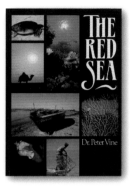

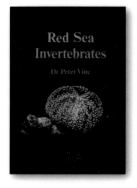

The Red Sea
Immel Publishing 1985

This book marked the start of my writing career with Immel Publishing, and of my collaboration with Sheikh Gazi Zainy.

Red Sea Invertebrates
Immel Publishing 1986

Several books on Red Sea fishes already existed, but nothing provided an overview of the Red Sea's invertebrates: corals, crabs, molluscs, etc. My book included descriptions of over 2,000 species.

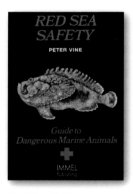

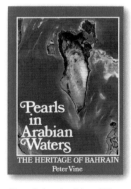

Red Sea Safety
Immel Publishing 1986

This book provided a quick guide on how to respond to stings, bites, and other shocks to the system. The cross on the cover was supposed to suggest First Aid, but such crosses are offensive in Arabian/Islamic culture, and the book was not openly sold in Islamic countries.

Pearls in Arabian Waters
The Heritage of Bahrain
Immel Publishing 1986

This was my first volume in a series of books covering the history, natural history, traditions, art, and modern development of Bahrain, Kuwait, Jordan, Qatar, UAE, Oman, and Seychelles.

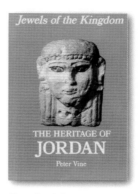

Red Sea Explorers
Co-authored with Hagen Schmid
Immel Publishing 1987

With a foreword by Dr Hans Hass, this
account of early exploration of the Red
Sea places the reader in the centre of the
narrative. It begins: 'The next problem was
where to bury the body', and it goes on to
describe the Arabia Felix Expedition and
those of other explorers.

Jewels of the Kingdom
The Heritage of Jordan
Immel Publishing 1987

One of the heritage series, based
on my own travels through Jordan,
a country that produced some
memorable experiences, including
places such as Petra, Wadi Rum,
the Dead Sea, and Gulf of Aqaba.

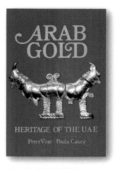

Immel's New Guide to Bahrain
Immel Publishing 1988

This was a pictorially based
guidebook with photographs by
National Geographic photographer
Adam Woolfitt. It had a long
shelf life. The clue is in the title.

Arab Gold *Heritage of the UAE*
Immel Publishing 1989

One of the heritage series of books I wrote
for Immel, *Arab Gold* was a popular title at
a time when most books on this region
concentrated solely on Dubai or Abu Dhabi,
rather than all seven emirates that form the
federation. The UAE government's positive
response to the book led to fifteen years of
writing and publishing the UAE yearbooks.

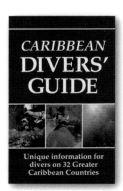

Caribbean Divers' Guide
Immel Publishing 1990

Both a guide to marine life in the Caribbean and a country-by-country account of popular dive sites and diving facilities, this book was written in co-operation with a large number of people involved in the Caribbean's nascent dive tourism industry.

The Heritage of Qatar
Immel Publishing 1992

Written when Qatar was still underdeveloped. It was quite a challenge to find interesting material to attract the general reader. Since publication, the country has gone through massive, fundamental transformation.

Bahrain National Museum
Immel Publishing 1993

Paula and I spent many fascinating hours researching the stories behind the artefacts so beautifully displayed at Bahrain National Museum. The museum displays span over 7,000 years, with intriguing connections to the epic of Gilgamesh.

Seychelles
Immel Publishing 1994

The Seychelles is a remarkable country that might be described as the Galapagos of the Indian Ocean. My first encounters with it came in the form of two biological expeditions in the early 1970s, before later writing the book, and finally renewing my acquaintances on a memorable sailing holiday.

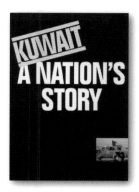

Kuwait *A Nation's Story*
Immel Publishing 1994

Whilst researching and writing about the country's history, culture, environment, economy, and development, the project was suspended due to Iraq's invasion. When I returned after the war, Kuwait was a very different place.

The Heritage of Oman
Immel Publishing 1995

Few countries on earth offer the variety of scenery and the wealth of wildlife that forms Oman's natural heritage. I loved this project.

Natural Emirates
Trident Press 1996

This book was primarily based on research by amateur naturalists who were members of the Emirates Natural History Society. It was the first time that the information had been gathered into a single publication.

UAE in Focus
Trident Press 1998

A primarily picture-driven title that portrayed the emirates that make up the UAE. Development happened so rapidly after its publication that cities like Dubai and Abu Dhabi are hardly recognisable from these photographs taken in the late 1990s.

Sîr Banî Yâs *An Arabian Ark*
Trident Press 1999

Paula and I walked and drove all over the island to create this small guidebook. The wildlife on Sîr Banî Yâs is remarkable, and the island today supports several tourist resorts.

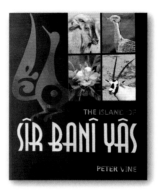

The Island of Sîr Banî Yâs
Trident Press 2000

The island of the Banî Yâs tribe has been inhabited by humans for thousands of years, and contains remains of a Nestorian monastery, together with pre-Islamic and Islamic artefacts.

Tides of War
Eco-Disaster in the Gulf
Boxtree 1991

I wrote this book during the height of the Gulf War, when oil slicks were killing turtles, birds, fish, and other creatures. Oil wells had been torched, and the scale of the environmental catastrophe was still a matter of debate. It won Best Environment Book at the Frankfurt Book Fair.

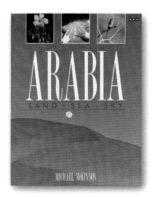

Arabia
Sand, Sea & Sky
BBC Books 1990

Accompanying a film of the same name, produced by Michael McKinnon, I jumped at the opportunity to write this book under contract to McKinnon films. I loved working with Michael who is an accomplished artist and brought integrity and creativity to his film making.

UAE Yearbooks 1995 to 2010

The UAE Yearbooks were published each December and covered events of the previous twelve months. They were hugely labour intensive in terms of research, writing and all other aspects of a major publishing project, usually in five or more languages.

18   The Sky's the Limit

In addition to book publishing, there were no limits to Gazi Zainy's enthusiasm for new ventures, and the waters around him were not always calm or predictable. Sometimes it felt like my role was to follow close behind and pick up the pieces. I recall sitting in our very rudimentary garage/office one cold and wet afternoon, trying to write a book on Qatar, when the phone rang.

'May I speak to Dr Peter Vine?'

'Speaking.'

'Can you confirm that you are a director of International Airboats Limited with an office in London?'

'That's correct. How can I help you?'

'Your aircraft has just made an unauthorised emergency landing on our military airport in Iceland, at Keflavik Airbase.'

'Sorry, I have nothing to do with that. You must have a wrong number.'

'You did say you are Peter Vine. Your address is Clifden, County Galway, Ireland?'

'Yes.'

'And this is your telephone number.'

'Well, obviously.'

'And you are a director of International Airboats Limited?'

'Well, yes, but it does not own any aircraft that is transiting the Atlantic. We just have a Lake Renegade aircraft, and she is in Kenya.'

'I'm afraid that you are the registered owner of this aircraft, and we have the American FAA documents completed in your name,' the Icelandic voice told me.

'You have what?' I said with an increasing sense of alarm. Was I dreaming? How could this be happening? 'Who signed those papers?' I asked.

'Well, apparently you did, and we have the pilot here. He insists that the plane is owned by your company.'

'What's his name?'

His answer sent shivers down my spine. It was a delivery pilot who had legitimately flown our small six-seater Lake Renegade aircraft from Florida to Kenya, via a series of refuelling stops, about six months previously. Apparently, when he took the controls of this particular plane in America, he used my name and contact details – completely unbeknown to me.

The military officer summed up my dilemma.

'She is incurring costs. You need to make arrangements to move your plane off our runway.' Then the line went dead, leaving me staring into space with a strong feeling of disorientation. *This can't be happening*, I thought. But it was happening, and it was about to get worse.

I put a call through to my business colleague and publisher, Sheikh Gazi Zainy, telling him what had just happened. 'I smell a rat,' he said. 'Did you speak with David?' He was referring to our pilot who had been flying the Lake Renegade in a series of demonstrations for the Kenyan Wildlife Service. Some months previously we had signed an agency agreement to become Middle East and Africa exclusive agents for marketing the plane. David's optimism had proved ill-founded, and we suspected that he was behind the current debacle.

When I eventually spoke with David, the story began to unfold. As we had guessed, he had been trying to set up himself and Bill, our pilot, in the second-hand aircraft business – buying planes at cheap prices in the USA and flying them to Africa, where they were much more valuable. The aircraft now sitting on the runway in Iceland had been bought, and paid for, by David's next-door office neighbours, who operated an air charter business from the domestic airfield near Nairobi. They were getting impatient with the apparent disappearance of their purchase.

I suggested to Gazi that we should send our own plane to Saudi Arabia before something worse happened. We immediately hired a local pilot and gave him instructions to collect the keys from David. But David's office neighbours were a step ahead of us and had placed a Mareva injunction on the plane. She wasn't going anywhere until the 'Iceland plane' was in their hands, or until they got their money back.

Nobody would listen to my protests of complete innocence in the affair. A long chain of documents had my name on them, from the purchase receipt and sales document to the flight plan and customs declaration. I became deeply impressed by this fact when I eventually arrived in the Nairobi courthouse and heard the charge sheets issued by both American and Icelandic authorities – all confirming me as the legal party responsible for the aircraft. Lawyers were having a field day, and my repeated proclamations of innocence were widely disbelieved. The judge gave us three months to resolve our disagreements with David's client. I flew to Jeddah empty-handed and without any idea of how to extricate ourselves from a hefty fine and legal demands.

Before I left Nairobi, there was one meeting that I had been asked to hold in connection with a genuine interest in setting up an air cargo business between Holland and Kenya. We wanted to know whether we could be granted a licence to run such a business, bringing Kenyan flowers to Holland's blossoming flower market, and back-hauling Dutch fruits to Kenya's burgeoning food market. I was ushered along a crowded corridor to meet the individual involved. After a brief introduction, and just as his secretary was delivering a pile of papers for signature, I was given the green light, subject to a 'facilitation fee' of $500,000. Following a call to Gazi, I was pleased to hear that under no circumstances would he, or his company, agree to such an arrangement.

Back in Ireland, trying to finish off my book on Qatar, continuing to brave the elements in our makeshift office, I was aware of weeks ticking by with no solution in sight to extricate ourselves from an apparently unwinnable claim against us – both corporate and personal. Then, in the eighth week after the Nairobi court hearing, I received a call from Gazi.

'Did you ever hear of a bondsman?' he asked.

'No.'

'Well, one just saved our necks,' Gazi said. I never did get to the bottom of what exactly took place, but the injunction was lifted and our plane made it to Saudi Arabia, where it was sold and my own resignation from International Airboats was somewhat regretfully accepted. No more aircraft business folly for me!

19 Trident Press

On my fiftieth birthday, in October 1995, I informed Gazi that Paula and I had decided to set up our own publishing company. We were starting all over again, from the bottom up, establishing our own authors, and promising not to poach any of Immel's stable of freelance writers. It was a hard decision to make, and I knew it would upset Gazi, but for our family's sake we needed to turn our love of books into something that generated a reliable income. We would sink or swim depending on the publishing decisions we made in the coming year. I did not consider us in competition with Immel – we had different plans and new markets in mind.

A phone call that reached me on a diving boat off the southern Red Sea shores of Saudi Arabia provided the opportunity I had been seeking. It was from the UAE's Ministry of Information. 'We'd like to talk to you about creating a yearbook on the United Arab Emiirates,' the caller told me. My mind raced forward to address the challenges that such a project encompassed, especially in such a fast-moving region. One of the frustrations that I had experienced with Immel was its lack of interest in digital media and the Internet, both for content and marketing. Now I intended to turn this policy on its head, providing the digital infrastructure to save and archive every news story that was circulated by the UAE news media. Up until this point, the only way to research previous stories on a particular topic was to read through archived printed newspapers, page by page. It was a hopelessly time-consuming and inefficient research method. UAE Interact became the first comprehensive website on the UAE, providing stand-alone features on a wide range of topics as well as a rapidly searchable, constantly expanding database of news stories. It literally transformed the English-language news distribution service provided by the UAE News Agency, WAM, and by the Ministry of Information's own news section, which created its own online bulletin as a source of official news from the UAE government. As a free and independent service, UAE Interact took on a life of its own and was soon being translated into French, German, Spanish, Italian, Chinese, and of course Arabic. It was being read all over the world, with online statistics to verify its worth.

Not only was UAE Interact a great facility for news reporters, editors, students, business people, and the general public, it also provided us with a base from which to plan and create the *UAE Yearbook 1995*. We continued to publish this, in print and digital formats, each December for fifteen years, ending in 2010. Today, official information on the UAE is published online by the Ministry of Foreign Affairs and International Cooperation (mofaic.gov.ae), which is a professionally operated website acting as a source of information on a wide range of topics.

Since the 2010 edition of the UAE Yearbook, in six languages, was the last to be published by Trident Press, we were determined to make it special, living up to its high reputation. The bulk of the content was hosted on a DVD that also contained online links to create a living yearbook continuously updated via UAE Interact. It contained not only the 2010 edition but also the previous fourteen editions, in multiple languages, together with three films that we had produced on the country. In short, it was a digital–print hybrid reference source on the UAE. Led by Paula, it took a year to produce, and, as sorry as we were to see the project end, we knew that the title had broken new ground in the yearbook genre. Looking back at that edition, it still lives up to the recognition it received at the time, although the DVD format is no longer so widely supported, and its online links to UAE Interact are no longer functional, since that website is no longer live.

Trident published on a range of topics, in both non-fiction and fiction, and several of our titles really captured our hearts. *The Silk Weaver*, a novel by Gabrielle Warnock, is set in Dublin in 1798 and follows Anton Paradis, a silk weaver whose only desire is to create beautiful patterns on the finest of silk. He finds his life in turmoil when he is forced to betray his employer and friend, and is caught in a spiralling nightmare of events. Unable to put down the manuscript, we were delighted to publish it in 1998, and it received excellent reviews. On the non-fiction side, I would have to list as one of my favourites *The Emirates: A Natural History*, still the most comprehensive reference book on the entire range of wildlife in the United Arab Emirates. Written by thirty-four experts in their various disciplines, it is illustrated with original photographs, many taken by award-winning cameramen, and is aimed at readers with an interest in Arabia's natural world.

Having created printed media for Expo Seville 1992 and Expo Lisbon 1998, we contributed to Expo 2000 Hanover with an Internet lounge that delivered interactive presentations on the UAE in a range of languages. By this stage, the Internet was being widely used as a communications tool, and we successfully linked up to the servers in Hanover from our own computers in Ireland. We had installed web cameras as part of the exhibition, and when the Expo closed down we were able to watch from the comfort of our home office in Clifden as technicians in Hanover, unaware of our remote surveillance, set about dismantling the equipment. Just before they reached our servers and cameras, and without their knowledge, we remotely wiped the disks clean of data. I was hooked from that point on by the scope of the Internet to extend our communications reach.

For a while, when the Internet was a novelty, we had an amusing installation of a web camera at Abu Dhabi International Airport. Standing on a disk labelled *SMILE YOU ARE ON WEBCAM*, passengers could call or email their relatives and friends, who would then visit the webcam page of UAE Interact and see the photographed subject, generally waving at the camera. It was clunky and very quickly surpassed by applications such as Skype, but it was hugely popular among early adopters of the Web.

Trident became increasingly involved with film production, multimedia presentations, and the creation of supporting content for World Expos, where I played the role of pavilion project director for Expos in Zaragoza (2008), Shanghai (2010), Yeosu (2012), and Milan (2015). This strong background in the Expo movement led to our media contributions in support of Dubai's bid to host Expo 2020.

20   Films and World Expositions

The more we became involved with the UAE's Expo projects, the more I felt the need to discuss with government officials their meaning and purpose. I felt that participation needed to be carefully and strategically planned, with clear objectives in mind. I often found myself talking with business people whose idea of a World Expo was closer to a commercial trade fair than a cultural event devoid of politics or overt commercialism.

The business community did have a point, since Expos seem to wear two sets of clothes: on the one hand encouraging countries to dress their pavilions in a cultural veneer with technological trimmings, and on the other hand displaying blatant commercialism, advertising the country's assets, goods, and services, whilst wrapping the whole package in a camouflage of national pride. The dress code adopted by the individual pavilions generally owed more to the architectural teams who pitted their skills against each other, than to the official theme which, in theory at least, was supposed to inform all the key design decisions. The constant pressure to justify state participation on commercial grounds, whilst disguising these objectives under the pretexts of culture, science, and the arts, is hardly surprising when we consider the roots of the event. These lie in ancient and traditional markets that took place at strategic locations around the globe, where people from diverse regions came to exchange general goods, ideas, poetry, music, and utensils. Julfar and Dibba, in what is now the UAE, and the legendary Ubar, in Oman, are relevant examples.

The idea of emulating these highly successful local fairs, promoting cultural and scientific exchanges at a single, specially created mega-event, lay behind the first World Expo, which took place in London in 1851 at a massive, purpose-built glass and iron structure, designed by Joseph Paxton, known as Crystal Palace. Expo London 1851 is remembered more for the extraordinary architecture of this innovative building than for the fair itself. It was a trend that was set to continue with, for example, the world's tallest structure (at the time), designed by Alexandre Boenickhausen-Eiffel, erected to mark the Paris Exposition of 1889. The Eiffel Tower remains one of the iconic landmarks of the French capital. The success of such expositions – Paris alone organised six hugely popular ones, in 1855, 1867, 1878, 1889, 1900, and 1937 – led other cities around the world to follow suit. Each had its unique selling points but shared one thing in common: that cultural exchange and promotion of improved living standards were core objectives.

The Convention of Paris 1928, signed by delegates from thirty-one countries, was established in order to create a global organisation with a single set of guidelines that would provide the regulatory framework for all World and International Expos. It still performs that function today, under the guidance of the Bureau International des Expositions (BIE). World Expos held under the BIE banner take place every five years and last for six months. Participants include states, international organisations, civil society groups, corporations, and citizens. The Expo site can be any size, and participants may build their own pavilions. Meanwhile, International Expos under the auspices of BIE are also held between World Expos and last for three months. Participants are similar to those at the World Expos, but pavilions are provided by the organisers and customised by the participants. In both cases the Expo theme must reflect a global concern.

Themes of recent Expos

Location	Year	Theme
Seville	1992	The Age of Discovery
Lisbon	1998	The Oceans, a Heritage for the Future
Hanover	2000	Holland Creates Space
Aichi	2005	Nature's Wisdom
Zaragoza	2008	Water and Sustainable Development
Shanghai	2010	Better City, Better Life
Yeosu	2012	The Living Ocean and Coast
Milan	2015	Feeding the Planet: Energy for Life
Kazakhstan	2018	Future Energy
Dubai	2021	Connecting Minds, Creating the Future

Our company participated, to a greater or lesser extent, in all of the above, except for Aichi, where the UAE did not exhibit, and Kazakhstan. For four of these Expos I was the project director, and they were exciting times. The UAE made a strong mark at each Expo; it had one of the most popular pavilions at Expo 2000 in Hanover, won a gold medal at Expo 2008 Zaragoza, and came first in a survey of visitor opinion at Expo 2010.

The first Expo where I was responsible for design, content, and installation of the UAE pavilion was Zaragoza 2008. This International Exposition, lasting three months, had the theme Water and Sustainable Development and was situated close to the River Ebro. I was asked to take over as pavilion project director less than a year before the opening, and I recall huge pressure to create the story, design the exhibition, and produce films and other media to convey the UAE's message in relation to the theme. In the event, thanks to some excellent teamwork, it was all done with mirrors – literally – and the pavilion won the Gold Award for 'Excellence of Design and Quality of Items and Content on Display'.

Expo 2010 Shanghai

Probably *the* most important aspect of an Expo campaign is getting the building right. It should be eye-catching, attractive, inspiring, functional, and, not least, affordable. We added one other criterion: that it should be possible to take it apart, ship it back to the UAE, and rebuild it there. This was something which, to the best of our knowledge, had never been successfully accomplished in the past and which met with severe doubts in most quarters when we mentioned it during the early days of the 2010 project.

An unstated but assumed characteristic for a nation's pavilion is that it should have some connection with the country it represents. This is a challenge that, with some notable exceptions, most countries do not really meet. We live, after all, in a world where global trends in architecture have totally changed traditional urban environments. Expo provides a light-hearted celebration of innovative building design but not an architectural or cultural map of the world. The UAE entered this arena with the wish that its building would not fall into the trap of modernity for the sake of modernity, nor tradition for the sake of tradition. They wanted it to become an iconic and instantly recognisable symbol of the UAE: past, present, and future.

London-based Foster and Partners, who had been the main

architects for Masdar City and Abu Dhabi's Central Market, as well as other key projects in the UAE, were given the brief to come up with a design that met our hopes and dreams. Their initial proposal involved an elegant angular structure that drew inspiration from Masdar's sustainable energy project. A huge shroud of photocells covered the proposed building, and their renderings of this structure were quite stunning. Following presentations at the UAE National Media Council, they were given a provisional nod to develop their concept further, and those of us involved with the process breathed deep sighs of relief that the project work had finally begun and we were in professional hands. However, there were still niggling doubts as to whether the design actually met all our criteria. I raised this subject with Deputy Commissioner Salem Al Ameri at one of our regular review meetings.

'I'm not sure how this building design connects with the UAE,' I said.

'I agree. Why don't we build a sand dune?'

I had been thinking along exactly similar lines, and that was the turning point, which both he and I look back on with a deep appreciation of its significance for the entire project. I returned to Foster and Partners with a new set of instructions that had the words 'sand dune' written bold throughout. We were just in time. Whilst F+P were already making serious progress with the design of the angular, photocell-shrouded building, they did not reject our right to change our minds. But the big question on everyone's lips was: How do you turn sand dunes into buildings that will represent both the past and present UAE, and which will not look tacky?

The inspired answer came after several weeks, during a flight from the UK to the USA by one of F+P's senior partners. He scribbled his thoughts on a small notepad, and upon arrival at his hotel in New York, he faxed it back to head office. About a week later, representatives of the UAE Expo team attended a new presentation at F+P's London office. This time there was a palpable sense of excitement in the air. At last, we had the basic outline of our pavilion – very much a modern sand dune. It was beautiful, elegant, and iconic. It would even be possible to take it apart, ship it back to the UAE, and rebuild it in the capital city. Both the F+P team and ourselves shared a real excitement that we were going to create something special for Expo 2010. With key architectural and engineering issues taken care of, it was time to develop the exhibition itself, addressing the Expo theme.

The Chinese Expo Authority, which was responsible for winning the bid to host the 2010 World Expo, put forward as its main theme Better City, Better Life. Participating countries and organisations were expected to contribute to an improved understanding of this broad theme and to share their experiences in the fields of urban planning, infrastructural development, environmental protection, and social cohesion. The UAE's Expo media team was more than happy to do just this, since the country's own developmental story closely matched the scope of the theme. There were plenty of examples of how the UAE's cities had been undergoing constant improvement to create better lives for their inhabitants. Indeed, initiatives such as Capital 2030 and Economic Vision 2030 were the result of intensive research and planning, and provided impressive road maps for future developments.

Our own media team relished the challenge to tell the UAE's incredible story:

> Shooting in the UAE was an adventure I'll never forget, a once-in-a-lifetime experience. Flying over deserts, diving under the ocean, climbing mountain passes, and scouring ancient fortresses. Getting up close to dolphins, tiger sharks, falcons, flamingoes, oryx, beautiful Arab horses, and even giraffe. The diversity across all seven Emirates was amazing, and the hospitality everywhere truly warm and generous. Oh, and along the way, staying in some of the best hotels I've ever experienced. . . . A *Dream Journey* for sure. (Director of *Dream Journey* film).

Design work on the exhibition was initially undertaken by an international group, RAA, that has offices in New York, London, and China. They took our ideas and worked out how they could be accommodated within the challenging spaces of the pavilion itself. In addition to establishing the Better City, Better Life theme, we were able to adopt our own sub-theme: The Power of Dreams. Exhibitions in the pavilion expanded on this unifying concept to show how the UAE has harnessed its dreams of a better life and applied imaginative thinking to lead the twenty-first-century urban agenda. Before visitors entered the pavilion, they were greeted by a young Emirati shaikha (and granddaughter of Sheikh Zayed), who delivered a welcome message in flawless Chinese, reminding them that over 200,000 Chinese people lived in the UAE.

As visitors entered the pavilion, they were guided to twin theatres, designed to create an intimate and engaging viewer experience, that presented a six-minute widescreen film entitled *In the Blink of an Eye*. This focused on the extreme contrasts between the UAE at its formation (in 1971) and in the present (2010), when standards of living and urban environments were among the best in the world. The story was related by a father to his son on his eighth birthday. Rashid had been brought into the desert so his father could hand over to his son guardianship of a special family heirloom in the form of a handful of precious pearls. Both Rashid and the pearls featured in later parts of the exhibition.

The founding father of the UAE, Sheikh Zayed, used to say that wealth is measured in people, not money or buildings. To illustrate this we filmed interviews with, and the lives of, fifteen Emirati 'ambassadors', including a surgeon, an aeronautical engineer, an astronomer, a chef, and a fashion designer, all women, as well as a school boy and a series of men: an artist, a jockey, a racing car driver, a fisherman, a tour guide, a poet, and two brothers who had found success as hip-hop artists. Forty projectors created what was described as the biggest 'pixel-bending' exhibition in the world at that time.

After meeting the Emiratis, visitors entered the spacious volume of the large 'dune'. Here they were taken on a virtual journey through the UAE, following two young people who, thanks to one of Rashid's 'magic pearls', could swim like fish and fly with ease – no better way to gain a bird's-eye view of the incredible places and experiences that the UAE offers. *Dream Journey*, a film without narration but accompanied by an original musical soundtrack, was created by filming real locations on Super 35mm film, and by months spent in the studio, adding animated characters

(Rashid and Jerry). The result was a stunning part-real, part-fantasy spectacle with some exciting special effects. The film is still available to view on YouTube (at: 'filmsonuae'), and it became the most popular aspect of the iconic UAE pavilion at Expo 2010. It certainly attracted the people – two million visitors – and stood out from the crowd, being voted 'best international pavilion at the event' by the Expo visitors at this largest ever World Expo. Based on overall criteria, the top pavilion out of almost 200 was that of the United Arab Emirates, followed by Germany, Russia, Saudi Arabia, Switzerland, Australia, Italy, Belgium, Republic of Korea, and the United States.

Every day for six months, from opening time to closing, the pavilion had long queues of thousands of visitors patiently waiting their turn. It was a wait that regularly extended to three or four hours. Several major magazines led their Expo features with the UAE pavilion, rating it one of the top buildings at the Expo. These included *Lifestyle Magazine* published in Shanghai; Japan's major architectural magazine, *Casa Bravo*; and the USA's prestigious *Exhibitor* magazine.

The award of 'Best Midsize Structure' to the UAE pavilion at Expo 2010 by the Illinois Society of Structural Engineers brought international recognition. Previous buildings singled out for the society's awards include the Guggenheim Museum in Spain, the Jin Mao building in Shanghai, and the Bank of China building in Hong Kong. The *Chicago Land Construction* website described the building as follows:

> Elegant forms where structure becomes the concept. Very powerful in its natural form. The handsomely, dune-like form of this Expo pavilion owes a considerable debt to innovative design and construction technologies, from a diagrid shell structure to 'form-finding' structural analysis, to bolted connections that will allow the pavilion to be deconstructed and rebuilt in its home country.

Since its inception, the Chicago-based society had made 147 awards, of which only fourteen had been for projects outside the USA. In 2010, two UAE-related projects won awards: the world's tallest building, Burj

Khalifa, for innovation; and the UAE's dune-shaped pavilion at Expo 2010, for best building in the $2 million to $20 million range.

Looking back on the project, I feel a strong sense of pride, not only in my role as project director but in the excellence of the team that we put together and managed. It was an extraordinary project that helped to set us up for what was to follow. And that, of course, had to be bigger and better.

Expo 2012 Yeosu

We began planning for Expo 2015 Milan whilst we were working on the smaller International Expo at Yeosu, South Korea, in 2012. As with Expo 2008 Zaragoza, the organisers provided the building space, and the individual countries were responsible for fitting out their respective pavilions and creating their exhibitions. This had the advantage of removing the event from the realm of international architecture competitions.

The Expo theme for this event was right up my street: The Living Ocean and Coast. Our big attraction was *The Turtle* – a dramatic film, stemming from one of my dreams, that we produced for the event and which won a gold medal at the Cannes Corporate Film Festival. Organisers hoped that the Expo theme would highlight humankind's knowledge about the ocean and coast and identify ways to resolve challenges facing the ocean. They pointed out that since the United Nations Convention on the Law of the Sea went into effect in 1993, the ocean had emerged as an important element in resolving various problems, including those related to resources, food, space, and the environment. However, industrial activities had damaged the marine ecosystem and reduced fishing stocks. As a result, oceans faced a severe crisis. A damaged marine ecosystem, global warming, and natural disasters are not limited to a certain country or region but have global implications. Thus, Expo 2012 Yeosu Korea was planned to pave the way for reaffirming global efforts to resolve such issues.

It is hard to say what actual difference such projects make in the grand scheme of things. *The Turtle* definitely struck a strong chord with our mainly Korean visitors, who were emotionally affected by the plight of a turtle that swallowed a lethal quantity of plastic, and by the inspiring young boy who campaigned against the use of non-recyclable plastic.

The short film still resonates with viewers on YouTube, and such strong productions need venues such as World Expos to create the necessary funding. But did it persuade people, companies, or governments to change their behaviour in the face of global environment issues? I am not sure.

Expo 2015 Milan

Expo 2015 in Milan was our last Expo for the UAE, and it included the challenging task of supporting the country's bid to host Expo 2020. Considerable effort was made to align the building with the exhibition and to tie both into our story and visitor experience. The Expo's general theme (Feeding the Planet: Energy for Life) resonated deeply with Emiratis. It was not so long since what now constitutes the UAE was one of the poorest nations on earth, and the memory of what it is to be hungry is still very much alive. Life expectancy in the UAE surged from 52 in 1960 to 77 in 2012, and much of this dramatic improvement was connected to the increased availability of water, energy, food, and land for various forms of agriculture. This land–food–water–energy nexus was at the heart of the UAE's own theme of Food for Thought. The challenge that our central character, Sara, and her family were addressing was how to achieve a sustainable equilibrium between these essential elements, especially conservation of water, which is now more important than oil to the UAE.

The UAE pavilion's task was to look at this problem from many different angles, hoping to find a sustainable solution that would not just benefit the UAE but would also be of global significance. Was it possible that desalination using solar energy might prove viable on a large scale? Was it going to be feasible to use plant biomass to power commercial aircraft? How could the country optimise the use of fresh water in farming? These and many other questions were tackled in the pavilion, first in interactive cube installations on the ramp, and later in our dramatic film *Family Tree* and in the intriguing 4D experience *Future Talk*. As Sara put it:

> Our story today may be yours tomorrow, since many parts of the world will be experiencing the same difficulties that we

are encountering due to spiralling demand and the effects of climate change. By forming creative partnerships and sharing our knowledge and resources, we are helping to shape a sustainable global future.

The seamless narrative immersed visitors in the rich culture of the UAE, its extraordinary landscapes, its means of nurturing and nourishing life in difficult times, the welcoming warmth of its people, the rituals, taste, aroma, and conviviality of Emirati cuisine, and the UAE's quest through scientific, technical, and aid partnerships to ensure adequate food for all. The world-renowned architect Norman Foster summed up the task faced by his architectural team this time:

> Our challenge has been to design for two climates – to create a naturally cool, comfortable space for visitors in Milan, while considering the pavilion's ultimate reconstruction in the Emirates, where there is a need to provide shade from the intense sun. The design reflects our investigations into the form of ancient cities and our appreciation for the desert landscape. It also maximises the opportunities presented by the elongated site – the dramatic canyon-like entrance welcomes people inside, and the channels between the high walls provide intuitive circulation, naturally leading visitors to the auditorium, exhibition and courtyard spaces.

This was one of the first World Expos to truly embrace social media, and we integrated our messaging in different languages, using Sara as our voice. A lively communications programme, directed at potential visitors, sought to inform them about the exhibition and prepared them to gain the most from their experience at the UAE pavilion. Our creative and media teams, led by film director Robert Butcher and film producer Greg Hobden, produced the award-winning high impact movie *Family Tree*, inspired by a personal dream. It used dramatic licence to look back at how the UAE has changed and how vital it is to maintain our roots. This was followed by the 3D 'musion' production *Future Talk*, which tested our talents to the hilt, in terms of both filming and projection. The core messages were also addressed in five short movies that we made to focus on food culture in the UAE. All this media treasure trove is still available to watch on YouTube (filmsonuae), albeit without the numerous enhancements of the big screen and 'Pepper's ghost' effects.

Just before visitors started to leave the pavilion, Sara composed a rap that summed up her feelings about how we need to support our planet in order to provide food for all. It is a cry from the heart, heard and appreciated by many young visitors. We thought that music was a very effective way to communicate our message, and our Expo audience, singing at the top of their voices as they left the pavilion, clearly agreed.

> We have land and food and energy,
> the sun, the sand and the big blue sea.
> The people – the animals – I'm beginning to see
> are interconnected like a tapestry.
> With a legacy that can be lean and green
> through history if we believe and know
> that together we can choose to make our planet grow.
> So come on – stand up – shout out – let's go.
>
> I believe, I care, I'll come with you
> I'm in, I'm there, It's my planet too
>
> 'Cause what can I do? Alone and too small
> I need to be a giant who is ten foot tall.
> Together we can do it if we all step up
> with hope in our hearts and focused minds.
> Stand up – shout out – speak up – it's time.
>
> I believe, I care, I'll come with you
> I'm in, I'm there, It's my planet too
> I believe, I care, I'll come with you
> I'm in, I'm there, It's my planet too.

In response to many requests for a recording, we placed the song on iTunes and sent all revenues to a charity that was providing support to people in Nepal affected by the earthquakes that happened in April 2015, just before Expo opened its gates. You can still listen to Sara's song on iTunes in both Italian and English.

Expo Dubai 2020–21

Emerging into the calm of an oasis graced with towering palms, orange tree, and olive trees, visitors to the UAE's 2015 pavilion were invited to explore a presentation on the UAE's plans, having won a closely fought competition, to host World Expo 2020 in Dubai. Like many global events, the Covid-19 coronavirus eventually caught up with their agenda, but when it opens in 2021, under the theme of Connecting Minds, Creating the Future, it will be the first time that a World Expo will be staged in the Middle East, North Africa, and South Asia (MENASA) region.

But for me, the Expo experience was coming to an end, and it was time to face my own new challenges. World Expos, on behalf of the UAE, presented so many wonderful opportunities to tackle global issues and to communicate in entertaining ways that I will never forget. It was a long way from farming trout in Irish seas, and it has taken writing this account to explain to members of my own family and friends how it all happened.

Teamwork

I was never a team player in sports. My sense of competitiveness in sailing was legendary. I was the first to demand 'water' with piercing cries of 'Starboard' and the last to yield it when the rules dictated against me. Yet despite these traits, my life has been shaped by teamwork on many different levels, and I have preferred to work with others in order to achieve more than I could on my own.

First and foremost, I worked with Paula, my life partner, business partner, and collaborator in all aspects of our joint endeavours, from research and writing, to publishing, media production, and a range of creative projects. We initially operated out of three centres, with Trident Media, based in Ireland, involved in some content creation and other home-based projects; Trident Press acting as our publisher in London; and FQC Media dealing with film production in the United Arab Emirates. The yearbook and other publishing projects were particularly labour-intensive, and none would have been achieved without dedicated office staff, especially Anne Ashe. At times the number of people involved in a project easily exceeded a hundred skilled and experienced production staff. We had a collaborative approach, with key creative staff having their opinions heard and respected on pavilion and exhibition design as well as scriptwriting, film treatments, music composition, and a host of other media disciplines. From 2008 onwards, we established a core media production team comprising Paula as story coordinator, Robert Butcher as creative designer, and Greg Hobden as production manager. Whilst the four of us worked closely together, it was my role to ensure that Emiratis remained the driving force behind Expo projects at all levels.

In this regard I reported first and foremost to the UAE Minister of Foreign Affairs, Sheikh Abdullah bin Zayed Al Nahyan, son of the UAE's founder, Sheikh Zayed bin Sultan Al Nahyan. I had known Sheikh Abdullah for many years, and there was a mutual respect and trust between us that made things that seemed impossible, possible. Sheikh Abdullah is widely acknowledged among world leaders to have vision, imagination, and depth of knowledge on cultural and diplomatic affairs. He was a key contributor to the UAE's Expo participation. On day-to-day matters, I liaised with him through the offices of his director of external information, Ibrahim Al Abed, widely respected media guru for the UAE. Every now and then, face-to-face meetings were vital to keep things under control on these multi-million-dollar projects. The UAE prime minister and the Cabinet were ultimate arbiters, and they maintained strict budgetary controls, encouraging all our team to optimise returns for their support. It was a high-pressure atmosphere and one that demanded close attention of the UAE Expo team, headed by Salim Al Ameri, who was supported by Abdulla Al Aidarous and Mubarak Al Daheiri. Later in the relationship, when we became involved in film production for Dubai Expo 2020, I liaised with that project's general manager, Reem Al Hashimi. These were all dedicated people for whom the UAE pavilions at various Expos were a great source of pride.

When it came to the projects themselves I must mention that our main architects for both 2010 and 2015 were Norman Foster and Partners. It would be difficult to find a better team, and I am both humbled by and proud of what was achieved. I have no doubt that Expo Dubai will break new ground and make its mark as one of the most successful Expo events ever.

TOP Peter Vine with media partners Rob Butcher and Greg Hobden.

ABOVE The pavilion at Expo 2010.

I persuaded American film-maker, Robin Lehman, to come to Connemara
to film basking sharks which are regular visitors to the west coast of Ireland.
When the massive sharks failed to appear we had to divert a whole production
crew to a different story. Our 'plan b' resulted in the production of a film called
Nightlife, which was nominated for an Academy Award in 1976. © Alamy

Films

JUNE 27, 2019 / SHORT

Nightlife (1976)

★★★★★ 4.3 (4)

An exploration of the fantastic variety of color and forms of life found beneath the Irish Sea.

Director: Robin Lehman.

1976 Cannes Film Festival – Winner Jury Prize.
1976 Cannes Film Festival – Nominated for the Palme d'Or.
1977 Academy Awards – Nominated for an Oscar for Best Short Film, Live Action.

The graphics shown above are from official records of the Motion Picture Academy also known as the Academy Awards. *Nightlife* began as a film about basking sharks off the west coast of Ireland, but the sharks never appeared, so we turned our attention to filming the wide range of invertebrate marine life that inhabits these waters. In the end we were forced to cut the film based on what we had managed to shoot. Much to our surprise, the film was nominated for Academy and Palme d'Or awards and also took the Jury Prize at the 1976 Cannes Film Festival.

Nightlife

Arabia: Sand, Sea & Sky

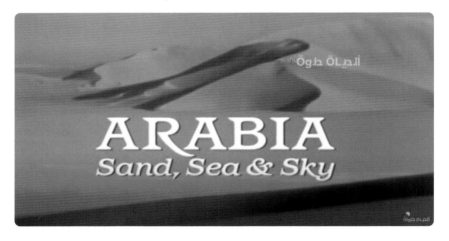

TOP During filming of *Nightlife*, diving with a Rollei SLR66 stills camera in custom housing, with compass jellyfish in Clifden Bay. © Hagen Schmid

ABOVE *Arabia: Sand, Sea & Sky* was a three-part series produced by Michael McKinnon and broadcast by the Discovery Channel, BBC, and National Geographic. I acted as biological assistant on the Red Sea episode, taking the team to Mesharifa for manta rays and to Sanganeb where we filmed mimic cleanerfish.

The Power of Partnership

True North: Dubai 2020's Voyage of Discovery

TOP The UAE in general, and Dubai in particular, has built its success on partnerships, not just within the UAE but on a global level. This short film was made to support Dubai's impressive and successful bid to host World Expo 2020.

ABOVE In late 2011 the ex-Volvo Ocean Racing yacht *True North* set out on its own voyage of discovery – to engage with ordinary people around the world and to learn about the challenges they face. They also wanted to share the thrills and excitement of sailing one of the world's fastest yachts.

People of the UAE

Ali's Film

TOP Almost 200 nationalities live and work in the UAE. This film, made as part of Dubai's bid for hosting Expo 2020, emphasises the diverse, multicultural nature of the country.

ABOVE Ahmed Al Dhuhoori became a recognised Emirati celebrity thanks to his performances in *The Turtle*, *Ali's Film*, and other productions.

Expo 2012

The Turtle

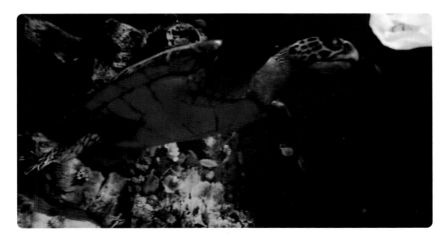

TOP   At Expo 2012 our core theme was marine conservation.

ABOVE   *The Turtle* was the main film showing in the UAE pavilion at Expo 2012 Yeosu, South Korea. It won the Gold Dolphin Award at Cannes Corporate Media & TV Film Festival.

3 Days to Change the World

Kosovo: The Hand of Friendship

TOP E-learning is at the heart of Education Without Borders, a student-organised movement that is expanding the boundaries of knowledge through the creation of a worldwide network of young people who are riding the wave of the electronic revolution.

ABOVE *Kosovo* documents the UAE's humanitarian mission in Kosovo during 1999, where a simmering ethnic conflict exploded into violent civil war. Moved to compassion by the scenes of horror being broadcast around the world, the UAE acted quickly and decisively to help civilians caught up in the conflict.

Feast of Dates: The Date Palm in the UAE

Lethal Legacy: Landmines and South Lebanon

TOP   Voted 'Best Documentary' at the UAE Film Festival, *Feast of Dates* has been broadcast worldwide on many national and global channels. This magical story travels back in time and far beneath the arid desert to reveal the secret life of the date palm tree, *Phoenix dactylifera.*

ABOVE   As a result of the unprecedented success of this project, the contaminated area, formerly occupied by Israel, was gradually being returned to the local residents, who would hopefully experience a future free from the dangers of concealed mines and unexploded ordnance.

Sheba's Greatest Treasure

ABOVE The massive dam at Marib, one of the greatest wonders of the ancient world, created a huge lake whose waters turned the desert green and enabled Marib's population to prosper. Sheik Zayed bin Sultan Al Nahyan, seen here in the early 1950s, was instrumental in the dam reconstruction project in Yemen.
Photograph by Wilfred Thesiger

Family Tree

ABOVE *Family Tree* is a dramatic account of one family and a very special tree. It was the main feature in the UAE pavilion at Milan in 2015. I wrote the initial story based on a dream that celebrated the date palm. We filmed from another helicopter as our fictional tree was moved from city to desert in a fight to save it from being swallowed up by development.

UAE Pavilion

ABOVE This film was made to launch the design of the UAE pavilion at Expo 2015 to the general public.

In the Blink of an Eye

Dream Journey

TOP Successful film from Act 1 at the UAE pavilion in Expo 2010 Shanghai.

ABOVE *Dream Journey*, the centrepiece of the UAE pavilion at Expo 2010, won four top awards at the New York Festivals' Television & Film Awards and raised the bar for future media that we produced.

24/7

Emotions

TOP   UAE from dawn to dusk, as shown in the UAE pavilion at Expo 2008.

ABOVE   We made this film on 15 June 2012, to show how visitors engaged with the displays and films that formed the UAE's *Living Seas* exhibition at its Expo 2012 pavilion.

Over the Emirates

ABOVE A 26-minute film showing the UAE from above. It includes stunning footage of the largest continuous sand desert on earth – the Empty Quarter – rugged peaks of the Northern Emirates, exquisite offshore islands and every major city in the country.

Then and Now

From this...1950

ABOVE & OPPOSITE   Both the extent and rate of development in the UAE is impressive. *Then and Now* was a short film that I produced to compare historical footage with contemporary views of the country. During the course of production we unearthed some seldom viewed footage of life before oil was discovered.   © Alamy

To this...2020

21 Living With Parkinson's

HBO2

October 2015 marked my seventieth birthday, diagnosis of early onset of Parkinson's disease, and the end of Expo 2015. I celebrated my birthday in Venice with all the family and cried when Paula played 'By All Means Necessary', a humorous review of my life as told by many friends and relatives around the world. It had been created by my two media partners, Rob Butcher and Greg Hobden, who applied all their professional skills to the task. It was a most thoughtful gift and one that made me determined to keep going despite the health setbacks. To begin with, after the diagnosis, I tried to avoid any meaningful contact with Mr Parkinson, but gradually, over time, I saw the benefits of mounting a rearguard action against his rude interference in my life. Part of this change of heart came after a chance meeting with an acquaintance in Galway who had set up a hyperbaric chamber.

As a long-time diver, I was fascinated to discover that the technology that has saved the lives of so many scuba divers over the years is now being used to help people, like me, referred to in the literature as PwP (People with Parkinson's). The European Committee for Hyperbaric Medicine publishes a long list of conditions that anti-inflammatory hyperbaric oxygen therapy (HBOT) is reported to affect. Galway's commercial chamber's website (www.oxygeneration.com) mentions over thirty reported successful interventions for this therapy, from stimulating healing of diabetic ulcers to treating glaucoma, sports injuries, ageing, and certain skin conditions and enhancing general well-being.

Despite the absence of Parkinson's disease from this wide-ranging list, anecdotal reports conveyed some glimmers of hope. However, my professional medical advisers each suggested that I should not raise my expectations too high, since this is still relatively uncharted territory in terms of proven therapy and side-effects. In late January 2019, I began a course of HBOT, initially with one session per day but soon moving to two one-hour sessions daily with breaks at the weekends. I joined an eclectic mix of fellows, each with a story to tell. Among the ailments for which they sought relief were tendon damage, glaucoma, Parkinson's, back pain, MSA (multiple system atrophy), concussion, chronic tiredness, meningitis after-effects, and some other neurological conditions.

In addition, a member of the Galway hurling team was checking out the chamber for general fitness enhancement.

As the door closed and the pressure inside the chamber gradually rose towards its operational level of 2 ATA (equivalent to a dive to 10 metres), there was the feeling of a shared journey, not knowing quite where it would lead. Reassurance was eagerly offered by 'old-timers' with scores of sessions under their belts. Eight minutes later the calming voice of the centre's session manager informed us that we had reached our operation pressure and could therefore put on our breathing masks, relax, enjoy the video, and breathe in almost pure oxygen. I put on the facemask and waited for the day's video to run. It was a space documentary presenting explorations of the universe – sufficiently engaging to take one's mind off the fact that we were not going anywhere for the next hour or so. Apart from the video soundtrack, the only other noise was the deep, rhythmic breathing of the cylinder's occupants as we all sucked in oxygen at twice normal atmospheric pressure.

I don't think anyone is claiming that HBOT is a cure for Parkinson's, but there are many PwPs who swear to its beneficial impact. Used as an adjunct to traditional therapy, it has been reported to reduce some Parkinson's symptoms and to improve well-being in some PwPs, but clinical trials have been elusive or inconclusive. HBOT increases the amount of oxygen that the blood can carry, resulting in hyper-oxygenated plasma and an increase in oxygen delivered to the tissues. It is this enhanced oxygen supply, attacking areas of inflammation, that triggers the many healing effects that have been attributed to HBOT. After 60 minutes of our rhythmic 'breathe-in', the pressure fell back to normal, and we could exit the chamber and carry on with our day's activities. It was time to tune in to how we felt. Was it doing any good?

The short answer in my case was that after that first session, I could not recognise any change in my well-being or reduction of my Parkinson's symptoms. This was not unexpected. A standard course of HBOT involves around forty sessions. Still hoping for a positive outcome, I signed up for ten sessions and set up a routine of doing two per day while I stayed at a nearby hotel, enabling me to get eight sessions completed in the first week. With that initial tranche behind me,

I remained disappointed that my tremors had not noticeably reduced, but others with whom I had been sharing the chamber claimed that they could see improvements. I signed on for an additional ten sessions, after which I noticed that my daily exercise walk seemed easier and my walking style had improved. I was no longer dragging my left leg, and I had a new spring in my gait. This was both unexpected and encouraging.

At a weekly session with my physiotherapist, we noticed that I was showing impressive improvement in the length of time I was able to balance on each leg. By the end of week two, I was used to hearing comments about improved skin condition, general movement, and speech, as well as less obvious tremors. My physiotherapist put me through my regular paces before stating that she had noted significant improvement in movement, strength, and endurance, as well as skin tone. I concurred with her observations.

With forty sessions completed in early March 2019, I looked back on how I had felt before I began HBOT and compared that to my current state of health. I believed the HBOT had delivered a more positive attitude to fighting the disease, improved gait, better balance, recovered sense of smell, improved skin tone, more energy and endurance, stronger voice, and a general improvement in overall well-being. Aware of the amazing power of the placebo effect, I decided that whilst HBOT may not be a cure for Parkinson's, it did appear to partially mitigate some of its effects. I kept going with the HBOT for a few more months but eventually decided to give it a break. It seemed to me that the improvements were not lost when I suspended the treatment, so I was interested to see what would happen, going forward.

As I write these lines in early 2020 (under self-isolation thanks to the Covid-19 virus), the disease is slowly progressing, but I have not given up with HBO2 therapy. I suspect that I will go back to the hyperbaric treatment for another session later in the year. In the meantime, I will keep following my doctor's and my specialist consultant's advice – keeping to a strict schedule with medicines, drinking plenty of water, taking regular exercise, and enjoying a healthy diet. I am especially thankful to my medical team: general practitioners John Casey Snr and John Casey Jnr; my physiotherapist, Sarah Casey; and my consultant neurologist, Prof. Timothy Lynch at the Dublin Neurological Institute. Above all, I will continue to treasure each day that I live this blessed life with Paula and our growing family.

Diving with Parkinson's

I realised my tremor was causing confusion when the dive guide kept looking at me and formed an 'O' with forefinger and thumb – underwater symbol for 'Are you OK?' Paula and I were down at around 15 metres in one of the world's most pristine coral reefs, Wakatobi in Indonesia. Mesmerised by the sheer profusion of marine life, my excitement had triggered tremors in my right arm – a departure from my usual left-side shakes.

I had been keen to fight the gradual impact of Parkinson's disease that made itself felt in a multitude of mostly annoying but sometimes amusing ways. But I soon discovered that things previously taken for granted could no longer be relied upon. Most disturbing was the sudden onset of leaking facemasks. For decades, I had been able to pick up any facemask, jump into the sea, keep my eyes dry, or clear any slight leakage with no fuss. Now I was finding it difficult to identify a mask that didn't leak pretty much all the time.

Determined that this would not mark the end of my diving, I searched for a solution, testing a series of masks both in the sea and in a local swimming pool. Some desk research also indicated that I was not alone among Parkinsonian divers plagued by once-reliable facemasks leaking throughout their dives. Thanks to a bottom-mounted pool mirror that enabled me to observe air bubbles trickling out of the mask next to my slightly depressed temples, I was beginning to understand the source of the problem. My Internet research mentioned leaks due to divers scrunching up their faces, and I could see that my own wrinkles were pronounced around the leaks. It was clear that I needed to find a mask that would create a strong seal to my face regardless of skin folds, facial tremors, or a revised cranial contour.

I initially decided to try a 'full facemask' of the kind that television presenters or oil rig divers use to talk to one another. The seal takes in both nose and mouth and continues around the top and back of the head rather than just the eyes and nose. There was just one problem: it presumed that ears could be cleared by just pressing silicone nose-plugs into the nostrils and blowing, rather than actually blocking them off with a good nose squeeze – something that I often found necessary. Unless the mask facilitated easy ear-pressure equalisation, it would be useless, and I was beginning to lose confidence that this more bulky rig was the answer to my problem.

I went back to the Internet to search for 'no leak facemask', and Google quickly found a review of four masks that manufacturers claimed were 'no-leakers'. I was drawn to the SCUBAPRO Synergy Trufit Twin Mirrored Mask, which had very positive reviews. I placed an urgent order with Simply Scuba and tested the mask as soon as it arrived. There were no bubbles leaking out from the side of the mask, so I packed it with my other gear and set off for another coral reef adventure. At Wakatobi, I put my faith in the new SCUBAPRO mask and was not disappointed: no leaks even at the temples. And what an amazing place to be – clear water, a plethora of creatures that were new to me, and the sweet relief of regaining confidence I had built up over five decades of diving. Hence my Parkinson's-induced right-arm tremors, triggered by my excitement at actually being able to see what was happening underwater.

Not all Parkinson's symptoms are so easily banished. I still need help getting into my gear and sometimes struggle to keep up with other divers. Manoeuvrability, particularly in a current, can be challenging, and I am getting used to feeling like a 'birdman', being pushed this way or that by well-meaning dive partners or guides who reckon I need a helping hand. But these are minor niggles when it comes to the sheer joy of gliding across dazzling reefs like a visitor from outer space. The effort to solve the minor issues that were holding me back has been worthwhile. Perhaps there is a broader lesson to make those extra efforts to overcome obstacles when under Mr Parkinson's insidious influence.

Notes for Parkinson's-Affected Scuba Divers

- Dive shallow using a dive computer, and take special care to avoid decompression sickness.
- Avoid alcohol during vacations involving multiple dives.
- One or two dives per day is probably safer than three.
- Loose-fitting, possibly shorty, wetsuits are worth considering for warm-water diving.
- Ensure access to gauges, weight-belt release, and buoyancy control buttons.
- Buddy-dive, and discuss your limitations with your buddy beforehand.
- Agree a hand signal for 'Give me a hand'.
- Double-check your gear.
- Test facemasks prior to a dive trip.
- If necessary, try the SCUBAPRO Synergy mask or similar with wide, soft, pliable seals.
- Make sure you have access to assistance at the end of each dive.
- Be aware of current research on the effects of scuba diving.

22 Last Words

Family

'Family are thick,' one of our three daughters explained to a confused friend in the heat of the moment. What she had meant was that the bonds that bind our family together are strong. When the chips are down, whatever the circumstances, we support each other and will always be there to help one another. Both Paula and I are fortunate to have solid family backgrounds: Paula's parents, with unshakable religious and work ethics, were renowned for their caring nature and generous support for their five children, John, Michael, Paula, Cathy, and Eugene, making sure they all received good educations. My own parents put a high value on the five of us – Dad, Mum, Sue, Andy, and me – creating a happy, cohesive household where we each had our responsibilities. When I look back now at both families, one feature stands out: despite our close-ness, there are strong differences between us all – our individuality could hardly find greater expression.

My Dad's life was defined, to a certain extent, by chronic health conditions, including a weak heart. He was an essentially shy person who internalised the stresses connected with trying to keep head above water in the aftermath of WWII. Despite this he was highly respected by a few close friends, who admired his eclectic knowledge, intellect, and love of good food. He was an excellent cook, quietly accomplished artist, and skilled carpenter. He loved the countryside, sea, nature, and good social conversation. The health issues precluded any significant sporting achievements, although he was an accomplished tennis player in his youth and a mean snooker player in his later years, winning several competitions at our local sailing club. As a parent, he was supportive, encouraging, and trusting of my ability to get on with things. I think he took great pleasure from his visits to us in Greece and from my academic achievements, although he always wondered how I would make a living.

Mum had an outgoing personality that complemented Dad's in many ways. Whilst my father was a country gent, my mother was a town lover who liked to dress up, sing, dance, and speak Welsh. Her musical skills led to involvement in several radio broadcasts and a fleeting acquaintance with Dylan Thomas. Faced with the financial pressures of raising a family, she focused on running our small family hotel in

Hoylake, on the Wirral Peninsula, whilst Dad became involved in a stationery business in Birkenhead and a café in nearby Heswall. Between them they managed to save enough to give us a modest, comfortable life, but it must not have been easy.

Their first child was my sister, Sue, whom I remember as a big sister, four years older than me, being pushed and pulled through her teenage years, alternately influenced by discreet romances, mum's opinions on how young girls should behave, and the annoyance created by two younger brothers who invaded her space all too frequently. She inherited my parents' interest in food and gained professional qualifications in that field. She spent nine years living in Zambia, where she honed her writing skills, contributing to two national newspapers, and developed a warm personality, relishing opportunities to explore the great outdoors and to engage with wildlife. Sue is still a keen walker, follower of the arts, concert-goer, reader, and social person, enjoying retirement and living close to her two daughters, Hilary and Linda.

Andy is my much-loved brother, with whom I alternately fought and played throughout our childhood, adolescence, and beyond. He has a high IQ, was in the top stream in grammar school (contrasting with my 'no hopers' stream), and bypassed sixth form and university to join an advertising company. His curtailed education may have been due to a general disaffection with formal education, the compelling attractions of getting one's own pay cheque, or an impatient desire for all that the liberal 1960s offered a young man for whom the world was his oyster. As a multi-talented musician and songwriter who could earn his living from a range of creative activities – cooking, wordsmithing, marketing, musical performances, and carpentry – he was well placed to enjoy a very full life. Starting out in Liverpool, he moved to London for a while before emigrating to Canada and living in Nova Scotia, Toronto, Montreal, Vancouver, and finally Cortes Island, close to the entrance of Desolation Sound. The sea is in his blood, and in his 60s he completed a challenging voyage around Vancouver Island aboard his 28-foot yacht, *Gwyneth*, named after our mother. Andy practices yoga and t'ai chi and remains in good health as he approaches his 80s. He built his own wonderful home on Cortes, where he hosts regular musical gatherings. A sensitive soul, well read and steeped in philosophy, Andy has spent many years suggest-ing to others, in poetry, prose, and song, how they should live their lives. He has two sons, Elgin and Simon, and a daughter, Michelle. They all live in North America and are all accomplished musicians.

Paula, with whom I have shared almost fifty wonderful years, appears throughout the pages of this book and does not require a separate intro-duction. Together, we raised Catriona, born in Sudan, Sinead, born in Saudi Arabia, and Megan, born in Galway, Ireland.

Catriona, or just Triona, entered this world at an Italian nuns' nursing home in Khartoum, close to the confluence of the Blue and White Niles. When I showed concern that no name tags were in place to identify the thirty or so crying or sleeping babies lined up, cheek by jowl, in identical tiny cots, I was reassured by a ward nurse, who explained that there was only one 'white baby girl' in the room, and she was ours. Triona's early childhood was influenced by our own careers that took us through the 1970s and early 1980s to live in Port Sudan, Jeddah, Athens, and Clifden, Ireland. She then fled the roost to live in France, the UK, and the USA, working as a barrister and becoming increasingly involved in human rights, death-row prisoners, injustices imposed on the Kurds, and finally, as a solicitor, helping to serve the needs of our local popula-tion. Married to Iain, a mathematical modeller and software developer who has adopted Irish citizenship, they are raising two daughters, Aoibh and Ella, and one son, Oisín, at their home next to ours, on the shores of Ardbear Bay.

Sinead was born in a hospital in Jeddah, Saudi Arabia, where the custom of tipping the nurses meant a small queue at the end of the bed after Paula successfully gave birth. Even the obstetrician seemed to expect his cut, with the result that the midwife tried to hold things back until, delayed by traffic, he eventually arrived. Paula lost no time in sug-gesting that it was she who deserved any rewards that were going. Sinead thus joined our family in Saudi Arabia – a fact that is duly recorded in her passport, resulting in a series of travel complications in the years that followed. I recall trying, unsuccessfully, to persuade a Ryanair check-in steward at Shannon Airport that Sinead, despite being born in Saudi Arabia, was not a Saudi citizen. I was told that without a visa to travel, she risked being deported. To our utter disbelief, Sinead was denied permission to board her Ryanair flight to London. Now a certified Irish citizen, Sinead is firmly rooted in Ireland, together with her partner, Pat, and his two girls, Katie and Sarah. She gained her degree in occupational therapy at Cardiff University and has forged a successful and rewarding career in this field. Her first love, despite some life-threatening falls, is ponies and horses. The story she wrote about buying the *Irish Times* journalist Michael Viney's pony Baínín was recycled as a set-piece essay on multiple occasions throughout her school days. At the back of our house we built Baínín a stable that Sinead decorated, complete with curtains. Now Sinead and Pat (Manufacturing Lean Sigma Blackbelt Expert in pharmaceuticals and recent Gaelic football team manager for Waterford Ladies) have built their own house in Dungarvan – with room for a pony.

There is no doubting Megan's nationality: she was born at University College Hospital, Galway, in 1984. My abiding memories are of running out to the shops to buy a comb for her and waiting my turn at a public phone box, where another Clifden resident was conveying to family members the death of her father. Megan, like Triona and Sinead, attended Clifden Community School, where she came under the spell of deputy headmaster Brendan Flynn. Her love of literature and drama eventually led her into bachelor's and master's degrees in drama and psychology. She is currently studying for a doctorate in social and community psychology at the University of Limerick. Married to Avi, a dedicated teacher, artist, and photographer, Megan has strong interests in human rights and injustices of the asylum process. She and Avi have been pivotal in establishing Melting Pot Luck in Galway: an organisation that helps to break down the boundaries between the local community and people who have experience of forced migration.

Finally

As readers will have gathered by now, this book comprises stories *from* my life rather than the story *of* my life, kickstarted by the discovery of old letters recording various travels and adventures. I am aware that there is more missing from this collection than the events that are included. It would be nice to think that I will one day fill in some of the more glaring omissions, but I am not sure that I will ever achieve that. Thank you for reading, and I hope you found it interesting – I certainly enjoyed writing it. Life goes on.

Family

TOP LEFT My mother and father outside our hotel in Hoylake.

TOP RIGHT My centenarian aunt Madge and sister Sue.
Madge was a professional herb gardener for much of her life.

ABOVE Paula and Pete.

LEFT TO RIGHT   Aoibh, Oisín, Iain, Ella, and Triona.   © Aoife O'Sullivan

LEFT TO RIGHT Pat and Sinead with Sarah and Katie, Angel and Misty.

TOP Pete, Sue and Andy.

ABOVE Megan and Avi.   © Aoife O'Sullivan

Acknowledgements

I never thought that I would write a book about my life. It all happened so quickly: once, I was a self-conscious schoolboy with a passion for sailing, music, and romance – the next moment I was a grandfather and retired director of a multi-million-dollar project representing a whole nation. A lot took place in between, but how to make sense of it? I am most grateful to Paula for her engagement, participation, and partnership in all aspects of our shared lives – this book being yet another example of her pivotal contribution to our abiding partnership.

Belief, interest, and encouragement also came from our three daughters, who feature from time to time in this collection of stories. Having repeated many of these tales at mealtime gatherings over many years, I owe all my family members recognition for continuing to be interested in these stories from my life. Whilst most of my relatives and friends will have heard some of these stories, or even been part of them, none will have heard all of them.

There is one couple outside of the family circle that deserve special mention: our neighbours, Danny and Suzanne Vaughan, who stand out for their kindness and warm friendship over forty or more years. They have been an inspiration and one of the solid rocks on which I have continued to build my life in Ireland.

The dark art of editing the text was undertaken, without a cruel word but no doubt some discreet clenching of teeth, by editors Siobhán Mannion and Stan Carey. I am also most grateful to Mary Ruddy and Vincent Murphy of Artisan House for their guidance and interest in this project, and for the professionalism with which they managed the whole process.

Photographers are separately credited, and my special thanks are due to them for helping to illustrate the book.

Appendix

The following is a list of my academic works, published under my name, together with a complete list of titles created by Immel Publishing, including books by other authors.

ACADEMIC PUBLICATIONS

Vine, P.J., 1970. Field and laboratory observations of the crown-of-thorns starfish, *Acanthaster planci*: Densities of *Acanthaster planci* in the Pacific Ocean. *Nature*, 228 (5269), pp. 341–342.

Vine, P., 1972. *Life on Coral Reefs in the Seychelles*. G.T. Phillips.

Knight-Jones, E.W., Knight-Jones, P., and Vine, P.J., 1972. Anchorage of embryos in *Spirorbinae* (*Polychaeta*). *Marine Biology*, 12 (4), pp. 289–294.

Vine, P.J., 1972. *Spirorbinae* (*Polychaeta, Serpulidae*) of the Hawaiian Chain, Part 1: New Species. *Pacific Science*, 26, pp. 140–149.

Vine, P.J., Bailey-Brock, J.H., and Straughan, D., 1972. *Spirorbinae* (*Polychaeta, Serpulidae*) of the Hawaiian Chain, Part 2: Hawaiian Spirorbinae. *Pacific Science*, 26, pp. 150–182.

Vine, P.J., 1972. *Spirorbinae* (*Polychaeta: Serpulidae*) from the Red Sea, including descriptions of a new genus and four new species. *Zoological Journal of the Linnean Society*, 51 (2), pp. 177–201.

Vine, P.J., 1972. Coral-reef conservation around the Seychelles, Indian Ocean. *Biological Conservation*, 4 (4), pp. 304–305.

Vine, P.J., 1973. Crown-of-thorns (*Acanthaster planci*) plagues: The natural causes theory. *Atoll Research Bulletin*, 166, pp. 1-10. Smithsonian Institution.

Vine, P.J., 1974. Effects of algal grazing and aggressive behaviour of the fishes *Pomacentrus lividus* and *Acanthurus sohal* on coral-reef ecology. *Marine Biology*, 24 (2), pp. 131–136.

Vine, P.J., 1977. The Marine Fauna of New Zealand: *Spirorbinae* (*Polychaeta*, No. 68). New Zealand Oceanographic Institute.

Vine, P.J., and Head S.M., 1977. Growth of corals on Commander Cousteau's underwater garage at Shaab Rumi (Sudanese Red Sea). *Jeddah Nature Journal*, 1, pp. 6-17.

Vine, P.J., 1980, January. Cultivation of fishes in the family Cichlidae in the Red Sea. In: *Proceedings of Symposium on the Coastal Marine Environment of The Red Sea, Gulf of Aden and Tropical Western Indian Ocean*. (Volume 2) pp. 9 –14.

Vine, P.J. and Vine, M.P., 1980, January. Ecology of Sudanese coral reefs with particular reference to reef morphology and distribution of fishes. In: *Proceedings of Symposium on the Coastal Marine Environment of the Red Sea, Gulf of Aden and Tropical Western Indian Ocean* (Volume 1) pp. 88 – 140.

Vine, P.J. and Bailey-Brock, J.H., 1984. Taxonomy and ecology of coral reef tube worms (*Serpulidae, Spirorbidae*) in the Sudanese Red Sea. *Zoological Journal of the Linnean Society*, 80 (2–3), pp. 135–156.

Vine, P., 1986. *Red Sea Invertebrates*. Immel Publishing.

Vine, P. and Schmid, H. 1987. *Red Sea Explorers*. Immel Publishing.

Vine, P.J., 2019. Red Sea Research: A Personal Perspective. In: N.M.A. Rasul and I.C.F. Stewart (eds.), *Oceanographic and Biological Aspects of the Red Sea*. Springer Oceanography, pp. 215–238.

Nasr, D. H., Shawki, A.M., and Vine, P.J., 2019. Status of Red Sea Dugongs. In N.M.A. Rasul and I.C.F. Stewart (eds.), *Oceanographic and Biological Aspects of the Red Sea*. Springer Oceanography, pp. 327–353.

Rasul, N.M.A., Stewart, I.C.F., Vine, P., and Nawab, Z.A. 2019. Introduction to *Oceanographic and Biological Aspects of the Red Sea*. In N.M.A. Rasul and I.C.F. Stewart (eds.), *Oceanographic and Biological Aspects of the Red Sea*. Springer Oceanography, pp. 1–9.

IMMEL PUBLISHING TITLES

The Diver's Guide to Red Sea Reef Fishes
Caribbean Divers' Guide
Undersea Britain
Tropical Marine Life
Sea Life of Britain and Ireland
Reef Animals of the Pacific Northwest
Red Sea Reef Fishes
The Red Sea
Marine Wildlife of Atlantic Europe
Seychelles
The Natural History of the Burren
Marine Field Course Guide 1: Rocky Shores
Echinoderms of the British Isles
Mangrove: The Forgotten Habitat
Diver's Guide to Coral Reefs
Sharks of Arabia
Red Sea Safety
Red Sea Invertebrates
Guide to Inshore Marine Life
Nudibranchs of the British Isles
Red Sea Explorers
Red Sea Diver's Guide: Large Format
Bah Mar the Shallow Seas
Arab Gold: Heritage of the United Arab Emirates
Spirit of the Wind
Wetlands: Tealham Moor
Arabian Desert
Guide to the Maldives
Discovery Guide to Southern Africa
Discovery Guide to Yemen
Golden Days in the Desert
The Wild Flowering Plants of Bahrain
Socotra: Island of Tranquillity
The Making of Ireland
The Mineral Wealth of Saudi Arabia
The Desert Ibex
The Brown Trout in Ireland
The Natural History of Connemara
Inland Birds of Saudi Arabia